THE WORLD'S GREAT SMALL ARMS

THE WORLD'S GREAT SMALL ARMS

CRAIG PHILIP

First published in Great Britain in 1993 by
Brown Books, 255-257 Liverpool Road,
London, N1 1LX

ISBN 1-897884-03-6

Printed in Hong Kong by
Dai Nippon Printing Co. (H.K.) Ltd.

Colour origination by Hong Kong Reprohouse,
Hong Kong

Picture credits
Brown Packaging: 2-3, 28, 44, 46, 69, 90, 118-119, 130, 140 (top); **Ian Hogg:** 10, 18-19, 31, 36, 37, 41, 43, 47, 48, 51, 54, 60, 61, 66-67, 76, 78, 86, 88, 92, 93, 94, 96, 97, 101, 104, 106, 108, 111, 114, 115, 116, 120, 128, 136, 137, 140 (bottom), 146-147, 147, 150-151, 154, 155 (top and bottom), 156-157, 159, 163, 168, 169, 172-173, 173 (top and bottom), 174 (top and bottom); **IWM:** 15, 70; **Pacemaker Press:** 85; **TRH Pictures:** 6-7, 8-9, 12, 13, 14, 16, 18 (left), 18 (centre), 20, 21, 22, 23, 27 (bottom), 32, 33, 34, 38, 39 (top and bottom), 44-45, 57, 58-59, 62-63, 65, 68, 75, 80, 81, 82, 102-103, 122, 126, 131, 138, 142, 144, 164-165, 166, 170-171; **US DoD:** 24, 30, 72-73, 83-84; **US DoD, US Marine Corps:** 42-43; **US DoD, US Navy:** 98-99, 148-149, 153; **US Repeating Arms Co.:** 160-161, 161-162

■ PAGES 2 & 3: The British SA-80 bullpup assault rifle. Light, compact and a delight to shoot, it is a replacement for the 7.62mm Self-Loading Rifle.

CONTENTS

INTRODUCTION

BY IAN HOGG

Mankind is approaching the end of a violent century: there have been two major world-embracing wars, and not a year has passed since 1900 without some form of insurrection or other type of institutional violence taking place.

At the same time, the nature of war has undergone several significant changes since the turn of the century: from the open, long-range exchanges of fire of the Boer Wars, through the trench warfare of World War I, the *Blitzkrieg* of World War II, the human-wave attacks in Korea, the tunnels of Vietnam, to the highly fluid tactics in the open sands of Iraq and Kuwait in the 1991 Gulf War. Such changes have invariably been accompanied by changes in armaments – either new weapons to suit tactics or vice versa. In addition, at the same time there have been huge conscript armies in which men who might otherwise have never seen a gun in their lives have become familiar with a wide variety of firearms.

To cater for all these changes, weapons designers have been busy developing firearms to meet the various demands – tactical, economic and technical – that the military has placed on them. Most of these weapons have been serviceable, but some have attained immortality, becoming legends among allies and enemies alike. In some cases this was due to their sheer efficiency, as, for example, in the case of the Maxim Gun; in others immortality was achieved due to a combination of appearance and publicity, as with the Tommy Gun. Some weapons became infamous as a result of their unreliability – models such as the Chauchat machine gun. However, whatever the reasons for their fame, there is a collection of weapons that can justifiably be called the 'great guns of the century'.

It is this collection that this book sets out to explore. It is, of course, a selective list, one that reflects the opinions of the author. However, on the whole I think it is well chosen and includes the best and most famous weapons seen during the century. The more recent weapons featured might be subject to a re-appraisal in another 50 years or so, for they are as yet too young to have established for themselves a reputation on the battlefield. But the inclusion of such designs as the Minimi machine gun, the AUG and G11 assault rifles, and the Beretta and SIG handguns is justified by their technical innovation and their widespread adoption alone. It is, therefore, highly unlikely that future generations will find anything amiss with this current choice.

In a perfect world, of course, none of these weapons would be necessary. But we do not live in a perfect world; far from it, and it is as well to bear that in mind. And whatever your political or sociological view of warfare might be, put it aside for a moment and contemplate the firearm as an engineering triumph. Consider what the average machine gun does in loading and firing a cartridge, then remember that it does this several hundred times a minute for as long as you care to keep the trigger pressed and the ammunition flowing. If the car manufacturers could make a car half as reliable as the Vickers machine gun, for example, it would be hailed as a miracle. So with this in mind, turn the pages and investigate some of the minor miracles of the twentieth century.

Ian V. Hogg

LEFT: A tripod-mounted MG42 machine gun currently in use with Spanish troops. The weapon first saw action during World War II with German forces.

CHAPTER 1 RIFLES AND ASSAULT RIFLES

"You can keep your atom bombs, your tanks and your airplanes; you'll still have to have some little guy with a rifle and bayonet who winkles the other bastard out of his foxhole and gets him to sign the peace treaty." When General George Patton said these words just after World War II, he was stating a truism felt by most of the millions of 'little guys' who had fought for their countries in conflicts before and since. The twentieth century has seen dramatic advances in the technology of warfare. However, in the final analysis wars are decided by the courage and persistence of the individual soldier, the man who has to walk or ride into an enemy's territory, and who has to place his body in the line of fire.

For over 150 years the personal firearm has been the weapon of the soldier, for the most part consisting of a long-barrelled weapon firing lead or steel projectiles through a barrel engraved with spiral grooves, the latter designed to give a stabilising spin to the pointed bullet. This 'rifling' has given its name to the whole class of firearm that has dominated the battlefields of the world.

SMALL ARMS TECHNOLOGY

At first glance, the advance of small arms technology seems to have been a slow, incremental process: gradual evolution rather than dramatic leaps forward. When compared to the speed of progress in other areas of military hardware, such as computers, missiles, aircraft and warships, the infantryman and his tools seem to come at the end of the queue for new developments. Weapons such as the Soviet AK series, first manufactured at the end of World War II, are still being used by thousands of soldiers and guerrillas, some 50 years later. The current American standard-issue assault rifle, the M16, is a development of a design first seen in 1959, while many other armies use versions of the 1950s-vintage Belgian FN FAL.

There are good reasons for this seeming lack of modernisation of what is, after all, the cornerstone of military power. First, current weapons are, on the whole, extremely effective. They are the end products of hundreds of years of evolution of the military firearm. If something works well, there is little incentive to replace it. Second, and more importantly, the task of supplying a completely new weapon to a major army is a huge one and takes up vast amounts of time, money and resources. Many thousands of weapons need to be issued, with each soldier needing training in the use and maintenance of the new design. Millions of rounds of ammunition have to be produced, both for training and to provide sufficient stocks for wartime use. A new rifle often means changes to other items of the infantryman's equipment: his ammunition pouches and webbing equipment, which need redesigning. What is also often not appreciated is that to design and manufacture what appears to be a relatively simple device actually demands the highest standards of mathematical, analytical, ballistics and ergonomics skills, together with high-quality engineering and production facilities. Also, in a blow to the traditionalists, a new shape of weapon often demands changes in ceremonial foot drill.

■ LEFT: A member of the Alpini, Italy's crack mountain formation, takes aim with a Beretta BM 59 rifle. This weapon is a Mk Ital, which is derived from the Mk III.

RIFLE REQUIREMENTS

All infantry rifles possess common characteristics, to a greater or lesser degree. Every design is a compromise, the exact nature of which depends upon the tactical philosophy of the user army and on the individual skills and biases of the designers and manufacturers.

The bullet the weapon fires must be able to kill, or at least disable, anyone it hits. All else being equal, a large, heavy projectile will usually cause more damage than a lightweight one, although certain design techniques can be used to increase the effectiveness of lighter rounds. These include creating a bullet that 'tumbles' inside the target, or one which uses soft materials or hollow tips to cause expansion in the target. Often, such techniques are outlawed by the Geneva Convention, although cartridge design constantly skirts around the edge of such restrictions.

A rifle should carry a reasonable number of cartridges in its magazine to allow the

AKM ASSAULT RIFLE

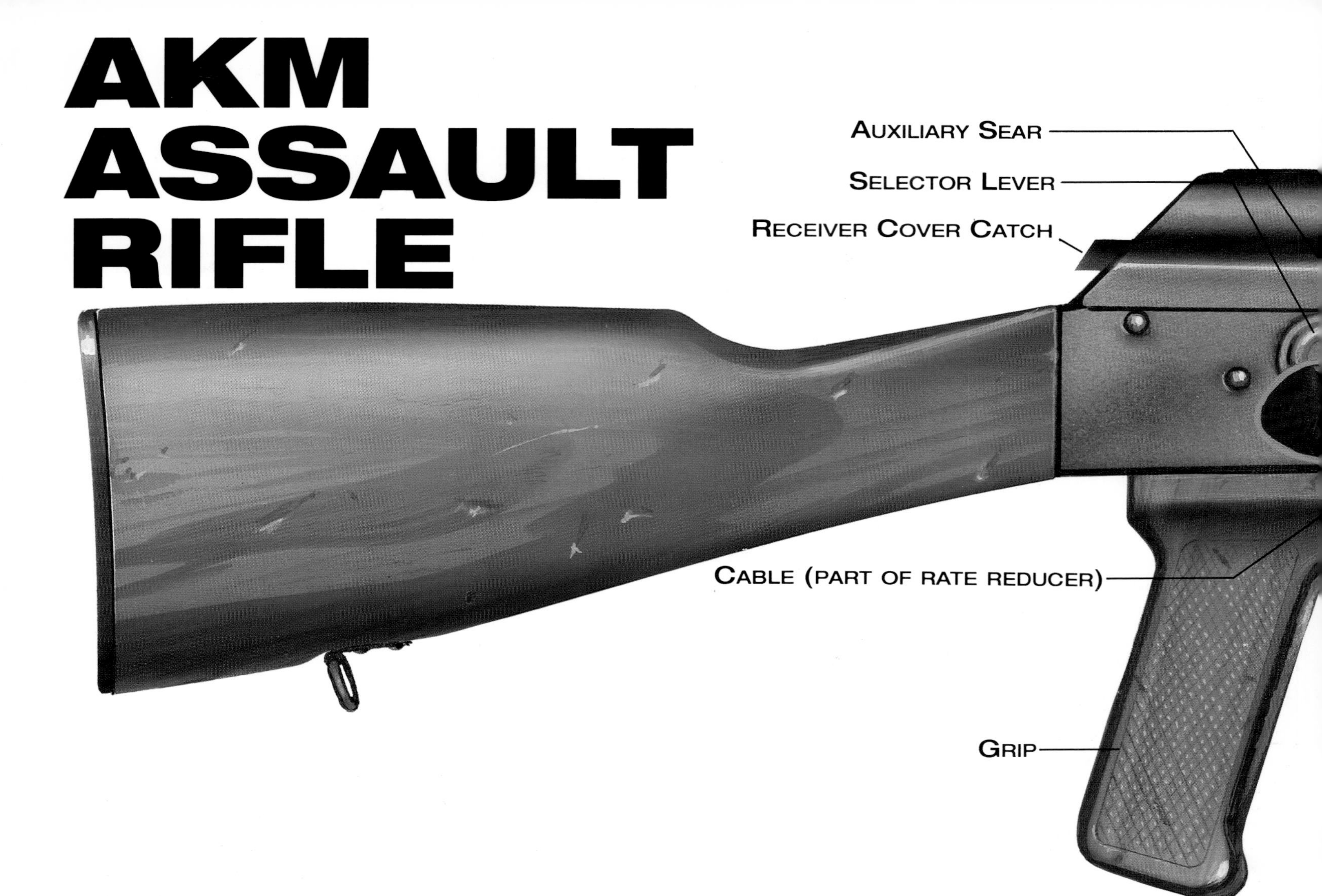

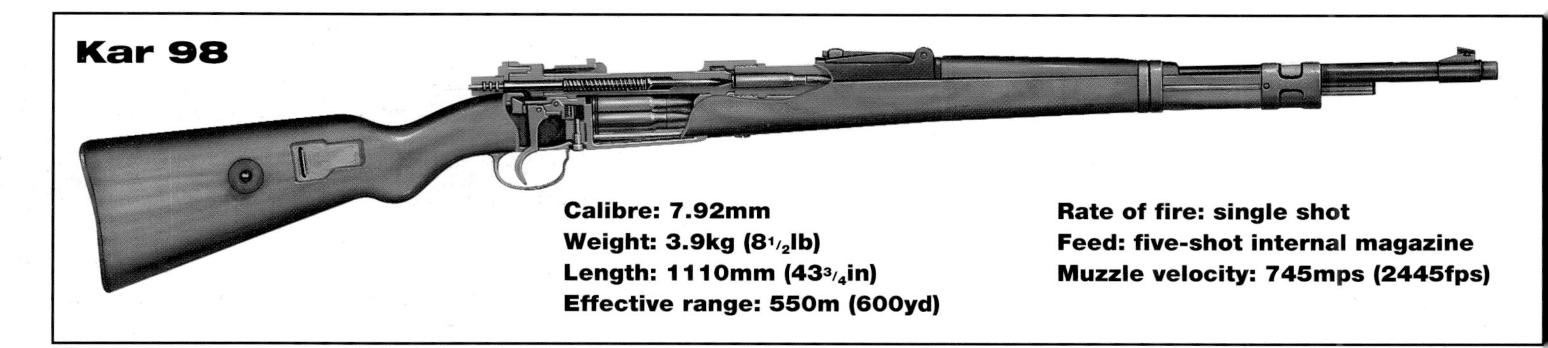

of it: the Rifle No 4. The No 4 was similar in length to the KAR 98K (1130mm), but slightly heavier at 4.11kg (9lb). The British rifle could hold 10 rounds of .303in calibre and had a bolt action which made rapid fire easier than with the KAR.

A bullet from one of these rifles could kill at a range of over 1830m (2000yd), though 450m or so was a more realistic range for a trained rifleman to hit a man-sized target on the battlefield. The bolt had to be worked between each shot and this, combined with limited ammunition storage, meant that an individual rifleman could only fire around 20 rounds per minute. These weapons were also relatively heavy and cumbersome, resulting in an awkward load for the soldier to carry when on the move. Both had attachments for long bayonets, though the 1939-45 conflict provided few occasions where hand-to-hand bayonet fighting actually took place. The British eventually developed a shorter version of the Rifle No 4 (known logically as the Rifle No 5) for fighting in close terrain such as the jungle. The No 5 was lighter than the standard weapon, so absorbed less recoil and gave the operator more of a 'kick' when fired. The shorter barrel resulted in a brighter muzzle flash, therefore a cone-shaped suppressor had to be fitted to prevent the firer being dazzled.

THE SELF-LOADER

Since the early years of the twentieth century, there had been a number of experiments with 'self-loading' rifles, ie weapons that automatically eject the empty cartridge case after firing, feed the next round into the breech, and cock the mechanism ready for the next shot. Once Hiram Maxim had shown how such a concept was possible with his machine gun, designers had been trying to devise rifles using similar principles.

The weapons use the energy created by the explosion of the propellant in the cartridge to operate the mechanism. Some use the force of the recoil, some use the

LEFT: A German infantryman in action in Russia during World War II. He is armed with a Kar 98 bolt-action rifle, a weapon that was both reliable and resilient.

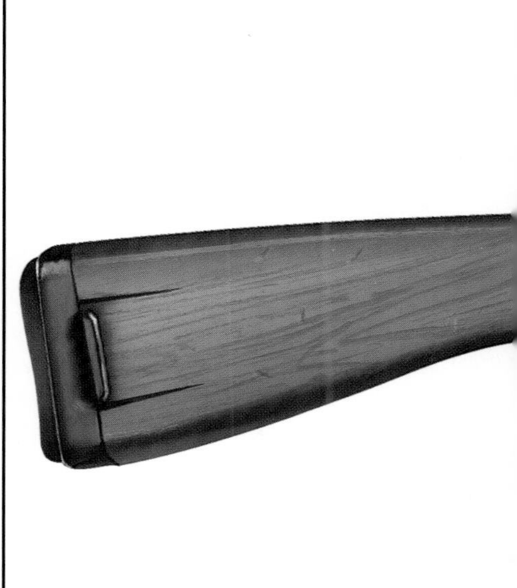

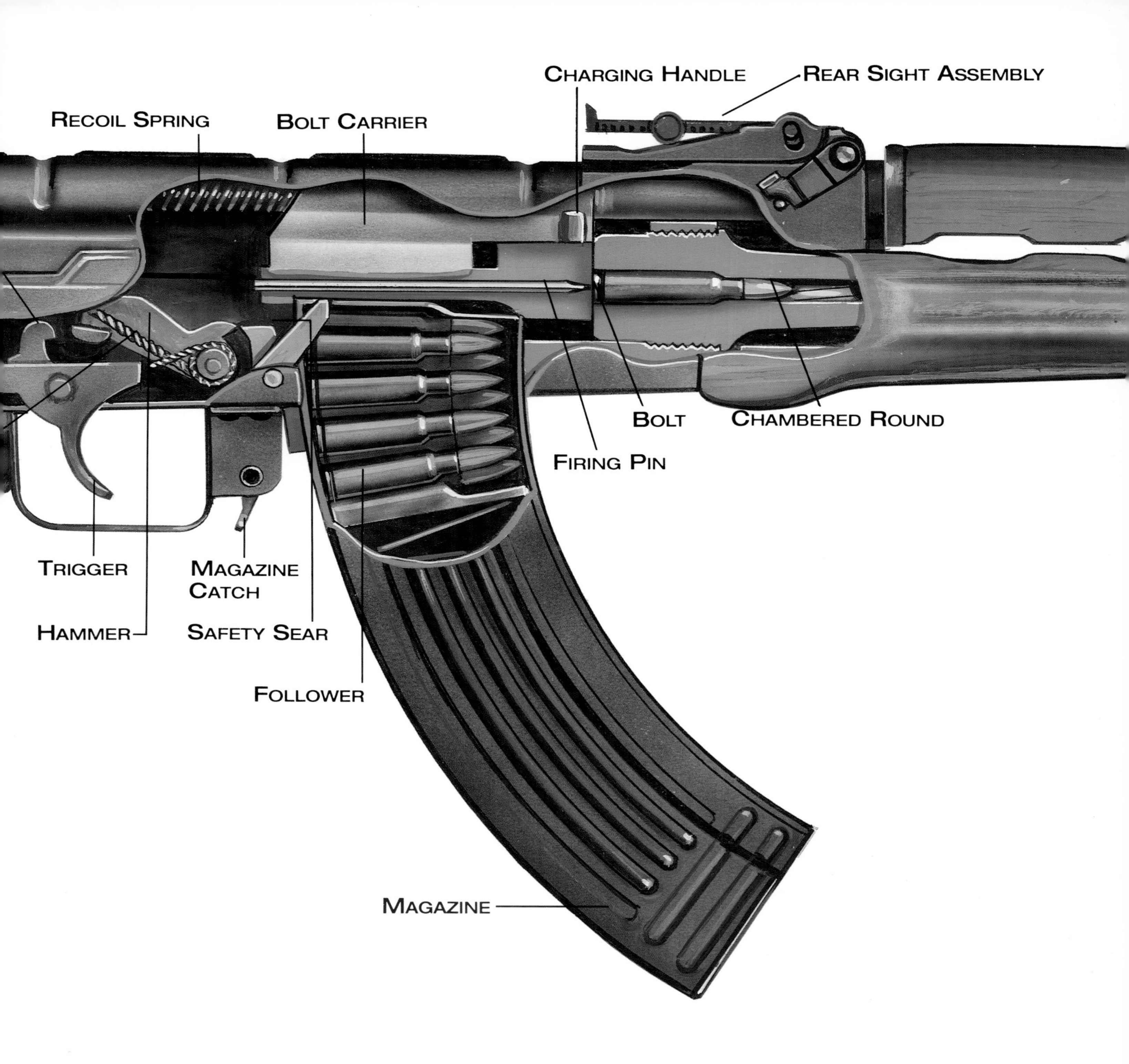

■ **LEFT: The Kalashnikov family. The AKM is held by two of these soldiers – far left and second from the right. The other weapons are AKMS assault rifles.**
■ **FAR RIGHT: The father of the AKM, the famous AK-47 assault rifle. The only major difference is that the AKM's bolt locks into a sleeve and not directly into the barrel.**

Calibre	7.62mm
Weight	3.15kg (7lb)
Length	876mm (34½in)
Effective range	400m (440yd)
Rate of fire	600rpm (cyclic)
Feed	30-round magazine
Muzzle velocity	715mps (2350fps)

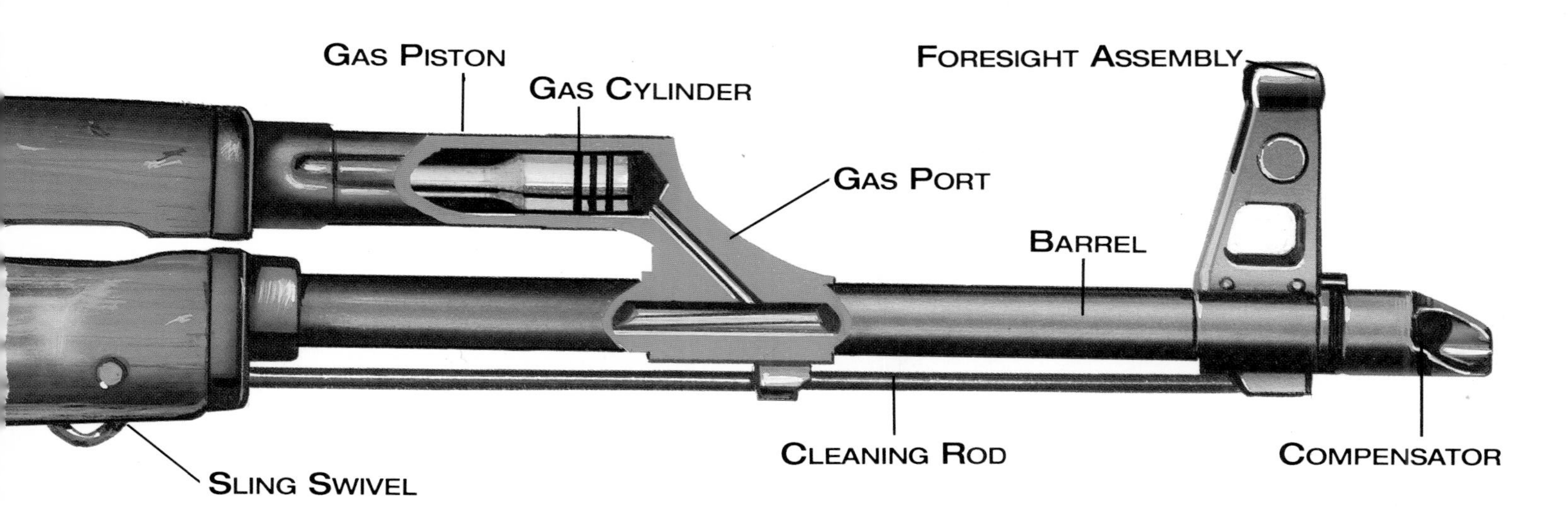
GAS PISTON
GAS CYLINDER
FORESIGHT ASSEMBLY
GAS PORT
BARREL
CLEANING ROD
COMPENSATOR
SLING SWIVEL

LEFT: An Afghan-made copy of a Lee-Enfield .303in bolt-action rifle in the hands of a Mujahedeen tribesman. The Lee-Enfield is very reliable and accurate.

user to engage multiple targets quickly. An automatic rifle with a high rate of fire can also increase the firepower of an individual soldier, although the trade-off is usually a reduction in accuracy and an increased expenditure of ammunition.

RELIABILITY OR ACCURACY?

Accuracy is important: the soldier should have a good chance of hitting his target. A heavy gun with a long barrel, firing powerful ammunition, imparts a high velocity to the bullet, creating a much straighter trajectory than a smaller, lighter weapon (this takes no account of the all-important interaction between the rifle and the firer, on which accuracy also depends). A large, heavy rifle with a powerful round and associated noise and recoil demands a highly trained and skilled firer to be accurate. A lighter alternative weapon which is more comfortable to fire may not be intrinsically as accurate as its heavier counterpart, but a conscript soldier may achieve much better results with it.

Long-range accuracy is usually not necessary. Most infantry actions take place at ranges of under 275m (300yd), and specialist snipers are normally the only people interested in precise shooting at much longer ranges. In battle, enemy infantrymen try to use as much cover as is available, giving the firer only fleeting snap shots of targets. In addition, most soldiers are not particularly good shots. Peacetime professionals can be trained to a reasonable degree of marksmanship, but the standards found in a conscript or wartime army are by necessity somewhat lower.

Weapons manufacturers and marksmen emphasise accuracy, but the lowly foot soldier usually prefers total reliability. This can be designed into a weapon by various techniques, such as keeping the number of moving parts to a minimum, using simple, well-proved principles, using high-quality ammunition, and by making the components strong and rugged. All military rifles are built to withstand exposure to mud, dust, extreme heat, snow and ice, rain and salt spray, to work with minimal maintenance and to survive the knocks and hard treatment likely to be received in battle. Reliability is also a function of ease of use and ease of maintenance. If a weapon demands careful, skilled attention, and has a large number of small components to clean in the field, then it is more likely that a tired, scared conscript soldier will fail to keep it in proper condition.

The weapon must also be portable. A rugged, accurate rifle firing powerful ammunition invariably means a heavy weapon. If the soldier is to carry it easily, along with the ammunition and his other equipment, then compromises must be made to allow for a reasonable weight. Modern lightweight materials such as plastics, fibreglass and carbon fibre composites have helped by largely replacing wooden stocks and butts. Weight and cost can be reduced further by using metal stampings and pressings welded and riveted together, rather than components machined from solid metal. Length and bulk can also be a problem, especially for soldiers of small stature, or for jungle or urban operations. Most soldiers now travel into battle in trucks or armoured personnel carriers, and a long rifle can be a hindrance when entering or leaving the vehicle.

Finally, a weapon for mass issue must be cheap and easy to manufacture. Should a nation take part in a major war, it may need to expand production of such weapons rapidly, and a rifle that demands sophisticated industrial facilities and takes unnecessary time to manufacture can be a logistical nightmare.

THE BOLT-ACTION RIFLE

Most of the combatants in World War II were equipped with bolt-action rifles that fired medium-calibre ammunition of around .30in (7.62mm) in diameter. German soldiers were equipped with the KAR 98K, a typical example of this class of weapon, and one which could trace its lineage back to the Mauser rifle of 1888. Nearly 1110mm ($43^{3}/_{4}$in) long, it weighed 3.9kg ($8^{1}/_{2}$lb) and fired the powerful 7.92mm x 57mm cartridge (the first dimension is the diameter of the bullet, the second is the length of the cartridge case from base to neck). An integral box magazine held five rounds which were fed into the chamber by working a long bolt above the trigger. The bolt pushed the top round from the magazine forward into the breech, then locked it in place by twisting the operating handle downwards.

The British Army used the SMLE (Short Magazine Lee-Enfield) and a development pressure of the resulting gases against the cartridge case ('blowback'), while others tap these high-pressure gases from the barrel to operate a piston system ('gas operation'). The latter is better suited to a powerful rifle cartridge because the slight delay inherent in the system, and the energy absorbed by the piston, reduce the force applied to operate the mechanism to a safe level. Gas operation also incorporates sufficient delay so that when the bolt opens there is no rush of high-pressure gas back into the mechanism and towards the firer.

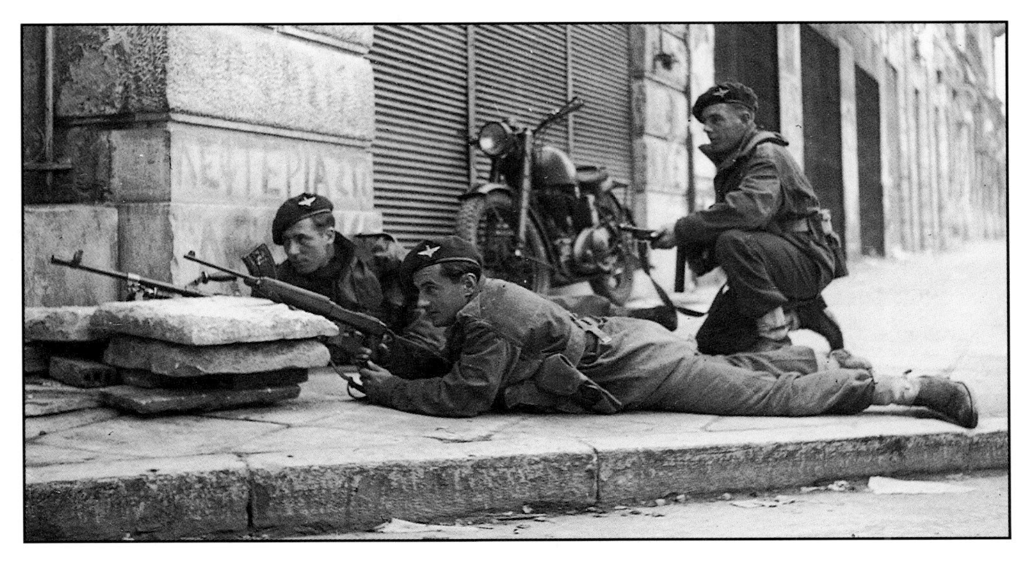

ABOVE: The M1 Carbine (foreground) was a very successful semi-automatic rifle.

OPEN AND CLOSED BOLTS

In a gas-operated weapon, a tiny hole is normally drilled in the barrel at a point along its length. As the bullet passes this hole, some of the high-pressure gases behind it are tapped off. They enter a pressure cylinder which holds a piston, the shaft of which runs parallel to the barrel. The gases push the piston backwards, which pushes back the bolt or, more likely, a bolt-carrying piece, thus instigating the whole extraction and reloading cycle. A gas-operated weapon can usually be identified from the parallel cylinder, which starts some distance behind the muzzle and runs above or below the barrel. Most modern automatic rifles and machine guns use some form of gas operation, though a significant minority use direct blowback.

As the bolt carrier accelerates backwards, this initial short movement normally unlocks the bolt itself from the barrel. Some bolts are locked by a series of lugs around their front face, and these are usually freed by being rotated through 30 degrees or so by a cam system on the carrier. Others are locked at the rear by lugs on the rifle body, and are freed by being tipped downwards by a sloped surface in the carrier. Once unlocking is complete, the bolt is free to move backwards with its carrier, and an extraction claw on the bolt face usually pulls the empty cartridge case backwards out of the chamber. There is normally a small protrusion in the path of the case which flips it sideways out of an open ejection port and away from the firer. Meanwhile, the bolt and carrier slam back against a powerful return spring. As they do so, they push the firing hammer and trigger mechanism back into the cocked position, ready for the next shot.

Most self-loading rifles employ a 'closed bolt' principle. With this system, the compressed return spring immediately pushes the bolt and carrier forward again, catching the round at the top of the magazine (held there by the magazine spring) and pushing it forward into the chamber. Once the bolt comes to a halt, its carrying piece continues forward for a short distance, locking it into place again. The rifle is now ready to fire the next round. If it is set to fire bursts (automatic) and the firer is still pressing the trigger from the previous round, the hammer will fly forward immediately. If the weapon is set to fire single shots (semi-automatic), the hammer mechanism stays locked in place by a catch until the trigger is pulled once more.

Once released, the hammer flicks forward, propelled by its spring, and will normally hit the rear of the long, thin firing pin. This spring-loaded pin is slammed through the bolt and carrier into the small sensitive initiating charge at the rear of the cartridge, which detonates the main

Rifle No 5 Mk I (jungle carbine)

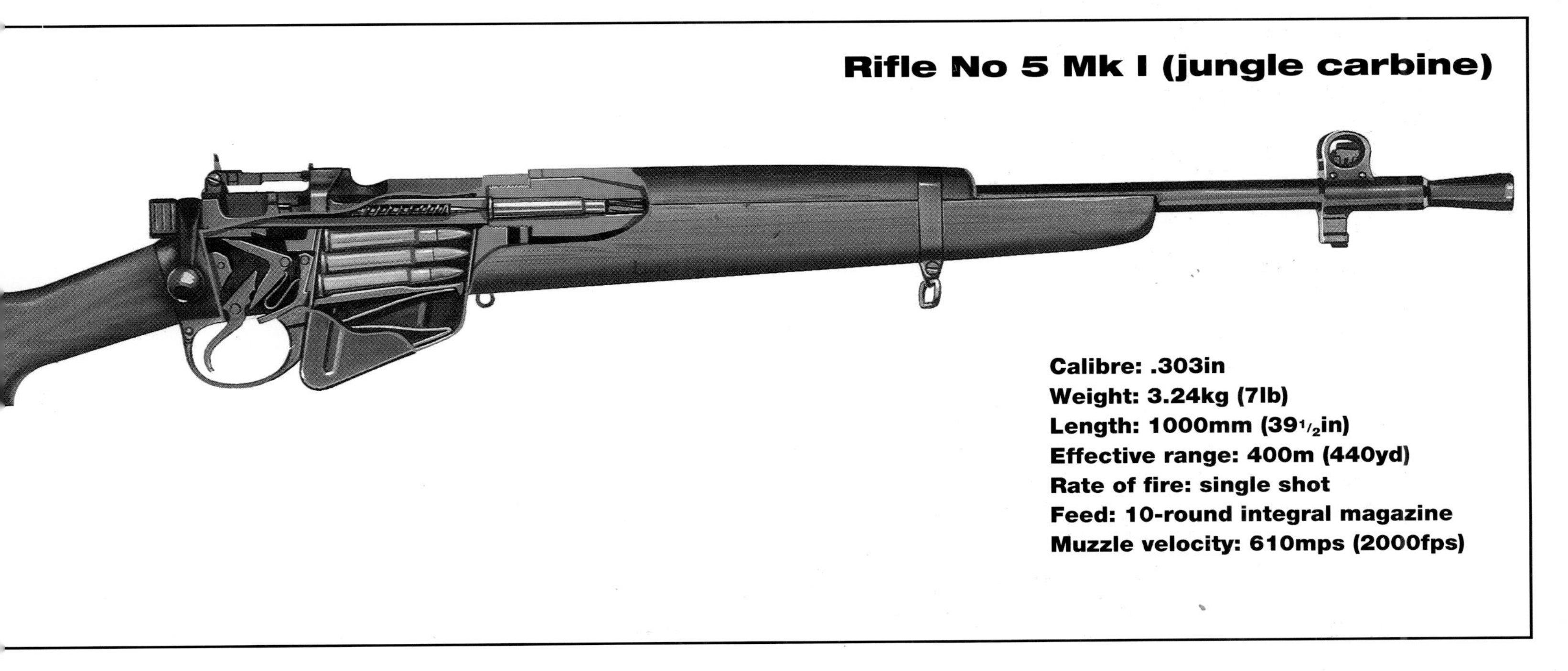

Calibre: .303in
Weight: 3.24kg (7lb)
Length: 1000mm (39½in)
Effective range: 400m (440yd)
Rate of fire: single shot
Feed: 10-round integral magazine
Muzzle velocity: 610mps (2000fps)

BM 59 Beretta Rifle

Calibre: 7.62mm
Weight: 4.6kg (10lb)
Length: 1095mm (43in)
Range: 600m (660yd)
Rate of fire: 750rpm
Feed: 20-round magazine
Muzzle velocity: 823mps (2700fps)

ABOVE: The Beretta BM 59 rifle is an Italian copy of the venerable US M1 Garand. There are a number of variants, including a squad automatic version.

propellant charge. The ensuing explosion causes an extremely rapid release of hot, high-pressure gases which propel the bullet along the barrel and towards the target. The gases from this explosion are used to start the whole cycle again.

Some rifles and submachine guns operate by means of an 'open bolt'. In this case the bolt or its carrier is held back against the compressed return spring by the trigger mechanism. When the trigger is pulled the bolt is released to move forward, again picking up the next round and pushing it into the chamber. As the bolt slams into its forward position, the firing pin is already protruding, so the round is fired instantly. An open-bolt design results in a weapon that is less accurate than one using a closed bolt system. This is because the comparatively large mass of the bolt system flying forward just before firing causes the balance of the rifle to shift, affecting the aim of the firer. A bolt held open may also allow sand, grit or dust into the mechanism, thus increasing the likelihood of a stoppage.

THE M1 GARAND

The advantages of the open bolt include simplicity of construction and the ability of the firer to see (through the cartridge ejection port) if the magazine is empty. The first warning the firer of a closed-bolt weapon has of an empty magazine is the dull click of the firing pin as it jabs into an empty chamber. Another plus for an open bolt mechanism is that it allows air into the chamber area between shots, which helps cool the rifle. With a closed-bolt system a round is left in the chamber between shots, and if there is a long pause after a period of heavy firing, the heat may detonate the propellant and fire the round accidentally (the dreaded 'cook-off'). Many closed-bolt rifles allow the firer to lock the bolt open manually to allow cooling when not firing.

Many countries had experimented with self-loaders, but the first army to use a self-loading rifle as a standard-issue weapon was the United States. The .30in calibre M1 Garand entered widespread service in 1936 and was to prove itself a reliable, tough and effective rifle. Operated by gas and piston, it had an integral box magazine holding eight M1906 rounds. The piston sat in a cylinder beneath the barrel, and in turn was connected to an operating rod. There was no bolt carrier; instead a cam pin on the side of the bolt was acted upon by a cam recess in the operating rod. When the rod was forced back by the piston, the cam system forced the bolt to rotate to the left, moving the two lugs on the bolt face and unlocking it from the receiver. The rod then carried the bolt to the rear, extracting the empty case and compressing the return spring. Once rearward movement had halted, the operating rod was pushed forward carrying the bolt with it. Once a new round was taken up and fed into the breech, the cam sytem again rotated the bolt, pushing its locking lugs into position.

This rifle was to be the mainstay of the American infantryman throughout World War II and beyond, and many were still in service in Vietnam during the early 1960s. The Garand was a heavy weapon – 4.37kg

M14 Rifle

Springfield M1903

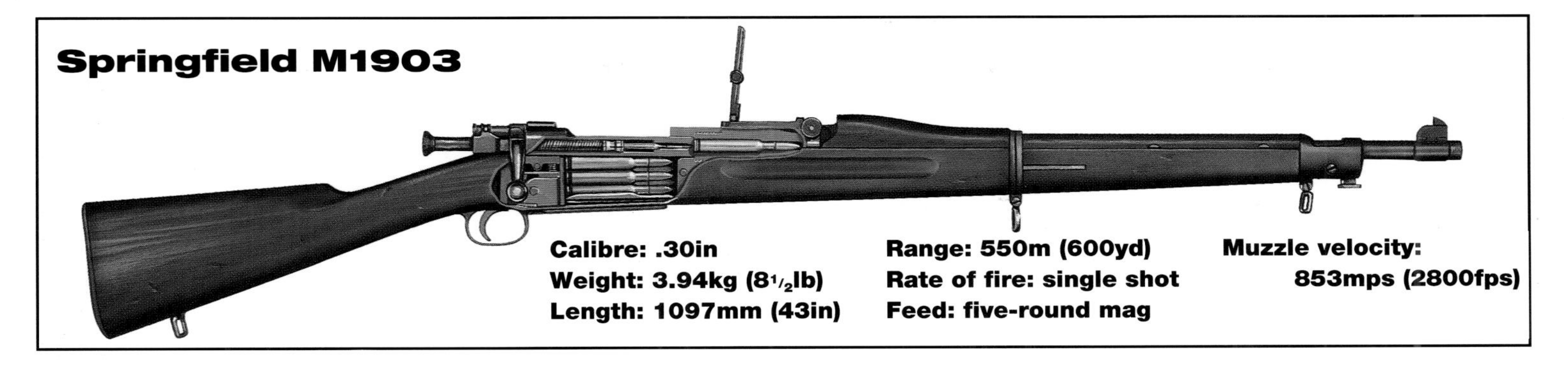

Calibre: .30in
Weight: 3.94kg (8½lb)
Length: 1097mm (43in)
Range: 550m (600yd)
Rate of fire: single shot
Feed: five-round mag
Muzzle velocity: 853mps (2800fps)

(9½lb)– which had wooden furniture and stock and was robust and reliable. Perhaps the only fault of the Garand was that it relied on a special clip pre-packed with eight rounds to reload the magazine. While the clip speeded up this action, it also meant that only a complete load of eight rounds could be inserted. A half-empty magazine could not be 'topped up' in a lull in the fighting – the firer had to wait until his rifle was empty before reloading. When the last round was fired, the clip was ejected out of the top of the rifle, giving off a distinctive clunk that was sometimes dangerously obvious to an enemy in close combat. The Garand was also licence-built by Beretta in Italy, and by the time production ceased in the 1950s, over five million had been manufactured. There were very few modifications to the rifle during its service life – a sign of an excellent design.

Another American attempt at a semi-automatic rifle was the .30in Johnson. Tested just before the outbreak of war, it was initially refused by the US Army and Marine Corps in favour of the M1 Garand. When war threatened, however, M1 production could not keep up with the demands of military manpower expansion, so the Johnson was procured for Marine Corps reconnaissance troops and airborne forces. The Johnson was unusual in that it used recoil operation rather than gas. A concept more often used in handguns and machine guns, recoil operation has the bolt locked to the barrel, and the force on the cartridge case moves them both rearward within the casing of the rifle. Once the pressure inside the barrel has dropped to a safe level, the barrel is stopped in its movement, while the bolt is unlocked and allowed to continue rearwards. Once the case is ejected, the bolt and barrel travel forward to load a new round and lock together in the firing position.

ENTER THE M1 CARBINE

The Johnson also had an unusual rotary magazine which held 10 rounds and, unlike the M1, could be reloaded at any time. Unfortunately, reliability was not the Johnson's strong point, and it remained less than popular with many users. One saving grace was a barrel that could be easily removed or replaced, allowing the rifle to be carried by paratroopers as a compact package. It was in this role that the Johnson achieved a certain amount of success.

The most widespread American weapon of World War II was not a rifle, handgun or even a submachine gun, but, rather, a strange hybrid of all three: the M1 Carbine. In 1938, the army requested a light weapon for use by officers, NCOs, drivers, machine gunners, signallers and others who would find a rifle an awkward hindrance. At first the request was refused owing to a shortage of funds, but by 1941 the M1 Carbine had been selected and was entering service. Some 1.8kg (4lb) lighter than the Garand and 190mm (7½in) shorter, it rapidly became popular with the troops. The M1 Carbine fired the same calibre ammunition as the rifle, but used a shorter, less powerful pistol-type round which had a shorter range and less stopping power. The two types of ammunition were not interchangeable. The Carbine was also a gas-operated semi-automatic. A short-stroke piston did not impinge directly on the bolt, but, rather, caused an operating rod to rotate then move the bolt backwards. Up to 15 rounds could be carried in its magazine, and a 30-round box was available later in the war.

Calibre: 7.62mm
Weight: 3.88kg (8½lb)
Length: 1117mm (43½in)
Effective range: 550m (600yd)
Rate of fire: 750rpm (cyclic)*
Feed: 20-round magazine
Muzzle velocity: 853mps (2800fps)

*** normally only single shots are employed**

■ LEFT: The heavy-barrelled version of the Belgian FN FAL. When being carried, the bipod folds up beneath the barrel.
■ BELOW: LIke most Soviet weapon designs, the Simonov SKS rifle was simple, easy to operate and reliable.
■ RIGHT: The AKS-74, the folding butt version of the Soviet AK-74 assault rifle.

The M1A1 variant was designed with a simple folding metal skeleton stock, to be used by paratroopers, and the M2 incorporated a selector for continuous bursts. There was also an M3 which could mount various sniper scopes and night sights. The M1 series proved so popular that over six million of all variants were produced in total. Up to the mid-1980s some were still in use with various police forces around the world, such as the Royal Ulster Constabulary.

Other countries continued to experiment with self-loaders during the war years, and some of the most important developments took place in Germany. The Germans had been pioneers in the field of self-loading rifles and actually had a complete regiment so armed by 1901. In World War II, the first semi-automatic rifle in large-scale German Army service was the Gewehr 41(W). Designed by Carl Walther, it looked like a conventional rifle but had a cap at the end of the barrel that deflected the muzzle blast back to force an annular piston to drive an operating rod and hence move the bolt. It again had an integral magazine (10 rounds of 7.92mm Mauser ammunition) but was heavy, poorly balanced and not particularly reliable. Despite this, the Gewehr 41(W) was issued in reasonably large numbers to troops on the Russian front.

A much more effective weapon, and one that doesn't look dated even by today's standards, was the FG42. Made largely of metal, with only a little wood around the rear of the barrel, the FG42 was designed to fire single shots or bursts (usually referred to as 'selective fire'). This weapon is more fully described in the machine guns chapter.

The next German self-loading rifle was probably one of the most significant developments for the modern infantryman, and the concepts it used were to be followed by virtually every new design over the next 50 years. In the 1930s, tactical studies had shown that infantry combat in World War I had taken place at ranges of around 300m, much less than originally envisaged. The German Army came to the conclusion that the long-range firepower of the standard-issue rifle was largely wasted. It therefore instigated the development of a shorter, less powerful version of the 7.92mm cartridge which was known as the 7.92mm *Kurz* (short) Patrone.

A new weapon was needed to take advantage of this less powerful round, and the model selected was Haenel's Maschinenkarabiner 42, or MKb42(H), designed by Louis Schmeisser. An initial batch of 8000 saw service on the Russian front and, after modifications, the weapon entered mass production as the Maschine Pistole 43 (MP43). Made largely from metal stampings and pressings, the MP43 looked unlike any previous rifle. It was gas operated, with a piston and cylinder above the barrel. The piston was attached to the bolt carrier, and drove the carrier back until the bolt unlocked by dropping down from a locking recess in the carrier. The whole mechanism then moved back through the extraction and reload cycle. The weapon had a pistol-style grip and trigger placed below the receiver, in front of which was a curved, detachable box magazine containing up to 30 rounds of the *Kurz* ammunition.

The less powered round resulted in a shorter rifle than before – 940mm (37in) – though it was still relatively heavy at 5.25kg (11½lb). Controllable automatic fire was achievable, and was much more effective than that from short-range submachine guns. The MP43 gave German soldiers firepower at the ranges that counted, and the plan was for the MP43 to replace the rifle, submachine gun and light machine gun in infantry units, though there weren't enough produced to make this possible. In 1944, the designation changed to MP44, and later that year Hitler was supposed to have coined the term *SturmGewehr* (assault rifle), which has now passed into usage as the general term for this type of weapon.

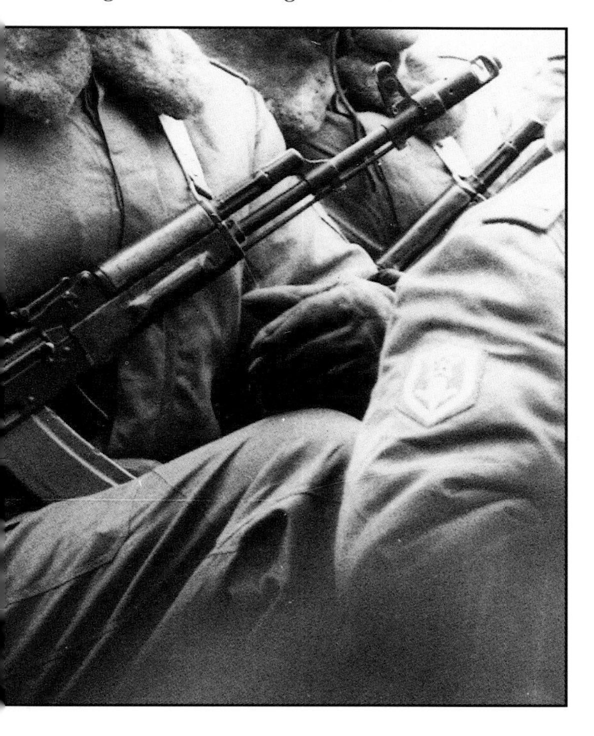

The Soviets had been experimenting with self-loading rifles throughout the 1920s and 1930s, but had not come up with a design suitable for large-scale production. They had also examined the characteristics of 'intermediate' rifle cartridges, but it took the appearance of the innovative German MP43 during the war to spur them into rapid development. The cartridge they eventually chose was a version of the Soviet standard 7.62mm round with a case shortened to 39mm in length and designated the 7.62mm x 39mm M1943.

A semi-automatic carbine known as the SKS was hurriedly developed and rushed into service to take advantage of the new cartridge. The Red Army was a firm believer in the value of massed firepower at short and medium ranges, and already had whole battalions equipped with submachine guns. The SKS was planned to provide heavy firepower at longer ranges than the submachine gun. Gas operated, the SKS overall was a rather heavy and cumbersome design which had a mechanism copied from the PTRS anti-tank rifle. A pressure cylinder sat above the barrel, and the bolt was locked in place by a tipping motion. The detachable box magazine only held 10 rounds. Despite its shortcomings it was tough and easy to use, and many thousands were produced, staying in service with Soviet allies and second-line troops for many years.

The SKS was only a wartime stopgap, however, and the design of a true assault rifle was only undertaken in the latter stages of the war. A design team led by Mikhail Kalashnikov eventually produced a compact, robust weapon which was able to fire single shots or bursts, and was reasonably accurate up to 275m (300yd). Known as the AK-47 (*Avtomat Kalashnikov* 47), the new rifle was quickly approved for service and was in widespread use by 1951.

The AK-47 is probably the most famous assault rifle of modern times, having been used by more armies, guerrilla forces and terrorist organisations than any other weapon. Short (880mm), well balanced and easy to handle, it is still quite heavy at 4.3kg (9½lb). The AK uses a much-copied gas system which involves tapping the gases from the barrel. There is no selectable gas regulator, though there are a row of small holes to vent excess pressure from the cylinder. The gases impinge upon a piston which extends from, and is part of, the bolt carrier. This carrier moves back 8mm or so while a cam pin causes the bolt itself to rotate through 35 degrees, releasing the front locking lugs that fix it to the barrel while the round is fired. By the time the bolt is released, the gases in the chamber have dropped to a safe level, and the bolt starts to travel back with its carrier. A large claw on the bolt face pulls the empty cartridge case back for ejection. The bolt and carrier are pushed back against the return spring, before moving forward and picking up a new round. Once the bolt has pushed the new round into place, the carrier continues to move forward and the cam pin rotates the bolt until its locking lugs are fixed once more.

ATTRIBUTES OF THE AK-47

The AK has a large change lever on the right side of the receiver. When this is in the top position, the trigger is locked and the bolt cannot be pulled back to load a round. As the weapon fires from a closed bolt, the firer may need to inspect the chamber and magazine to see if there is still ammunition available, so the bolt can be pulled back just enough to see inside or to insert a finger to check. When the change lever is in the middle position, the weapon will fire continuous bursts, and single shots when it is in the bottom position.

A distinctive curved magazine protrudes below the receiver (the main part of the body), and holds up to 30 rounds. The AK-47 has a wooden pistol grip and butt, together with wooden furniture around the front grip and gas cylinder. The foresight is

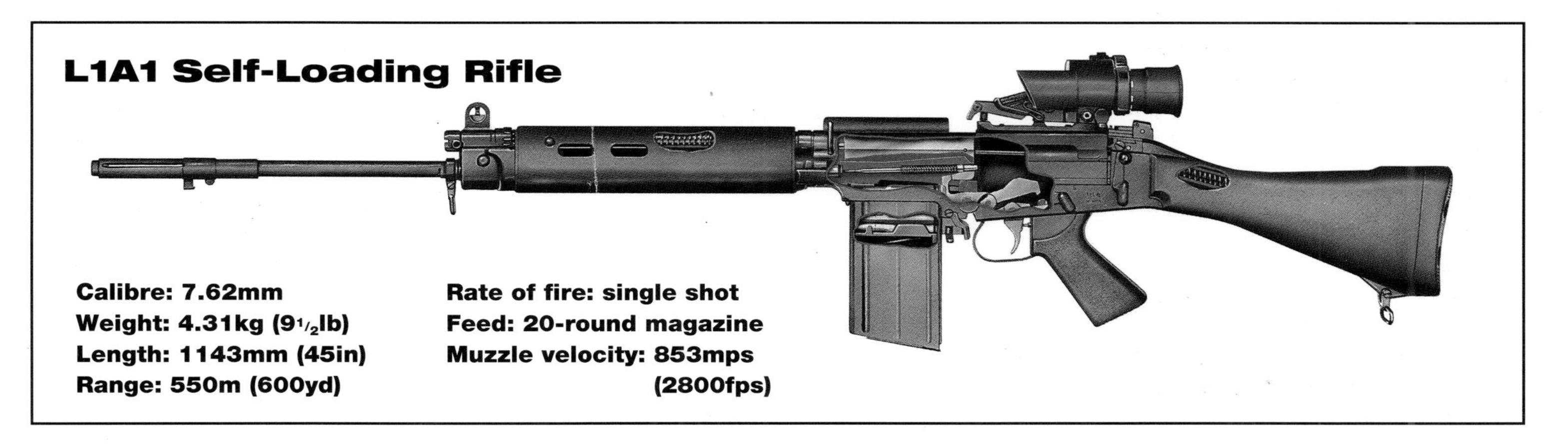

L1A1 Self-Loading Rifle

Calibre: 7.62mm
Weight: 4.31kg (9½lb)
Length: 1143mm (45in)
Range: 550m (600yd)
Rate of fire: single shot
Feed: 20-round magazine
Muzzle velocity: 853mps (2800fps)

LEFT: The British L1A1 Self-Loading Rifle, one of the finest assault rifles ever.

a simple post protected by a large guard, and it can be adjusted in elevation and azimuth. The rear sight is a simple notch at the front of the receiver, above the chamber, and is adjustable for ranges up to 800m (880yd). There are also small tritium luminous dots on the sights, one below the rear sight notch and one on a flip up post behind the foresight. In poor light conditions, all the firer needs to do is align the two dots, one directly above the other, to know that he is pointing at his target.

At first glance the AK-47 appears to be a very mediocre weapon. Not particularly accurate, only effective at medium ranges, firing a moderately powerful round and crudely finished. Closer inspection, however, reveals its strengths. It is well finished where it needs to be, with the barrel lining chrome-plated for longevity and the bolt face precisely machined. It is designed to be reliable under tough conditions, having few moving parts and less that require attention from the user. By using the rotary bolt locking system, only the chamber, the bolt face and the locking lugs need to withstand the full stresses of firing, enabling steel of lower tensile strength to be used for the rest of the bolt and firing mechanism. The AK bolt carrier has grooves cut on its external surface to scrape out dirt and fouling, and the system will continue working in conditions that would jam most other weapons of this class. Even if the mechanism does eventually seize up, the cocking handle is permanently attached to the bolt, and thus can be forced forward

Stoner M63

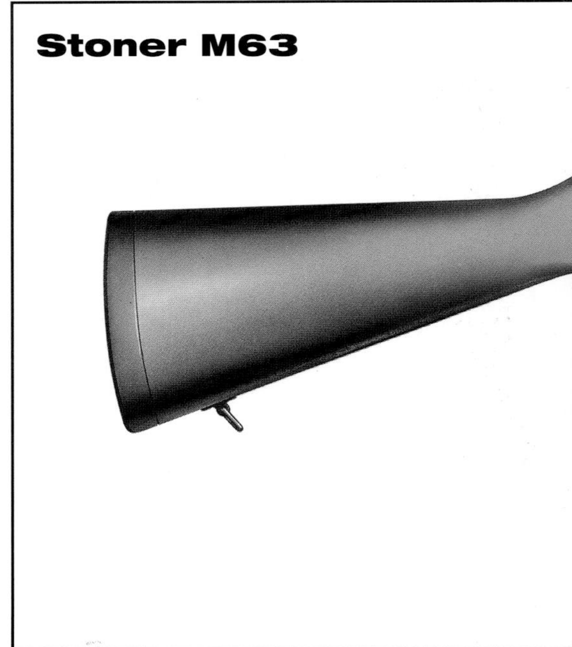

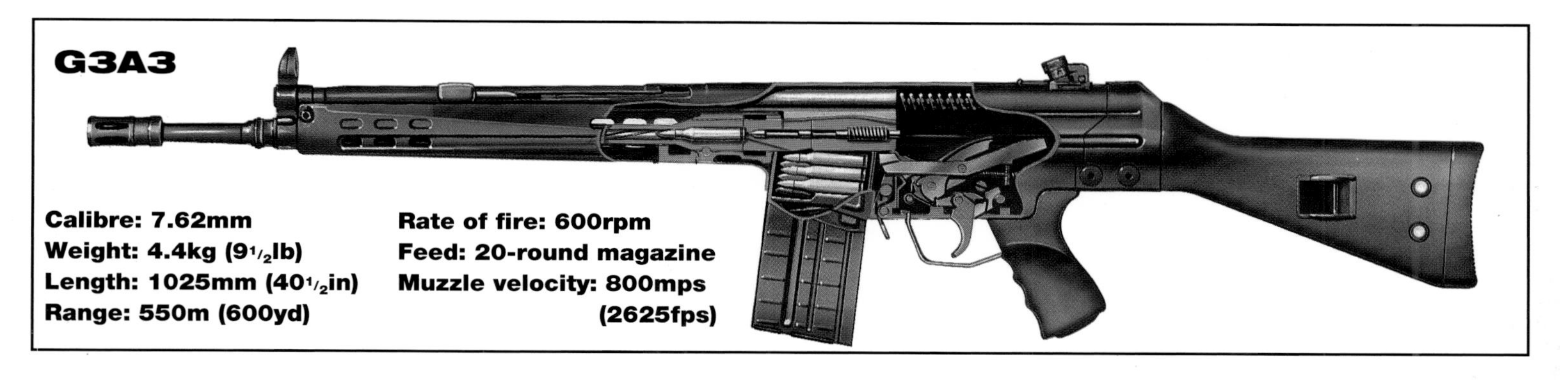

G3A3

Calibre: 7.62mm
Weight: 4.4kg (9½lb)
Length: 1025mm (40½in)
Range: 550m (600yd)
Rate of fire: 600rpm
Feed: 20-round magazine
Muzzle velocity: 800mps (2625fps)

by hand to load the next round. The AK is remarkably easy to operate and simple to maintain, and conscript soldiers can be taught how use it in the minimum of time.

The AK is not designed to win engineering design awards, for long-range precision shooting, or to look smart on a drill square. It is designed for one purpose only: to be used by conscript soldiers in combat. Effective at the ranges that mattered, able to deliver devastating firepower from comparatively untrained hands, the AK-47 quickly became the standard weapon of the Red Army. It also entered service with most of the Soviet Union's allies and 'client' states, many of whom set up their own production lines. The Chinese manufacture an almost exact copy known as the Type 56; Hungary makes AKs under the designation AKM-63; former Yugoslavia has the M70 series; Poland the PMK; North Korea the Type 68; and Romania the AKM. Some of these weapons have slight modifications from the original design: laminated wood or even plastic furniture, folding stocks, or modified pistol grips forward of the magazine. The simplicity and robustness of the design has made it popular with guerrilla forces around the world, and this, combined with Soviet and Chinese willingness to support revolutionary forces, has made the AK the most widely used weapon ever. No one knows for sure, but it is estimated that over 30 million AKs of all types have been produced since 1951.

The Soviets themselves were not slow to modify the design, with a version appearing with a folding metal stock for use by vehicle crews and paratroopers. The first major development, however, was the AKM. This is really an AK-47 re-engineered for ease of production. Sheet metal pressings, riveted and welded together, replace some of the forgings and castings used in the earlier rifle, creating a weapon that is significantly cheaper and quicker to produce and at the same time is over 900g (2lb) lighter. Other differences include a small delay device to prevent the hammer striking the firing pin until the bolt is fully locked, and a simple compensator device built into the muzzle which diverts some of the gas upwards to help resist any muzzle climb on automatic fire. The AKM can be identified from the AK-47 by a number of

■ ABOVE: The very practical G3 assault rifle is made from sheet metal stampings and has plastic furniture.

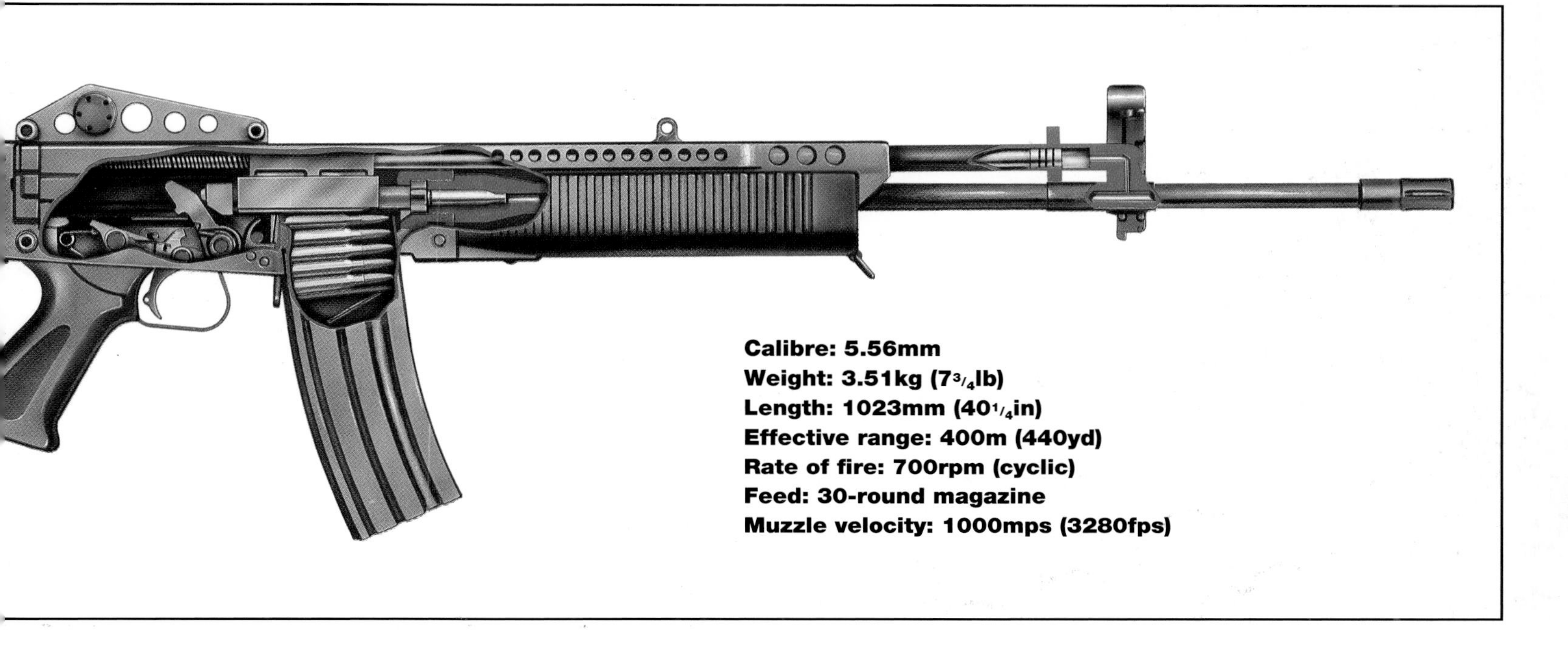

Calibre: 5.56mm
Weight: 3.51kg (7¾lb)
Length: 1023mm (40¼in)
Effective range: 400m (440yd)
Rate of fire: 700rpm (cyclic)
Feed: 30-round magazine
Muzzle velocity: 1000mps (3280fps)

LEFT: The Stgw 57 7.5mm assault rifle. In service with the Swiss Army, it is a version of the SIG SG510-4 rifle. Minor changes include the addition of a bipod.

ribs across the top of the receiver and a horizontal groove on the front grip. There is also an AKMS with a metal skeleton stock, which folds up underneath the body of the rifle. The AKM has an unusual, short bayonet: there is a small lug on the scabbard which inserts into a slot at the end of the blade to make a pivot. The scabbard, which is electrically insulated, has a hard metallic edge which, combined with the bayonet blade, turns the whole assembly into a makeshift wirecutter.

The AK has proved so effective that some Western nations have also copied the design. The Finns developed a modified AK as their M60 Valmet assault rifle. Firing the same round as the AK, major differences are a tubular steel butt and a plastic-covered steel fore-end. The rear sight is at the rear of the receiver and there is no trigger guard, thus enabling the weapon to be fired while wearing thick arctic gloves. After a few years of operational experience the improved M62, incorporating some changes to the original design, was brought into service. The M62 has a trigger guard, uses more plastic in a revised fore-end, and incorporates tritium night markers on the sights. There is also a further improved model, the M78, and another variant has been developed for fire support tasks (which has a longer, heavier barrel). The Valmet (and thus the AK) also formed the

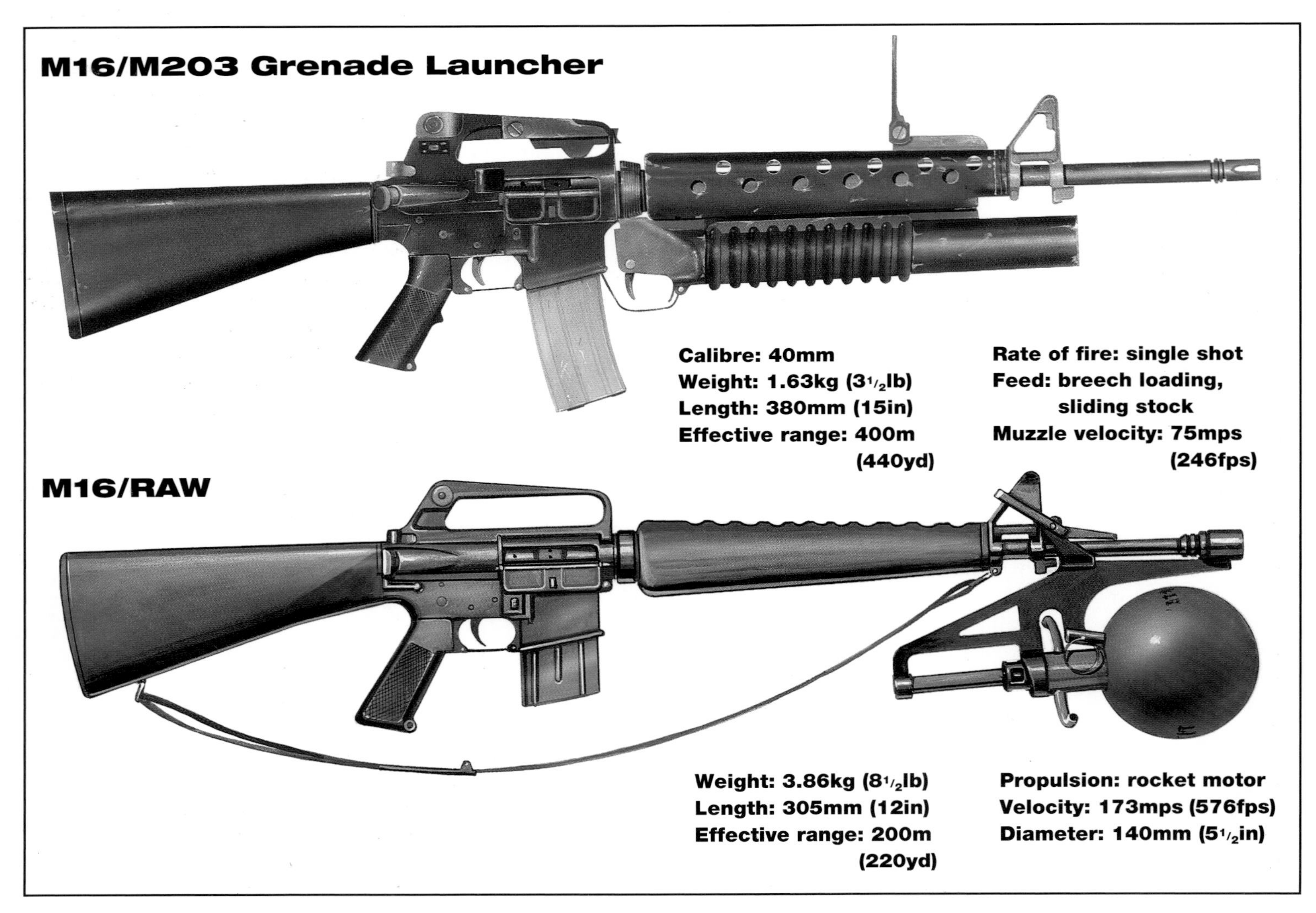

LEFT: The M16 rifle. It was first sold as a self-cleaning weapon. Unsurprisingly, there were problems with jamming. Cleaning kits were hastily issued!

basis of the Israeli Galil assault rifle which was developed in the early 1970s.

Following the end of World War II, many of the former combatants were starting to look at replacing their wartime bolt-action rifles. With the onset of the Cold War and the formation of NATO, attempts were made in the West to create common standards for military weapons and equipment. Much of this effort came to nothing, but one area where a successful agreement was achieved was in the field of small arms ammunition. In 1953, the NATO countries agreed, under strong American pressure, to standardise on a 7.62mm x 51mm round that could be fired by whatever infantry rifle an individual country would develop.

THE AMERICAN M14

Many regarded this decision as a retrograde step, with the NATO countries missing the opportunity to incorporate wartime experience and develop a lighter, less powerful round. The Americans, however, were happy to keep to this heavier ammunition, especially as it was based on their old .30in cartridge but with a slightly shorter case. Developments in propellant technology meant that the new round was just as powerful as the old, and effective at much longer ranges than the Soviet intermediate 7.62mm x 39mm bullet.

As the machinery used to manufacture the .30in round could be easily modified for the new cartridge, the United States was well placed to re-equip its forces. In the M1 Garand the United States Army already had an effective semi-automatic rifle in service, one which would require very little work to convert to the new ammunition. The M14 was devised as a logical development of the Garand, entering service in 1957. Capable of semi-automatic, single-shot or full-automatice fire, the M14 looks very similar to its predecessor, having a wooden 'rifle' butt and stock. A detachable box magazine extends below the receiver and holds 20 rounds, the designers having dispensed with the awkward eight-round loading clip of the Garand. Some were fitted with bipods to provide a light machine gun capability, but the weapon was too light for any degree of sustained fire. A version with a heavier barrel was developed but it never entered service. In the event, many M14s issued to soldiers were permanently set for semi-automatic fire only.

The M14 was an effective and reliable weapon which was used by many other countries, and saw active service in US hands during the Vietnam War. While it was criticised for being heavy and cumbersome, many soldiers liked the punch and man-stopping capability of its 7.62m round (later versions included sniper models). By the time production ended, around one and a half million of all types had been made.

The most successful Western rifle of the 1950s and 1960s, and the one that came nearest to being a NATO-wide standard-issue firearm, however, was to come from Belgium. The Brussels company of Fabrique Nationale (FN) had already produced a licence copy of the American BAR automatic rifle/light machine gun before World War II, and were experimenting with self-loading rifles in the late 1930s. Work was suspended during the German occupation (1940-44), but quickly restarted after the war. The Belgians realised that there would be a large market for a cheap self-loading rifle, and soon the Model 49 was successfully in use with a number of armies. A gas-operated weapon available in a number of calibres, it was to form the basis of the next FN design: the *Fusil Automatique Légèr* (FAL).

THE BELGIAN SELF-LOADER

First seen in 1950, the FAL was originally designed to fire the German 7.92mm intermediate round. Once NATO had taken the decision to standardise on 7.62mm x 51mm, the rifle was quickly re-designed to use this calibre. The FAL was an immediate success, eventually being sold to over 90 countries. It is not a compact nor a light weapon, being 1067mm (42in) long and weighing in at 4.31kg (9½lb). However, the length makes it accurate for a self-loader, and the weight implies a robustness and reliability that has made it popular with troops all over the world. The FAL is gas operated – a plug above the barrel diverts the gases into a long cylinder and against the piston. When the piston strikes the bolt carrier, it starts to move backwards for 6mm (¼in) of free travel while the pressure in the chamber drops to a safe level. At the end of this travel, a cam on the bolt carrier causes the rear of the bolt to tip upwards into the carrier, unlocking the bolt and extractor. The complete mechanism moves to the rear, with the extractor pulling the empty cartridge case free. When the return spring pushes the bolt and carrier forward again, the next round is taken up by the bolt and fed into the chamber. Once the bolt stops moving forward, the carrier continues to move and the cam forces the rear of the bolt downwards into a locked position.

The FAL always fires from a closed bolt, and most models can fire in semi- or full-automatic modes, though the 7.62mm x 51mm round is really too powerful for controllable hand-held automatic fire. The adjustable gas plug controls the amount of gas diverted against the piston. If the rifle becomes fouled or is fired in sand or dusty conditions, extra gas pressure against the piston will overcome any tendency to jam.

The first models had wooden butts, pistol grips and foregrips, though since the

ABOVE: Heavy firepower. A Colt M4 Carbine with an M203 grenade launcher. The M4 is a shortened version of the M16.

1960s most have been finished with fibreglass. The weapon has a distinctive long, straight outline, with the firer's eye position as near to the level of the barrel as possible. A straight 20-round magazine protrudes below the receiver, in front of the pistol grip and trigger group. There is a simple lever above the pistol grip which is used as a safety catch and selector lever for single shots or bursts. The FAL is sometimes criticised for being too heavy and cumbersome, and as being unnecessarily powerful for most combat ranges, but its reliability and stopping power has ensured it has remained enduringly popular with its users.

Licence production in a number of countries has resulted in several variants of the FAL. The paratrooper model, for example, employs a side-folding tubular metal stock and shorter barrel to make a much handier weapon, and there is also a folding stock variant with the full-length barrel. Another variant is the light machine gun model, which has a heavy barrel and integral bipod. The early FALs had a simple open muzzle, but later models have various designs of flash hider and grenade mounts.

Britain ended World War II with huge stocks of obsolescent Lee-Enfields. A new weapon was needed, and so a team at the Royal Small Arms Factory at Enfield began work on a startling new design. They intended to take account of wartime experience to produce a light, compact weapon able to fire single shots or bursts using lighter, intermediate ammunition. A .280in round was developed that would be effective in infantry combat, but light

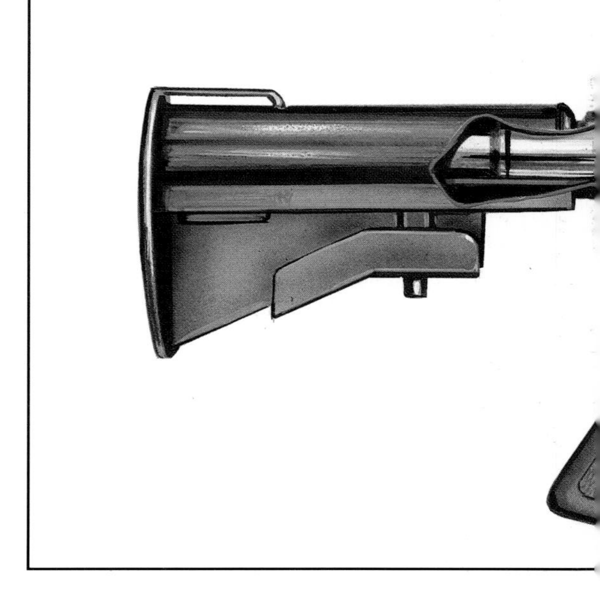

enough to fire in accurate bursts from a hand-held weapon. The rifle developed in 1949 to fire this round looked like nothing else that had ever been seen before, and was called the No 9 Mk 1, or EM2.

To reduce length, the Enfield team had put the magazine, breech and bolt mechanism behind the grip and trigger, with the butt becoming an extension of the body. This configuration, known as 'bullpup', allowed for a surprisingly long barrel (62cm/$24\frac{1}{2}$in) in a compact weapon (89cm/35in). Having the grip and trigger near the centre of the weapon made for good balance, and a firer could bring it to bear on a target quickly. The gas-operated mechanism used a closed-bolt system, with the bolt recoiling into the butt. A 20-round box magazine extended below the receiver, a few centimetres behind the grip. Care was taken to protect the mechanism from dirt and dust, with a hinged door covering the ejection port. The butt, receiver and barrel were all in a straight line, so the sights had to be raised a considerable height above the barrel. This was done by putting a non-magnifying optical sight on top of a fixed carrying handle above the receiver.

The EM2 passed user trials with flying colours, being easy to use, accurate and reliable. The only disadvantage of the bullpup configuration was that as the chamber and ejection port were alongside the firer's face, the weapon could not be fired from the left shoulder. To do so would mean the firer having to expose most of his head and shoulders to shoot from the left side of any cover. Nevertheless, the EM2 was felt to be a major leap forward in firearms design and was approved for use.

However, the EM2 never entered production. The Army had decided that it was imperative to use the standard NATO 7.62mm ammunition, which would have meant a complete re-design of the EM2. It was also felt that British Middle East commitments and the possibility of conflict in open desert terrain would require longer ranges than those offered by the EM2's round. There was also a certain amount of conservative suspicion of the radical new design, as well as doubts about its effectiveness in the rigours of extended combat operations. Time was pressing, so the Army went instead for the Belgian FN FAL (the British Army would eventually accept into service a bullpup weapon firing a small calibre round, but it would take another 30 years for this to happen).

BRITAIN ADOPTS THE FAL

The FAL was manufactured in Britain as the L1A1 Self-Loading Rifle (SLR). There were a number of modifications from the FN model, including the addition of a flash eliminator and removal of the full-automatic capability. SLRs also entered service with other nations, including Canada and Australia, with the Australians setting up their own production line. The SLR is normally equipped with a simple blade foresight and an adjustable aperture rear sight. Luminous tritium indicator marks can be fitted to the foresight for poor visibility, though if more sophisticated telescopic or night sights are to be used, the standard receiver top cover has to be replaced by one with a mounting bracket. The rifle has proved itself to be reliable and rugged, and few modifications have been necessary, the major one being an early change from wooden furniture to fibreglass.

Other nations were also rearming, some with the weapons of their former enemies. Italy, for example, had its armaments industry devastated by the war, so Beretta was licensed to produce US M1 Garands to equip the reconstituted army. Once NATO adopted the 7.62mm calibre, the Italians decided to follow suit, so a new rifle was required. Money was short, so rather than develop a completely new design they decided to modify and improve the M1.

The result, the BM 59, looks very similar to the M14, though the Italian designers created their own modifications to the barrel and gas cylinder. There is a 20-round detachable magazine that can be reloaded while attached to the rifle by using a charging clip. The BM 59 is designed to fire bursts as well as single shots, but as with other weapons using the full-powered 7.62mm round, it is difficult to control when firing full-automatic. A number of variants exist, including a paratrooper model with a pistol grip, folding skeleton stock and bipod, as well as a section automatic weapon which has a heavy bipod.

The French were quick to equip their army with a self-loader, deploying the MAS 49, which fired the French full-powered 7.5mm x 54mm round, in 1949. A large, hefty rifle, the MAS 49 has the look of a conventional bolt-action design, but has a 10-shot detachable box magazine protruding beneath the receiver. Though gas operated, there is no piston – the gases are directed straight to the face of the bolt. As the Americans were to find later, such a mechanism is prone to fouling, but the

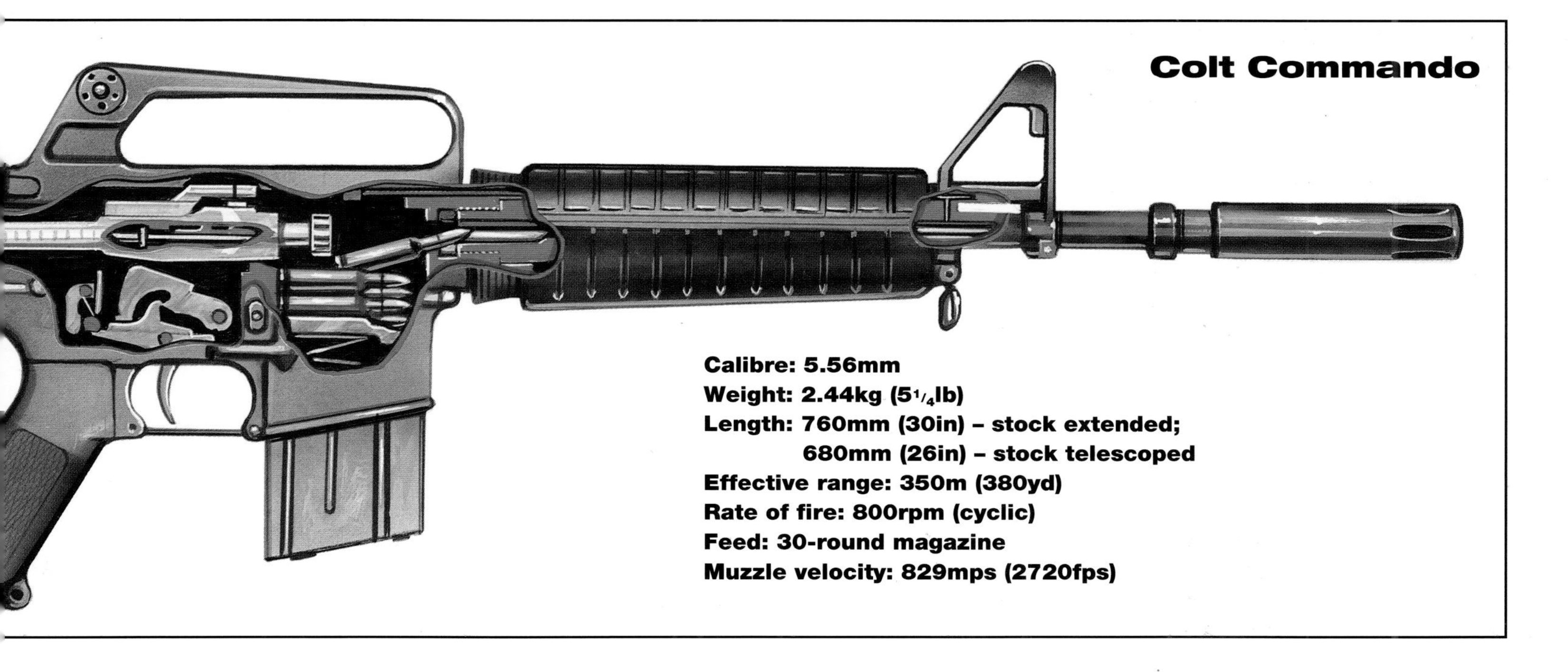

AR70

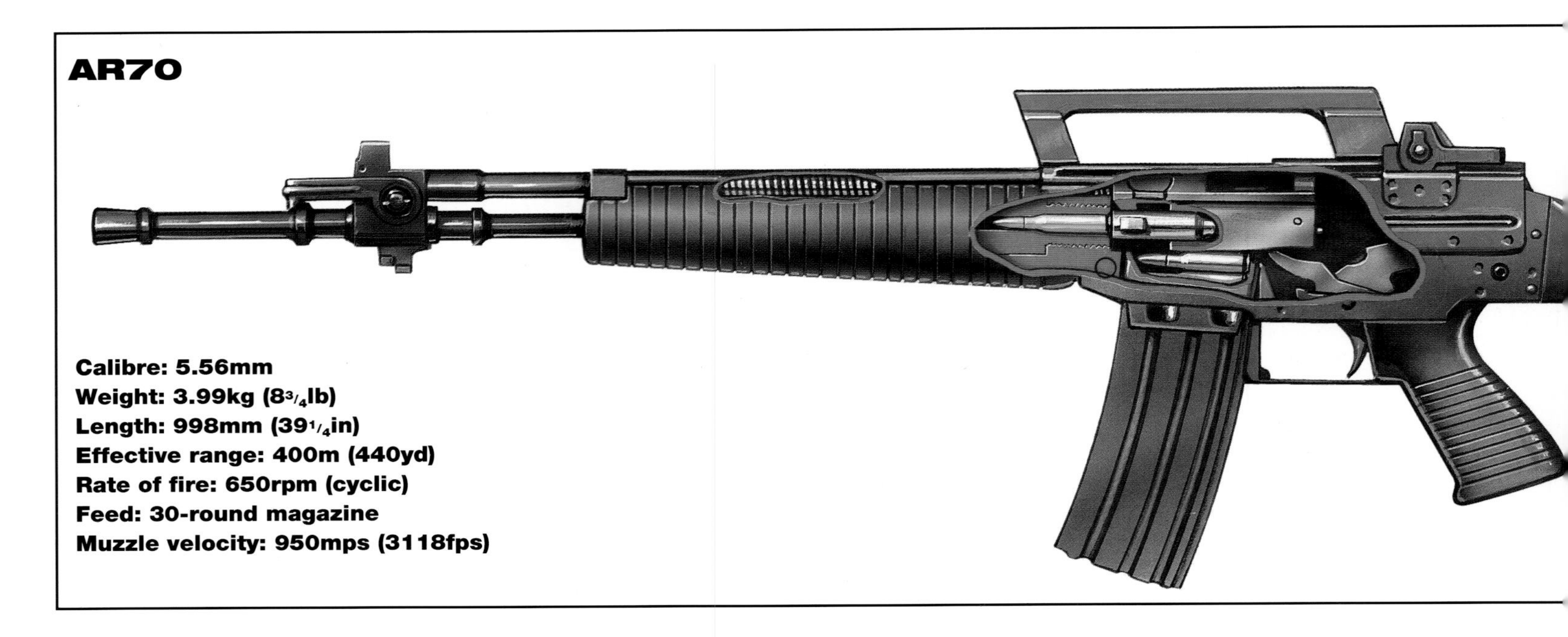

Calibre: 5.56mm
Weight: 3.99kg (8¾lb)
Length: 998mm (39¼in)
Effective range: 400m (440yd)
Rate of fire: 650rpm (cyclic)
Feed: 30-round magazine
Muzzle velocity: 950mps (3118fps)

French ammunition does not seem to have caused any such problems.

After World War II, German engineers in all disciplines found themselves working for other countries. Small arms designers were no exception. A German design team that had been working on self-loading rifles ended up in Spain, together with drawings and data on some of the projects that had been under way at the end of the war. This team started work for CETME (*Compania de Estudios Técnicos de Materiales Especiales*), developing a rifle based on the Mauser StuG45 which had existed in Germany in prototype form. The weapon was to use the unusual delayed blowback system that had been developed for the MG42 machine gun, and has formed the basis for many weapons ever since. The concept was actually devised by a Polish engineer, Edward Steicke, and the Germans found a prototype design when they overran his country in 1939. The StuG45 used the delayed blowback system, and the CETME team continued the development.

Straightforward blowback uses the gas pressure on the empty cartridge case to push back the bolt system. The advantages are a simpler and lighter weapon with no cylinder and piston assembly, though most blowback weapons fire from an open bolt and thus have inferior accuracy. The bolt usually has to be sufficiently heavy to provide some delay before it moves backwards, otherwise the gases will vent out of the breech at a dangerously high pressure.

CETME'S BLOWBACK DESIGN

The German design enabled blowback to be used from a closed bolt and had a unique mechanical system which delayed bolt opening in a reliable and safe way. There is a flat bolt head which pushes the cartridge case into the breech and forms the rear of the chamber. Behind the bolt head are two small vertical metal rollers, the axes of which are free to move outwards from the bolt. Behind them is a locking piece which contains the firing pin and has a sloping front face. The locking piece can slide into the rear of the bolt head and is held from behind by the heavy bolt carrier. When a round is fed into the chamber, the bolt head is actually forced into the larger diameter extension of the barrel and chamber. The locking piece is pushed up against the bolt head, and its sloping face forces the metal rollers outwards, where they lock into recesses in the barrel extension. Once they are fully locked, there is space for the firing pin to pass between them and through a hole in the centre of the bolt face. The trigger is pulled and a hammer drives the firing pin, which jabs the igniter in the cartridge, firing the round. The high gas pressure tries to force the bolt backwards from the barrel extension, but initial movement is opposed by the locked rollers. The rollers are eventually forced inwards by a shaped cam path and the bolt is free to move. The locking piece and carrier are forced back, extracting the empty case, compressing the return spring and cocking the hammer. The return spring then pushes the bolt assembly forward, picking up a

Galil

Calibre: 5.56mm
Length: 979mm (38½in)
Effective range: 400m (440yd)
Rate of fire: 650rpm (cyclic)
Weight: 4.35kg (9½lb)
Feed: 30- or 50-round magazine
Muzzle velocity: 950mps (3118fps)

ABOVE RIGHT: The rugged Galil assault rifle. All Israeli Galils have metal folding stocks to facilitate movement in and out of armoured personnel carriers by mechanised troops.

new round and forcing it into the chamber. The delay in unlocking caused by the movement of the rollers is enough to reduce the gas pressures to a safe level.

Case extraction can pose a problem for blowback weapons because the bolt and extractor move back very quickly, without any initial turning motion to release the case from the chamber. This sharp pull backwards can sometimes rip the base from the cartridge case, leaving the rest in the rifle. The solution used by the CETME team was to cut shallow flutes in the chamber where the case sat. Some of the gas leaks around the outside of the case, freeing it from the walls of the chamber and making extraction much easier.

An automatic rifle using such a roller-delayed system, and firing a version of the German wartime 7.92mm *Kurz* round with a lighter bullet, was produced in Spain. By the mid-1950s, the West German Army was being created and, in an ironic twist, the Spanish offered the Germans their own design back as an infantry assault rifle. The *Bundeswehr* liked the idea, but had already decided to follow the NATO standard, so requested that the weapon be re-designed for the more powerful 7.62mm round. The German company of Heckler & Koch took

RIGHT: The South African version of the Galil, the R4 rifle. An interesting feature is the nylon/fibreglass magazine, designed to save weight.

over development, and by 1959 the 7.62mm G3 (*Gewehr* 3) was in full production.

The G3 is very similar to the FN FAL, being only 28mm shorter and only 10g (22lb) heavier. Ammunition is also held in a 20-round detachable box in front of the trigger, and a lever just above the trigger is used as a safety catch and semi- or full-automatic fire selector. The rifle, which has plastic furniture, is largely made from pressings and stampings. At first glance the G3 looks rather like a gas-operated weapon, with what appears to be a gas plug and cylinder above the barrel. This tube actually contains the operating mechanism for the bolt, with the cocking handle protruding on the left side, well forward of the magazine. The tube extends into the receiver, where it holds the top piece of the bolt carrier then the long return spring. An adjustable rotary rear sight sits above the receiver, level with the trigger and pistol grip, while the foresight consists of a simple blade enclosed by a circular protective shroud. The G3 is a tough and reliable 'no-frills' weapon which has entered service with over 50 countries. There have been versions with retractable metal stocks, and specially selected rifles have been equipped with telescopic sights and used as police sniper weapons, called the G3SG/1.

THE SWISS Stgw 57

The Spanish also decided to change to 7.62mm calibre, though they developed a lower-powered round with a reduced propellant charge from that of the NATO standard. CETME reworked the original assault rifle design to produce the Model 58. The common parentage between this and the G3 is readily apparent, though the Spanish weapon is slightly shorter and heavier. The CETME has a slightly different mechanism, in that when automatic fire is selected it fires from an open bolt. The butt and grip are made from plastic, although many models still have a wooden foregrip, and some have a light bipod permanently attached. Owing to the unusual ammunition, the CETME has not had the same export success as the G3, though it is just as effective and reliable. In 1974, the Spanish adopted the full-power NATO cartridge and the CETME Model C was produced. Both the CETME and G3 have served their countries well, and both form the basis for further development, with Heckler & Koch in particular creating a range of rifles, submachine guns and machine guns all using the roller-delayed blowback system.

Swiss engineers were also familiar with the German StuG45, and were quick to develop their own rifle using the roller-delayed blowback mechanism. The result, the Stgw 57, entered service in the late 1950s and was designed to use the Swiss 7.5mm x 54mm round. The bolt mechanism is similar to that of the G3 and CETME, though there are some important differences: while the chamber has the same flutes engraved around the cartridge to allow some gases to pass around the case, there are two small holes in the face of the bolt that allow these gases to pass through and impinge on the locking piece, giving some assistance to the rearward movement of the bolt assembly.

A large (1105mm/43½in) rifle, the Stgw 57 is much heavier than most of its contemporaries, weighing in at 5.55kg (12¼in). Single shots or bursts can be fired, with ammunition being held in a 24-round magazine. An integral folding bipod folds under the metal cooling jacket which also forms the foregrip, and the weapon has a straightline configuration to enable control of bursts. It is perhaps too long and heavy to be a true assault rifle, but it is more than adequate for the Swiss concept of defensive operations in rugged terrain. It is extremely tough, reliable and easy to use and maintain, ideal qualifications for use by conscripts. The rifle has been developed to use the NATO 7.62mm round as the SG510 series, though these have not had much success outside Switzerland.

By 1960, a large proportion of the world's soldiers were equipped with some form of self-loading rifle. Those that belonged to armies aligned with or friendly to the Soviet Union were almost all equipped with some variant of the Kalashnikov, firing the 7.62mm x 39mm round. Nations with links to the United States and NATO were using the more powerful 7.62mm x 51mm cartridge, and firing it from a range of semi-automatic or selective fire assault rifles. There were other calibres in use, including the German wartime 7.92mm, but the two 7.62mm rounds dominated the world scene.

THE ARMALITE REVOLUTION

Weapons design never stands still, and some American and European engineers in the 1950s were already looking at the possibilities of smaller and lighter rounds optimised for medium and short ranges. The British had already tried to embrace this concept with the EM2 in the 1940s, but, as stated above, had abandoned it for the NATO 7.62mm round and the FAL. In America, however, Eugene Stoner, one of the most prolific arms designers of modern times, was also examining the characteristics of small calibres and lighter rifles.

■ ABOVE: SA-80 – the compact and lightweight bullpup assault rifle in use with the British Army.

In the mid-1950s, Stoner was an employee of the Armalite Division of the Fairchild Corporation, a concern that specialised in lightweight rifles, shotguns and aircrew survival weapons. In 1955 he had developed an unusual weapon known as the AR10, which he had tried to persuade the US Army to take instead of the M14. The AR10 used a two-piece bolt, in which multiple lugs locked the bolt in place as it was rotated by the carrier. The bolt face locking concept allowed most parts of the mechanism to be made from lightweight materials such as aluminium. Light alloys were also extensively used elsewhere on the weapon, reducing its weight to 3.4kg (7½lb). The AR10 also had a so-called straightline layout: the butt, receiver and barrel were all at the same level. Such a configuration transfers the recoil to the firer's shoulder in a straight line, helping to reduce muzzle climb when firing bursts. The sights were integral to a large carrying handle above the receiver,

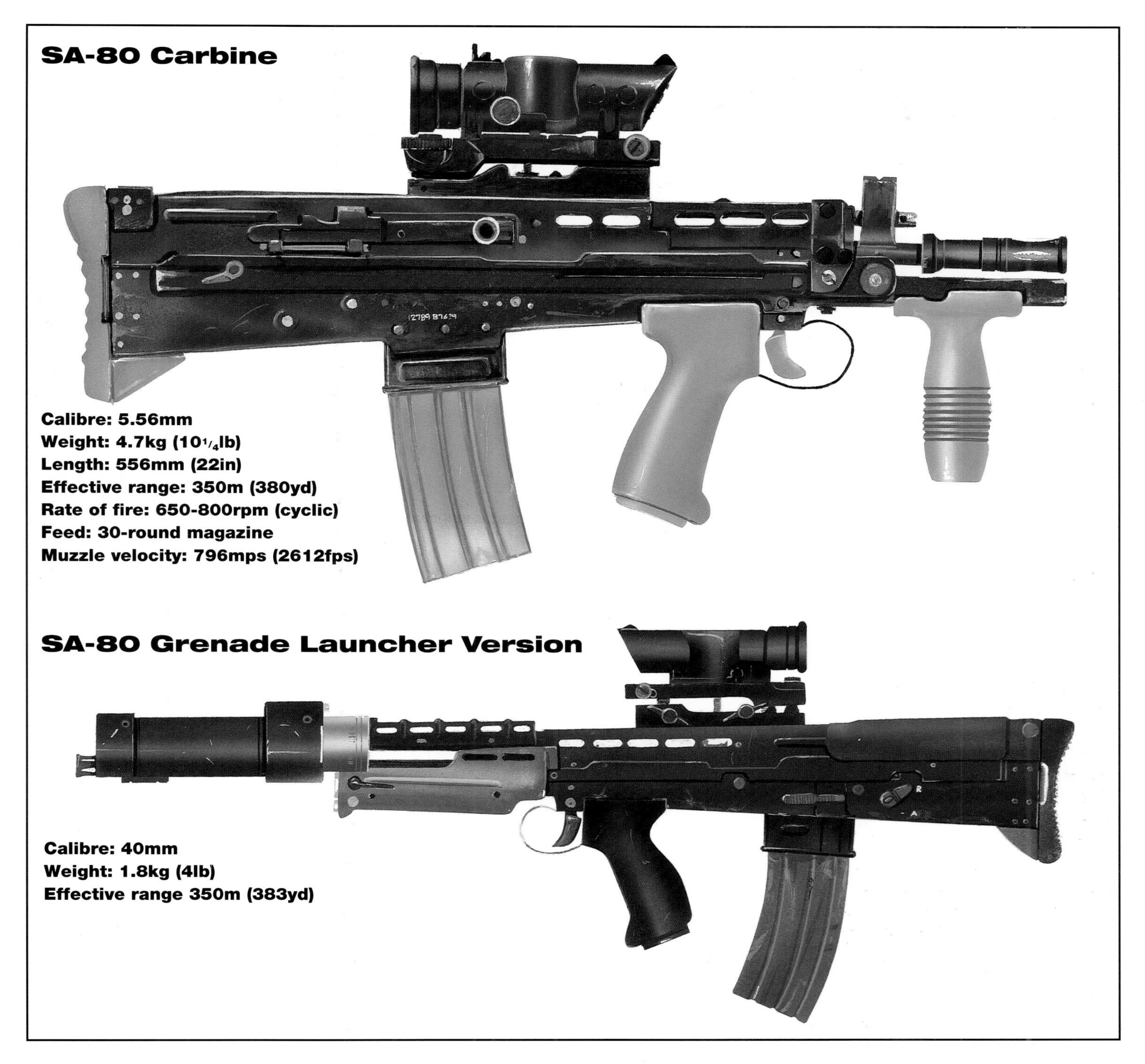

with the cocking handle lying just behind this assembly. The AR10 was gas operated, but dispensed with the weight and complexity of a piston and actuating rod. Gases were diverted into the cylinder, from where they impinged directly on the bolt carrier, causing movement to the rear. The whole weapon was a lightweight, effective design. Unfortunately for Armalite, the US Army was already committed to the M14, and as a consequence the AR10 only sold in small numbers to Guatemala and the Sudan.

However, the company continued to look at lightweight weapons, awaiting the development of an effective small-calibre bullet. Small cartridges already existed for target shooting and small game, but these were not effective as anti-personnel ammunition. By the late 1950s, however, Remington had come up with an improved version of their .223in round with a heavier bullet, and this was to be developed as the 5.56mm x 45mm M193 round. Smaller and lighter than the 7.62mm round, the M193 is effective up to a range of 366m (400yd). The bullet is designed to tumble on hitting a target, inflicting damage out of all proportion to its size. It also tends to fragment on impact, again dispersing its energy over a wide area. Being much lighter than the then current ammunition, more 5.56mm rounds could be carried by soldiers in battle.

Stoner saw that a rifle designed for this cartridge could be made significantly lighter than one firing 7.62mm ammunition. Recoil would be reduced and there would be less flash and a quieter report than from the more powerful round. He incorporated many of the attributes of the AR10 in the new design, which was known as the Armalite AR15. Another straightline rifle with the rearsight in the carrying handle, the AR15 makes extensive use of light alloys and has a black plastic butt, pistol grip and foregrip. Initially, a box magazine holding 20 rounds was provided, but a larger 30-shot item soon followed. Like the AR10, the AR15 has no piston, the gases

M16A1

Rear Sight Adjustor
Charging Handle
Forward Bolt Assist
Buffer Tube
Auto Sear
Selector Cam
Disconnect
Grip
Stock
Sling Swivel

bolt carrier. This worked well with the original 5.56mm cartridge used in development, but since then the Army had changed the propellant specification, which caused much more dirt and grease to coagulate on the bolt carrier and foul the weapon. This problem was compounded by a belief that the M16 needed minimal maintenance; indeed, it was originally sold as a self-cleaning weapon! Many soldiers were not even issued with cleaning kits. The realisation gradually dawned that the new rifle needed to be carefully looked after, and so a revised training philosophy was introduced. Fragile magazine lips also created jams in the feed system, though modification to the design soon overcame this. Once the US Army adapted to the characteristics of the M16, the rifle became a popular and effective weapon.

5.56MM VERSUS 7.62MM

Within a few years the M16A1 became the standard US Army infantry rifle in all theatres, much to the consternation of the other NATO states. Having been railroaded into accepting a modified American 7.62mm cartridge, and investing in production facilities, ammunition and new weapons, they now found that their standardisation agreements were waste paper as far as the Americans were concerned. For the next 15 to 20 years, the NATO alliance was faced with the possibility of going to war with one of their largest component armies using completely different ammunition from everyone else.

The American Army and Air Force were totally committed to 5.56mm calibre, though the Navy stayed with the 7.62mm M14. M16s also found favour with many other armies, and licence production was undertaken in Singapore, The Philippines and elsewhere. Over eight million have been made, and the basic bolt mechanism has been copied in many other rifles. The M16 is especially popular with special forces and reconnaissance troops, and has been used by the British Special Air Service (SAS) since its 1960s Borneo campaign.

Stoner's design forms the basis for a family of weapons, all with the same mechanism and general shape. The CAR15, or Colt Commando, was developed as a result of experience in Vietnam. The objective was to create a short carbine of similar size to a submachine gun but firing rifle ammunition. The barrel length is reduced to 259mm (10¼in) from the M16A1's 508mm (20in) and the Commando sports a sliding extendable butt. Using such a short barrel creates a massive muzzle flash, so a large flash eliminator is normally attached. The mechanism is almost identical to that of the M16A1 and most component parts are interchangeable. The Commando found ready acceptance with US Special Forces in Vietnam, and is used by elite units in many other countries.

THE PORT FIRING WEAPON

An unusual M16 variant is the M231 Port Firing Weapon. When the US Army introduced the M2 Infantry Fighting Vehicle into service, tactical doctrine called for its mounted squad to be able to provide suppressive fire from weapon ports in the hull. Rather than follow the Soviet example of clipping their issue rifles into open ports, the Americans fitted modified M16s to the ports, leaving them permanently attached to the vehicle. These M231s have no stocks or sights and they fire from an open bolt, though most of the mechanism and feed system are interchangeable with the M16A1. The M231 has a collar attachment for mounting to the firing port, and fire is directed at the target by using tracer and viewing the fall of shot through glass periscopes. When the soldiers exit the vehicle, they simply leave these weapons in place and take with them their own M16s.

Steyr AUG

Calibre: 5.56mm
Weight: 3.9kg (8½lb)
Length: 790mm (31in)
Effective range: 400m (440yd)
Rate of fire: 650rpm (cyclic)
Feed: 30- or 42-round magazine
Muzzle velocity: 970mps (3184fps)

As a result of further experience, the M16A1 was modified to fire the more effective SS109 bullet. This involved using

BELOW: The French FAMAS assault rifle. Like most bullpups, it is compact, light and comfortable to fire.

FAMAS

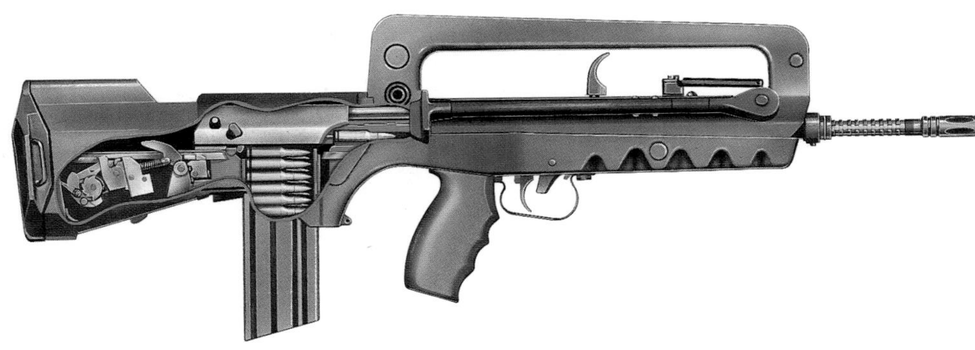

Calibre: 5.56mm
Weight: 3.61kg (8lb)
Length: 757mm (30in)
Effective range: 400m (440yd)
Rate of fire: 900-1000rpm (cyclic)
Feed: 25-round magazine
Muzzle velocity: 960mps (3150fps)

Left: The M16 assault rifle – this is an A1 version – is an excellent weapon, but it requires highly specialised machine tooling, a fact that tends to make unit costs expensive.

Right: The M16 is excellent for jungle warfare because it is short, light and has a high muzzle velocity – its bullet cuts to pieces anything it hits at close quarters.

Far Right: The M16s in US service can fire single shots or three-round bursts. The three-round burst facility was adopted in preference to full-automatic to conserve ammunition.

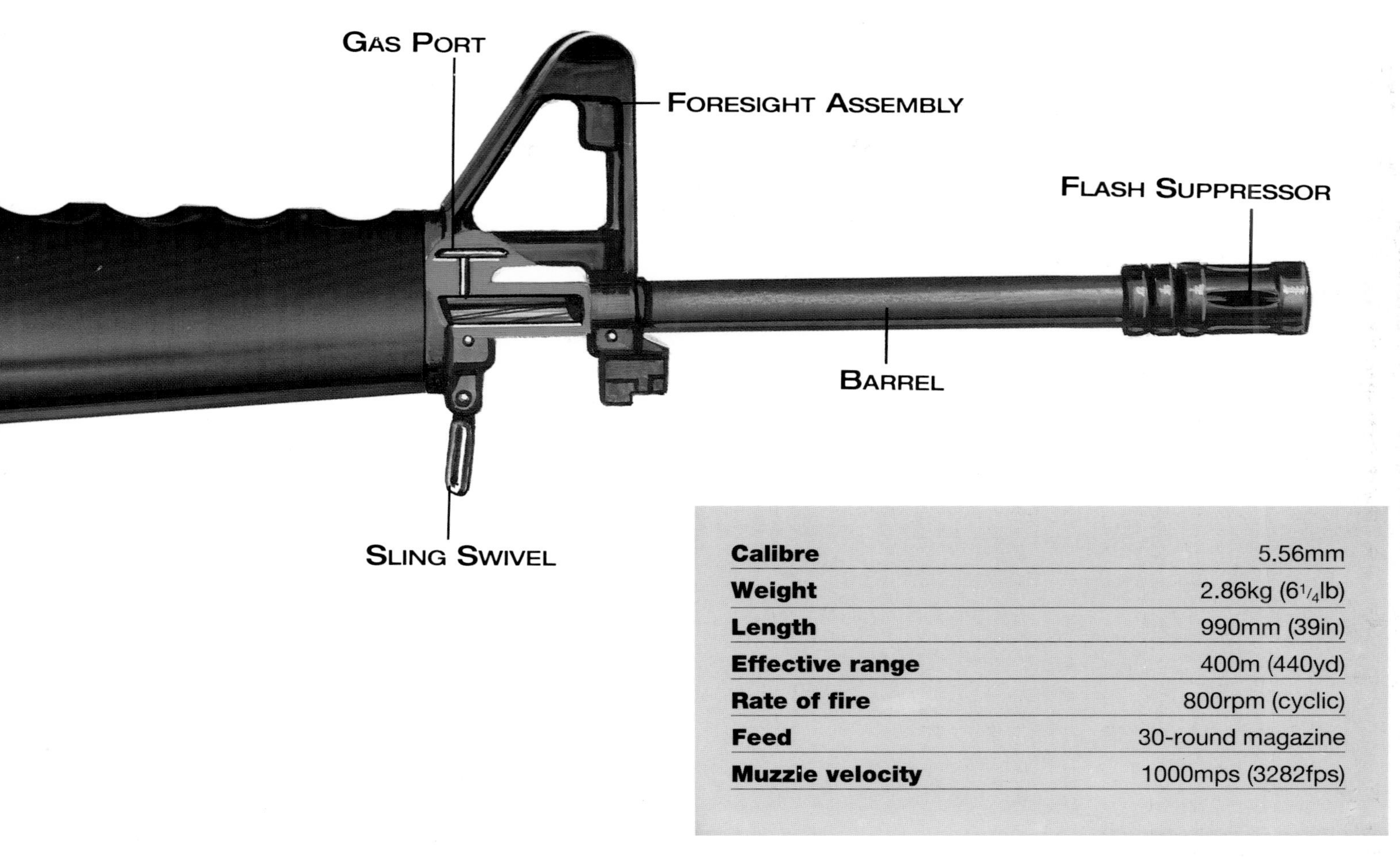

Calibre	5.56mm
Weight	2.86kg (6¼lb)
Length	990mm (39in)
Effective range	400m (440yd)
Rate of fire	800rpm (cyclic)
Feed	30-round magazine
Muzzie velocity	1000mps (3282fps)

being directed along a steel tube to impinge directly on the bolt carrier. The bolt has seven lugs around its face which lock into the barrel extension when it is rotated by the cam pin on the bolt carrier. The AR15 also has its cocking handle above the receiver, in the rear of the carrying handle. A large upright post in front of the foregrip holds the foresight, and there is a flash eliminator at the end of the barrel. A lever above the pistol grip is used to select single or automatic fire (the low recoil forces make bursts easily controllable). In 1957, the AR15 was licensed by Colt and large-scale production began. By the early 1960s, trouble was flaring up in Southeast Asia, and some countries in the area purchased the new weapon for their troops. Asian soldiers are generally of smaller stature than their Western counterparts, and the lightweight weapon proved ideal for their use.

US servicemen were initially suspicious of the new rifle. Low weight, light alloys, black plastic furniture and tiny bullets gave the impression of it being a toy. To men brought up on the M14, a real rifle was much heavier, gave a kick like a mule, was preferably machined from solid steel, and had polished wooden furniture. The AR15 didn't even sound like a proper rifle, giving off a light popping noise rather than the satisfying crack of 7.62mm calibres.

As the United States began its long and painful involvement in Vietnam, the Air Force selected the AR15 to equip its Vietnamese security guards. The Armalite thus entered service, being known as the M16. Once it started to see combat, more and more soldiers began to appreciate the value of the new design. A number gradually trickled into Army use, troopers finding the size and weight of the rifle ideal for jungle combat at short and medium ranges. In the sapping humidity of Southeast Asia, a rifle that was a few pounds lighter was a blessing to an overloaded infantryman. It could also be brought to bear faster than the heavier M14, and an infantry squad could put down a withering amount of automatic fire in an ambush. An unexpected benefit was that the lack of recoil, flash and bang meant inexperienced conscripts became accustomed to their rifles much more quickly than previously, which made marksmanship training much easier.

In the mid-1960s, there was uncertainty among the American military as to whether the new calibre should be more widely used. Many soldiers still preferred the stopping power and range of the 7.62mm round, believing it to be better at penetrating cover and able to cause more damage when it hit. The decision was made for them, however, when in 1966 General Westmoreland, Commander of US Forces in Vietnam, formally requested 100,000 of the new weapon for service in Vietnam, to be known in Army service as the M16A1.

ABOVE: The gas-operated Steyr AUG is largely made from synthetic materials, which means it is lightweight compared to other rifles. It is also comfortable to fire.

The M16A1 was modified slightly from the original M16, the main difference being a bolt closure device enabling the soldier to drive the bolt home if dirt and fouling were jamming operation. By 1967 thousands of troops were equipped with the plastic rifle and it rapidly became standard-issue in Southeast Asia. However, mass-issue brought a number of problems: persistent stories of stoppages and unreliability, and huge quantities of ammunition being expended with no result. Further investigation found that flaws in US Army training and lack of fire discipline were causing soldiers to blaze away in automatic fire without taking proper aim, burning up ammunition by the truckload. An average of between 50,000 and 200,000 rounds were being fired to inflict one casualty!

The difficulties with mechanical reliability were more serious, and the M16 got a reputation for constant jams and stoppages. The operating principle of the M16 uses hot gas diverted straight to the

a slightly heavier barrel and changing the rifling to optimise the spin given to the new bullet, which has resulted in the M16 having improved range and lethality. The new model is known as the M16A2, and was introduced into Army service in 1985. It is recognisable by the ribbed foregrip, which is made from stronger plastic. Ammunition wastage by firing long bursts was still felt to be a problem, however, so the A2 has been designed with no full-automatic facility. Instead, it has a special setting to fire three-round bursts on each pull of the trigger, which makes for a good compromise between accuracy and firepower. A new design of flash hider is fitted, overcoming the tendency for the muzzle blast from the M16A1 to kick up dust when it is fired from the prone position. The SS109 bullet is more accurate at longer ranges than the M193, so a more sophisticated rearsight is fitted at the rear of the carrying handle. As a result of extensive combat experience, the M16A2 is now one of the best fighting rifles in the world.

A shorter carbine version of the A2, known as the Colt M4, also exists. This looks almost identical to the Colt Commando, with the same extendable butt and shortened foregrip. It has the A2 rear sight, however, and a slightly longer barrel (368mm) than the Commando. The M4 also has the three-round burst system and is optimised for the SS109 bullet. An even shorter M16K model is offered by the La France company. There is also a light machine gun M16, and Colt have even produced a 9mm submachine gun model for police and security agencies. Additional extras available for the M16 family include large-capacity drum magazines, belt-feed kits and .22in training conversions.

An M203 40mm grenade launcher can be fitted to any M16 by clipping it underneath the foregrip and barrel, giving the infantry squad a useful high-explosive fire capability. This single-shot weapon does not interfere with the rifle's firing capability, having its own trigger system. Flip-up sights are also attached to take account of the high angled trajectory of the grenades. A more unusual grenade attachment is the Brunswick 140mm RAW (Rifleman's Assault Weapon). This is a large, almost spherical grenade with a rocket thruster which is clipped to a special attachment under the barrel of the M16. When an ordinary bullet is fired, gases exiting at the muzzle are tapped off to trigger the RAW launcher, igniting the rocket propulsion and sending the large grenade towards the target. There is little or no recoil felt by the firer, and the flat trajectory makes aiming easy. RAW has a large warhead which will blow a sizeable hole in concrete, brickwork, earth or sandbagged constructions.

THE MOVE TO SMALL CALIBRES

Designers in other countries had also been experimenting with smaller calibres, and most had followed American experiences with the M16 with great interest. Reports from Vietnam prompted the Belgian firm FN to investigate the effectiveness of such weapons, and its first attempt at a new

FN FNC

Calibre: 5.56mm
Weight: 3.8kg (8¼lb)
Length: 997mm (39¼in)
Range: 400m (440yd)
Rate of fire: 600-750rpm
Feed: 30-round magazine
Muzzle velocity: 965mps (3170fps)

design was the FN CAL of the mid-1960s. The CAL was more or less a 5.56mm derivative of the very successful FAL, though it used a rotating bolt rather than the earlier rifle's dropping bolt system. Unfortunately for FN, the NATO armies were in the middle of re-equipping with 7.62mm weapons, and were understandably reluctant to change calibres so soon. The Swiss also attempted to develop a 5.56mm weapon, and produced a design based on a modified 7.62mm SG510. This employed a hybrid version of the roller-delayed blowback system, in which a gas-operated piston provided the impulse to retract the rollers and recoil the bolt. The design was perhaps too complex, but the main obstacle to commercial success was again the NATO commitment to 7.62mm.

Limited success in marketing a 5.56mm weapon during the 1960s was achieved by the Italian company Beretta with the AR70/223. A lightweight, gas-operated weapon, the AR70 makes extensive use of steel pressings, spot welding and plastic furniture. The mechanism is similar to that of the AK-47: a rotary bolt with two locking lugs at the bolt face. A 30-round detachable box magazine sits under the receiver, and single shots or bursts are selectable. Rifle grenades can also be launched without modification to the rifle. The AR70 has proved to be a workmanlike and capable design. By replacing the fixed plastic butt with a folding metal wire model, the rifle becomes the SC70 Special Troops Carbine. There is also an SC70 variant with a 320mm (12½in) barrel, some 130mm (5in) shorter than standard, for issue to officers, vehicle crews, signallers and support troops. The Beretta series has been in service with Italian paras and special forces, though the rest of the army had to make do with the BM 59. The AR70 family has also seen service in Jordan, Malaysia and elsewhere.

THE NO-FRILLS GALIL

It was in the Middle East, however, that the 5.56mm calibre first came into widespread non-US use. After the 1967 Six-Day War, the Israeli Army felt the need for a lighter and handier weapon than the hefty FN FAL, which was then issued as standard. Israeli soldiers had been greatly impressed by the rugged, handy and effective AK-47s used by their Arab opponents, and requested similar characteristics from any new weapon. Never ones to ignore a good idea, Israeli Military Industries took many of the best features of the AK series and incorporated them in the new 5.56mm rifle (the first development batch actually used components from the Finnish M62 Valmet, itself a modified AK design). The Israeli weapon was more than just a copy, however, incorporating as it did the lessons of extensive combat experience.

Named after the designers, Yakov Lior and Israel Galili, the new weapon was called the Galil. Early in the programme the decision was taken to use a relatively heavy barrel, enabling the parallel development of 5.56mm and 7.62mm versions. The Israeli Army would only use the 5.56mm model,

■ LEFT: SIG's SG550 rifle. The design includes several weight-saving measures, including a plastic butt, hand guard and magazine, the latter being transparent.

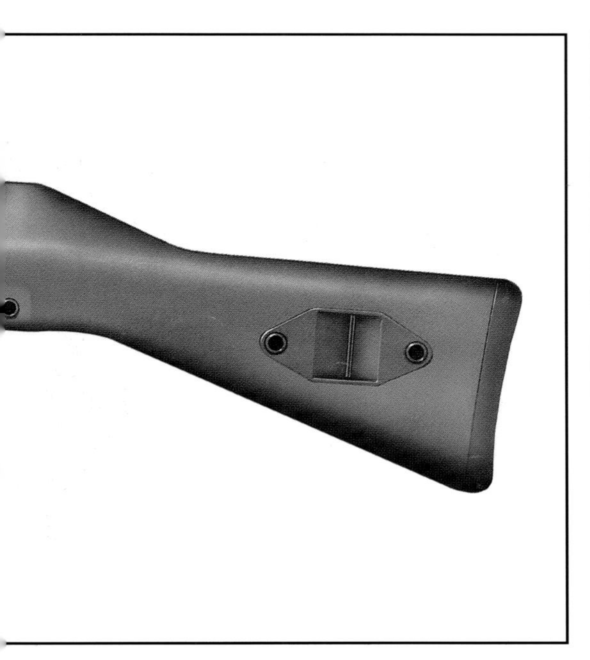

ABOVE: Heckler & Koch's 33E rifle, a 5.56mm gun that can fire rifle grenades.

but the 7.62mm has enjoyed some export success. The Galil is gas operated, with the piston and cylinder above the barrel. The bolt is based on the AK rotating bolt mechanism, and a Kalashnikov-style 35-round magazine protrudes below the receiver. Like the AK, the Galil fires from an open bolt. There are a number of variants, including a light machine gun (with a 50-round magazine) and a highly modified sniper rifle. The standard Israeli model is the 5.56mm ARM, which has a folding metal stock, integral bipod and carrying handle. There is also an AR variant, with no bipod and carrying handle, and an SAR which is a shorter carbine model. Some export models have a wooden stock, and 7.62mm versions of all configurations are available.

Attention to detail is obvious in some of the unusual features of the Galil. The standard sights are a two-aperture flip sight to the rear, with a simple post at the fore, calibrated to 600m. For shooting in poor visibility, luminous tritium markers are fitted to all models. A V-shaped rear aperture folds up, which has one luminous spot on each arm of the V. A third spot is on a foresight post, which is also folded up. All the firer needs to do is to ensure all three spots are in a straight row, with the central one over the target. The rifle and light machine gun models have an integral folding bipod, the legs of which double as wirecutters. Perhaps the feature that has attracted more attention than any other is the bottle opener built into the magazine catch. This is a serious feature, as combat experience identified a number of cases where troops used the magazine lips on their FAL in this way, leading to damage and the possibility of a stoppage.

The Galil is extremely tough and reliable, being largely made from solid machined blocks rather than stampings and pressings. Demonstrations of this ruggedness were popular in the 1970s, when Galils were buried in sand, immersed in water, driven over by trucks and generally mistreated before firing hundreds of rounds without any problems. The Galil is a superb rifle from a nation whose combat experience is second to none, and whose survival has often depended on success in battle.

Other countries have also been impressed by the Galil, and have selected it for use with their own armed forces. The South African R4 rifle, for example, is a Galil with minor modifications, including the metal stock being replaced by a slightly longer one made from carbon plastic, plus a strengthened foregrip. Some small changes have been made to ease manufacture, such as the fibreglass magazine instead of the standard metal one. As with the Galil, the R4 has proved itself on extended combat operations in hot, dusty conditions.

SC70

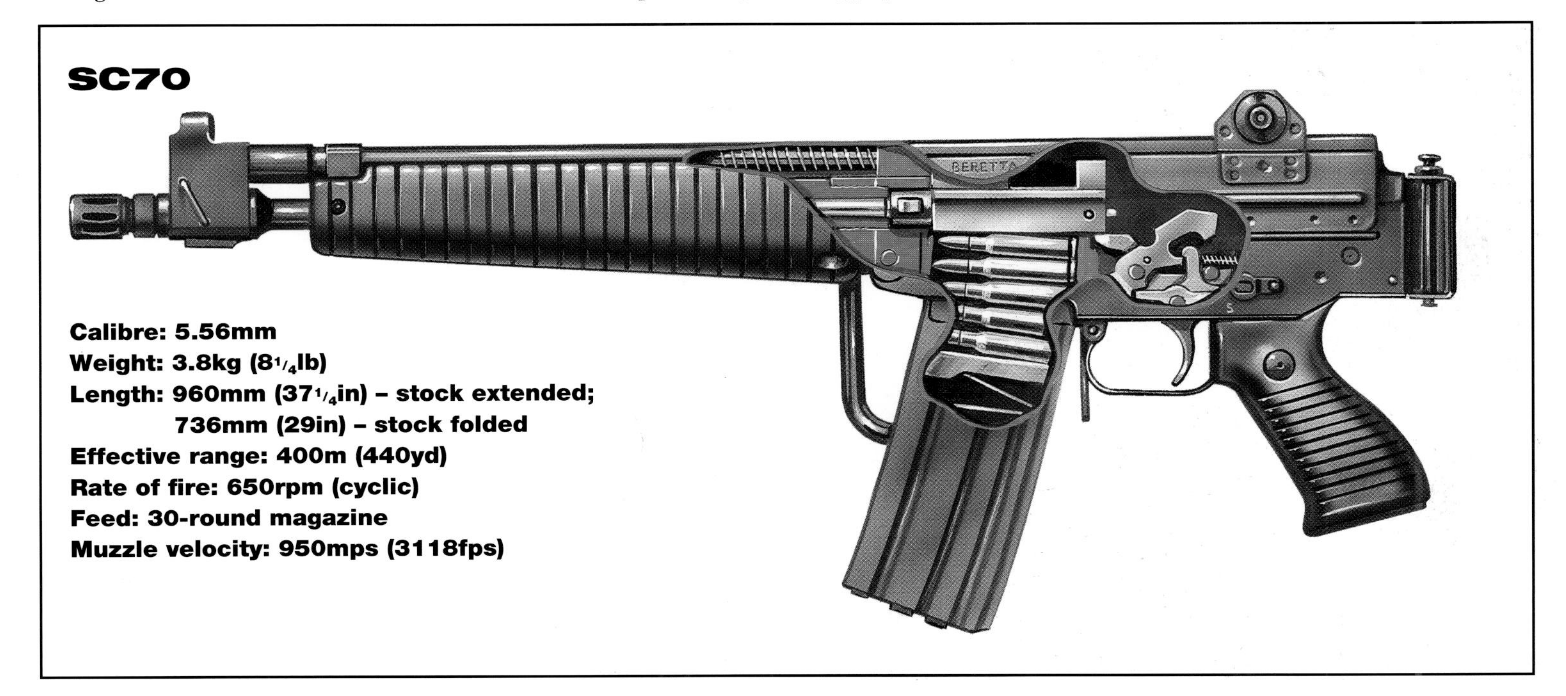

Calibre: 5.56mm
Weight: 3.8kg (8 1/4lb)
Length: 960mm (37 1/4in) – stock extended; 736mm (29in) – stock folded
Effective range: 400m (440yd)
Rate of fire: 650rpm (cyclic)
Feed: 30-round magazine
Muzzle velocity: 950mps (3118fps)

AKS-74

Calibre: 5.45mm
Weight: 3.6kg (8lb)
Length: 930mm (36½in) – stock extended; 690mm (27in) – stock folded
Effective range: 400m (440yd)
Rate of fire: 650rpm (cyclic)
Feed: 30-round magazine
Muzzle velocity: 900mps (2954fps)

By the early 1970s, most NATO countries were looking at replacements for their 7.62mm assault rifles. It was expected that the next generation of service rifles would use some form of smaller calibre, but this was still to be decided on an alliance-wide basis. In Britain designers were resurrecting the concepts behind the EM2, and began developing a small-calibre weapon. The new mechanism was based on that used in the American AR18, a 5.56mm assault rifle designed by Armalite after Stoner had left the company. Armalite had felt that the sophisticated manufacturing techniques required to produce the AR15/M16 series were such that very few countries had the resources to make these weapons. The AR18 was an attempt to develop a simpler 5.56mm weapon taking account of experience with the M16, and was deliberately designed for ease of production. A piston system was also incorporated, as opposed to the direct gas flow to the bolt which had caused problems with the M16. The US Army was fully committed to the earlier rifle, however, and the AR18 never entered service.

ABOVE: The grandfather of the AK-74, the AK-47 assault rifle. The AK-47 is 7.62mm calibre, whereas the AK-74 is 5.45mm.

RIGHT: Croatian fighters battle Serb gunmen during the current civil strife in Yugoslavia. The two men with assault rifles are armed with AK-47s, rather than the Yugoslav version of the weapon, the 7.62mm M70 assault rifle. The M70 rifle is similar to its Soviet counterpart, though an important difference is the grenade-launching sight that is permanently attached to the M70 at the gas port and which, when raised, cuts off the gas supply to the piston.

LEFT: The 5.45mm AKSU-74 submachine gun, a variant model of the AKS-74 rifle. Note the bell-mouthed flash hider.

L42A1

Licence production was undertaken in Britain (by Sterling Industries), Japan, Holland and The Philippines, though most potential customers were either happy with the M16 or intent on developing their own weapons (British readers may be familiar with the AR18 as the 'Armalite' rifle used by IRA terrorists as the symbol of their bloody struggle for Irish unification).

OF CALIBRES AND BULLETS

The design of the AR18 was sound, and engineers at the Royal Small Arms Factory at Enfield, London, used the basic mechanism for their new Enfield Weapons System (EWS). Looking rather similar to the EM2, the EWS is also a bullpup design, with the bolt, chamber and magazine behind the grip. It is, in fact, a completely different design, with virtually nothing in common with the earlier weapon. The EWS was planned to use a unique small-calibre round of 4.85mm, though the British engineers remembered the lessons of the EM2 and designed the new weapon to be easily converted to 5.56mm. This forethought was to stand them in good stead when NATO sponsored a series of trials to decide upon a new standard round.

From 1977 to 1979, various NATO states examined future rifle requirements, and tested a range of service weapons and prototypes. With the United States Army already equipped with the M16, it seemed a foregone conclusion that the new standard would be 5.56mm x 45mm. Where there was European dissent, however, was in the performance of the American M193 bullet. This was regarded as being only marginally effective at medium ranges and having inadequate stopping power. Reports from Vietnam had told of determined enemies still shooting back after taking multiple hits from M16s, while anyone hit by a 7.62mm bullet tended to stay down. NATO decided to use the American cartridge, but with a new bullet designed by the Belgian company FN. This projectile is heavier and longer than the M193, and is known as the SS109 or 5.56mm NATO.

The first generation of 5.56mm weapons were optimised to fire the American bullet, though it tends to become unstable very quickly and its range is poor. The NATO round demands rifling with a tighter twist than for the M193 – usually one twist in around 178mm (7in) rather than the 305mm (12in) of the M16A1. Some weapons use a compromise figure to allow effective performance from both rounds. Once the decision to standardise was taken, however, development of lighter 5.56mm assault rifles proceeded rapidly. As mentioned above, the United States Army also saw the worth of the new ammunition and produced the modified M16A2. A host of other NATO agreements created standards for details such as magazine feeds, sight mounts and other components. NATO soldiers of different nationalities may not have had the same equipment, but at least they could now use the same ammunition and supply each other with full magazines in an emergency.

Back in the United Kingdom, the Enfield Weapons System was quickly modified to the new calibre, and used the NATO standard magazine feed (which is actually that of the M16). Also referred to as the SA-80, the rifle is designated L85A1, and is the first weapon able to fire full-automatic ever to enter British service as a standard infantry rifle. The SA-80 manages to fit a reasonably long (518mm/20¼in) barrel into a compact (785mm/31in) overall package, and uses conventional gas operation with a rotary bolt system. Firing from a closed bolt, the carrier assembly recoils into the butt, riding backwards on two guide rods which also hold the return springs. The body of the rifle is largely steel pressings welded together, with the pistol grip, foregrip and cheek rest being made of high-impact plastic. Single shots or bursts are selected by a small lever behind the magazine, with the safety catch, easily reached by the forefinger, being just in front of the trigger. A cocking handle protrudes from the right-hand side of the receiver, and the ejection port is protected from dust and grit by a spring-loaded door which flies open when the first round is ejected.

SA-80 ACCESSORIES

A detachable metal box magazine holding 30 rounds protrudes from the receiver, behind the grip, and is identical to that of the M16A2. The rifle comes complete with a short bayonet which, following Russian innovation, combines with its scabbard to form a wirecutting tool. A flash eliminator is fitted at the muzzle, and the weapon can mount most infantry rifle grenades (though these are not generally used by the British). Like the M16, a 40mm grenade launcher can be attached to the foregrip beneath the barrel to give a useful support fire capability. The Hilton HG40 is a single-shot weapon with an independent trigger mechanism and its presence has no effect on the operation of the rifle.

In an unusual departure from conventional design, the SA-80 has been

Calibre: 7.62mm
Weight: 4.43kg (9¾lb)
Length: 1181mm (46½)
Effective range: 800m (880yd)
Rate of fire: single shot
Feed: 10-round magazine
Muzzle velocity: 838mps (2750fps)

designed from the outset to employ an optical sight. In British Army service the standard sight is the L9A1 SUSAT (Sight Unit Small Arms Trilux), a lightweight times four magnification fixed-focus unit. The aiming point is marked by the tip of an illuminated vertical needle and all the firer has to do is place this single marker over the target. SUSAT gives the infantryman the ability to bring his rifle to bear on a target much more quickly than if he was using conventional rear and foresights. His sight picture is also magnified, helping him to clearly identify targets at long ranges, under camouflage or in cover. In conditions of poor light, SUSAT also gives a clearer picture than the naked eye, and can double as a handy surveillance aid. For night operations, image intensifying sights are easily attached, using the same mounting brackets as for SUSAT. The British generally use the Pilkington Kite image intensifying sight, which is an advanced lightweight device able to identify a man-sized target in conditions of no moonlight up to a range of 300m (330yd).

There are three variants of the Enfield design: the L85A1 rifle or Individual Weapon (IW), the L86A1 Light Support Weapon (LSW), which is fully described in the machine guns chapter, and the manually operated single-shot Ensign, which is used by cadets and for training. British frontline troops have their rifles fitted with SUSAT, but their support counterparts are not issued with this expensive item. Instead, their L85A1s have a conventional aperture sight built into a carrying handle with a post foresight above the front grip. These can be removed and replaced by SUSAT in a matter of minutes. A combination of SUSAT and the well-balanced bullpup configuration has made the L85A1 one of the most accurate rifles currently in military service, making snapshooting, steady aimed fire and suppressive bursts much more effective than with most other 5.56mm rifles.

The SA-80 has had a number of problems, however, such as its overall reliability and difficulties with handling because of its unusual shape. A

■ ABOVE: The US M21 sniper rifle. Originally called the US Rifle 7.62mm M14 National Match (Accurised), it is now being replaced by the M24 Sniper Weapon System. A sound suppressor can be fitted to the muzzle if required.

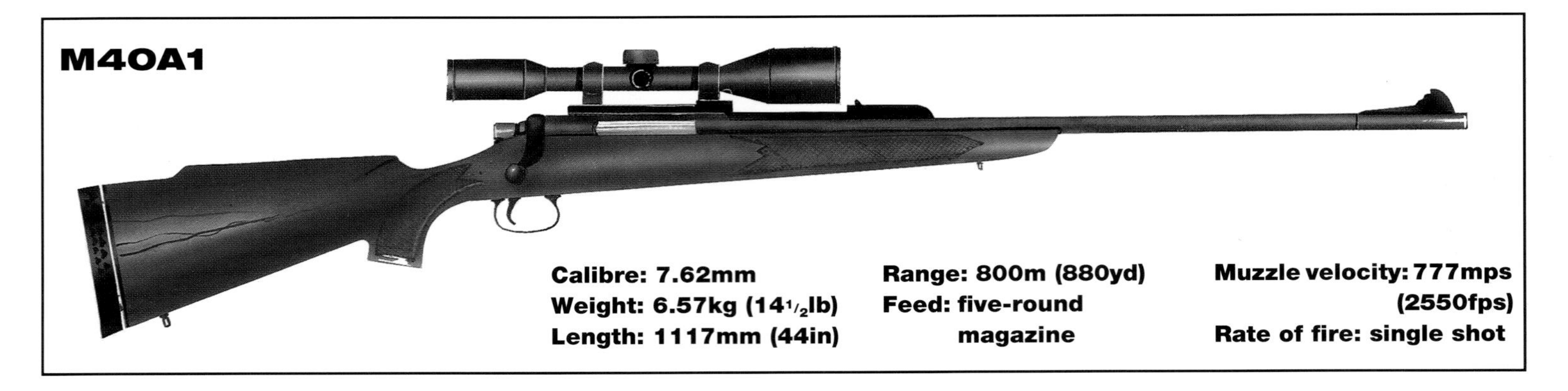

disadvantage of all bullpups is that the chamber and ejection port are level with the firer's face, making left-handed fire impossible, or at the very least extremely hazardous to the user. To shoot from the left side of cover with such a weapon means exposing a larger area of the upper body than if firing from the right side.

A bullpup also means that the magazine is behind the firer's grip, which can cause difficulties when trying to change magazines in the prone position. There were also early problems with the SA-80 concerning the magazine release lever catching on clothing and equipment and

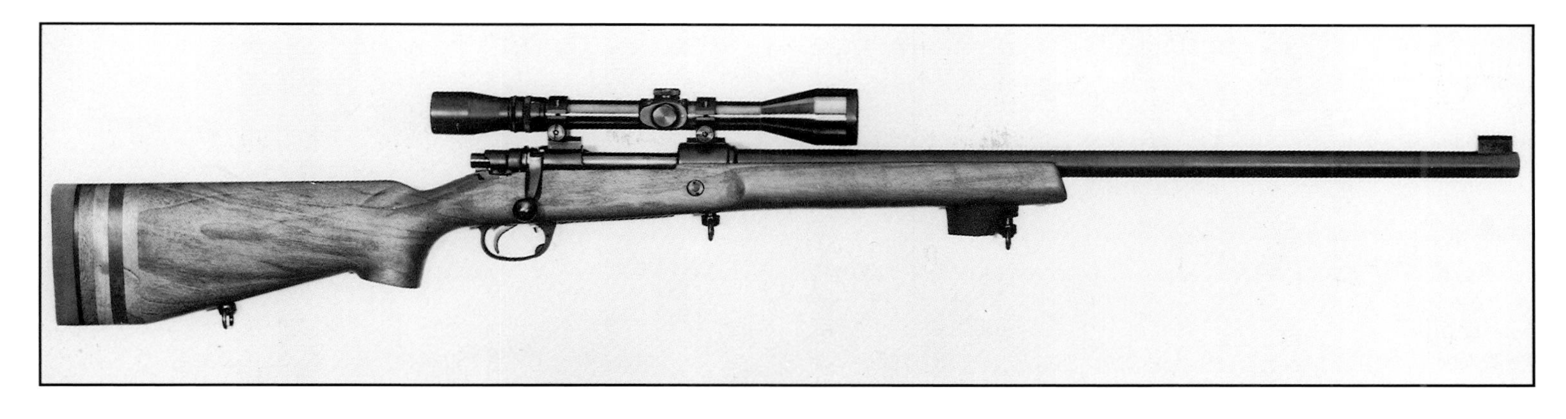

ABOVE: In service with the armed forces of Australia, Canada and New Zealand, the Parker Hale Model 82 is an excellent gun.

causing the ammunition supply to part company with the rifle, to the dismay of users. This has now been corrected, however. Notwithstanding the above, the British Army decided that these problems inherent in a bullpup shape are outweighed by the gains in accuracy over a conventional configuration.

Other problems with the SA-80 have been more serious, particularly the issue of poor reliability on operations. Cleaning and stripping are also awkward, with some components being difficult to clean in field conditions. Most of the reliability problems were caused by poor quality control and problems in the manufacturing process, which have now been solved. Once a weapon gains a bad reputation it can take many years to live it down, and the SA-80 seems to be suffering from this syndrome. It is noticeable that the British SAS, which has used the M16 since the 1960s, has retained the American weapon in preference to the indigenous design. In addition, it was noted during the 1991 Gulf War that some infantrymen kept their L1A1 SLRs, deciding that the extra stopping power of the 7.62mm weapon was a useful asset for the long combat ranges typical of desert terrain. Nevertheless, the SA-80 has now virtually replaced the SLR in frontline service, and will be the British soldier's combat rifle into the next century. Overall, it is a superb shooting weapon, and operational and manufacturing experience should overcome its teething troubles and ensure that it will have a long and distinguished service career.

FRENCH BUGLES

France also decided to follow the bullpup route for its new 5.56mm weapon, and the resulting FAMAS (*Fusil Automatique Manufacture d'Armes de St Etienne*) began to enter service in the early 1980s. A compact design, it is lighter than the British weapon and is easily recognised by the long carrying handle above most of the body. The French designers have incorporated some unusual features into the FAMAS, notably the ability to be converted to fire from either shoulder. As stated earlier, the chamber and extraction port of a bullpup weapon are usually alongside the firer's face, making left-handed fire impossible. The FAMAS has been designed to be fired from either shoulder by a few simple adjustments. There are two positions on the bolt face for the extractor claw. By removing the claw and fitting it in the alternate position the rifle can be made to eject empty cases in either direction. There are also left and right ejector ports, the one not in use being covered by a detachable cheek piece to protect the firer. This flexibility does not enable the firer to switch the rifle to either shoulder at will during a battle, but it does allow left-handed infantrymen to be more easily accommodated.

The FAMAS makes use of the blowback concept. As some form of delay is necessary to prevent high-pressure gases blowing into the ejection port, the French rifle employs a mechanical leverage delay system. Two short parallel levers, one on each side of the bolt, join the bolt to its carrier, their pivotal axis being a horizontal pin through the bolt. When the mechanism is closed the levers are vertical, with the lower ends extending past the bolt to lock against pins on the receiver, and the upper ends pressing against the inside rear face of the carrier. When the round is fired, gas pressure starts to force the bolt rearwards. The bottoms of the delay levers are held by the receiver locking pins, so the levers start to rotate backwards around their pivotal axis. The top of each lever presses against the comparatively heavy carrier piece, causing it to accelerate backwards, the force needed to cause this absorbing much of the initial energy of the recoil. Once the delay levers have rotated sufficiently for the lower ends

LEFT: Two US Marines, one armed with an M40A1 sniper rifle, man an outpost during Operation 'Desert Shield' in Saudi Arabia, September 1990.

SA-80

to clear their locking pins, the bolt is free to move back with the carrier. By this time the dangerously high gas pressures have been dissipated, and the bolt and carrier recoil into the butt, ejecting the empty case and starting the loading cycle.

The FAMAS fires from a closed bolt and has a 25-round box magazine protruding behind the grip. The grip and trigger are attached to a plastic handguard which forms the lower part of the body. The long carrying handle holds all the sights, and night vision equipment and telescopic sights can also be fitted to it. A lever above the pistol grip is used to select single shots or automatic fire, and there is also a position for choosing three-round bursts. If the latter fails, the configuration of the trigger and sear assemblies are designed to ensure that there is no effect on the other modes of operation. A folding bipod is integral to the weapon, and a short bayonet is supplied with each rifle. A version of the FAMAS with a shorter barrel is also available for special forces, paratroopers and bodyguards.

The short barrel and bullpup shape, combined with the long carrying handle, has given rise to the rifle's nickname: *Le Clarion* (Bugle). In the Bugle French soldiers have an accurate and reliable

BELOW: Put a Pilkington pocketscope on a British Self-Loading Rifle and what do you have? A perfectly adequate battlefield sniper rifle that can withstand knocks.

Calibre	5.56mm
Weight	4.52kg (10lb)
Length	785mm (31in)
Effective range	400m (440yd)
Rate of fire	800rpm (cyclic)
Feed	30-round magazine
Muzzle velocity	940mps (3085fps)

ABOVE LEFT: The SA-80 suffered a number of teething problems, such as fore-ends breaking and magazines falling off because of a badly placed magazine release catch, but these appear to have been rectified. Much more serious, there have been questions raised concerning its overall reliability on the battlefield.

LEFT: British Army personnel in Cyprus carrying SA-80s. The view of the average 'Tom' is that the rifle is sound, though many still prefer their trusted SLRs.

RIGHT: Overall, the SA-80 is well balanced, easy to fire and shoots well. It is also easy to carry inside Army APCs.

weapon which seems to have overcome most of the problems inherent in a bullpup design. The FAMAS has also been successfully exported and has entered service with some African and Middle Eastern armies.

THE UNIVERSAL AUSTRIAN

Looking like a futuristic science fiction weapon, the Austrian Steyr AUG (*Armee Universal Gewehr*) is a modern 5.56mm bullpup rifle of distinctive appearance. First seen in service in 1978, the AUG makes extensive use of advanced plastics on the body and receiver, with the barrel made from high-quality steel with a chrome liner. The AUG has been designed as a modular family of weapons (hence the designation 'Universal'), and different barrels, sights and trigger groups, together with folding bipods, can all be fitted without using tools. The basic 5.56mm AUG can be used as an assault rifle, short carbine, light machine gun, or even a 9mm submachine gun, all by changing a few components.

The barrel has an integral folding grip and a sleeve containing the gas cylinder and gas port. This unit locks into a cast aluminium receiver which includes the carrying handle. The whole unit is held by the large plastic body, which is also moulded to form the pistol grip, hand guard and butt. The Steyr design is gas operated, though there is no separate piston. Instead, the bolt carrier is attached to two guide rods, one on each side, which lie forward alongside the barrel, within the receiver. The left-hand guide rod protrudes into the offset gas cylinder and forms the piston, which drives the bolt assembly rearwards.

A rotating bolt is held by this carrier, which employs a front-locking system similar to that found on the M16. The AUG uses a similar method to the FAMAS of facilitating left-handed firing, in that the extractor claw can be moved to the left side of the bolt and a plastic blocking piece is moved from the left ejection port to the right. There is no fire selector on this weapon; pulling the trigger to the first pressure fires one shot while pulling it further fires a burst. A large guard protects the whole grip and trigger assembly, enabling arctic gloves to be worn by the firer. Ammunition is fed from a 30-round detachable box behind the grip which, in a clever touch, is made from transparent plastic to enable a quick check to be made on the number of rounds left. Sighting is by a 1.4x magnification optical unit integral to the carrying handle and receiver. The sight employs a simple black ring graticule which can be quickly placed over a man-sized target during combat. If more sophisticated telescopic or night sights are required, an alternative receiver with a flat mounting bracket can be fitted.

Known in Austrian service as the Stg77, the AUG has found export success in Australia, New Zealand, Morocco, Oman, Saudi Arabia and Ireland. Despite its strange appearance, it is extremely solid and tough, and can perform accurately in all climatic conditions. One of its pre-acceptance trials, for example, was to be driven over by an army truck several times. Only the glass in the optical sight broke, everything else remained in perfect working condition.

In the mid-1980s, the earlier Belgian FN CAL had been redesigned and simplified, and had reappeared as the FN FNC. The new design was an instant success, entering service with the Belgian Army and being licensed for production in Indonesia.

The FNC is light and largely made from stampings, pressings and plastic. Special consideration was given to ease and cheapness of manufacture, and the weapon is ideal for licence production by fledgling armaments industries. It is a conventional gas-operated rifle, with the piston and cylinder above the barrel. The pistol grip and foregrip are made from high-impact plastic, while the folding butt is of a plastic-coated tubular metal design. A solid plastic butt is also available. The NATO standard M16-style magazine holds 30 rounds and a safety lever is used to select single shots or

■ ABOVE: The current British Army sniper rifle, the Accuracy International PM, designated L96A1. The firm also makes a covert version of the PM which packs into an airline suitcase.

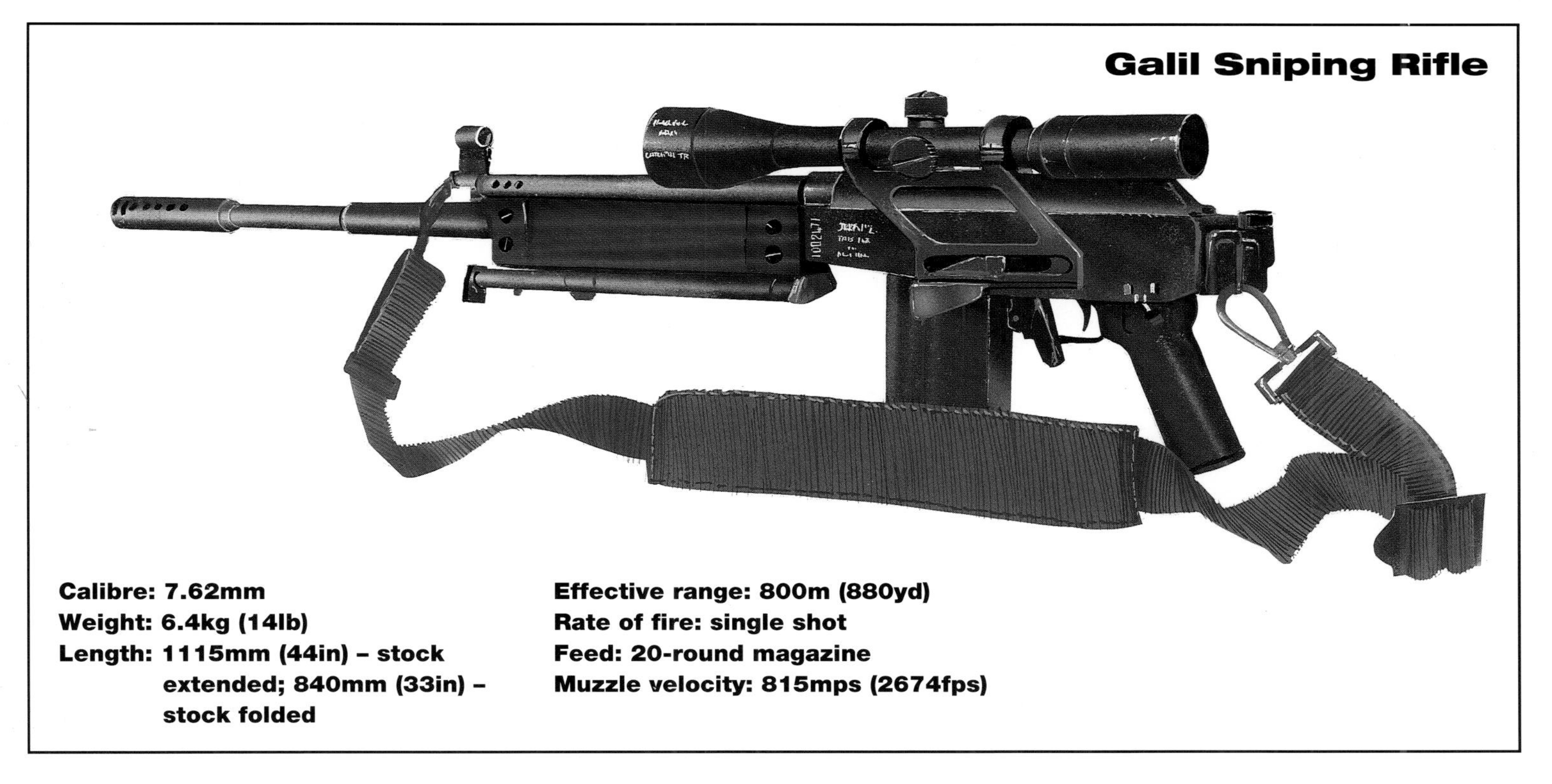

Galil Sniping Rifle

Calibre: 7.62mm
Weight: 6.4kg (14lb)
Length: 1115mm (44in) – stock extended; 840mm (33in) – stock folded
Effective range: 800m (880yd)
Rate of fire: single shot
Feed: 20-round magazine
Muzzle velocity: 815mps (2674fps)

automatic fire. Sighting is by a conventional aperture and post system.

FNCs can be purchased with their rifling optimised for either the US M193 bullet or the Belgian SS109. There is also a variant with a shorter barrel, which combines with the folding stock to make a surprisingly compact weapon. The Swedes procured a modified FNC as their standard AK5 rifle, one of the changes being a redesign to the rifling to reduce the wounding effect of the bullet. The FNC is a competent, workmanlike and effective design which is a worthy successor to the FAL.

Other Western nations to move to 5.56mm included the Swiss, who, after the commercial failure of the SIG SG530, persevered with the development of the simpler SG540. This dispensed with the Swiss version of the roller-delayed blowback system, using instead a conventional gas-operated rotating bolt. The SG540 is an effective 5.56mm assault rifle which fires from a closed bolt and uses a 20- or 30-round box magazine. It can fire single shots or full-automatic, and there is a mechanism for firing three-round bursts. The weapon is relatively cheap to manufacture and has been sold to over 27 countries. Manufactured under licence in France then in Portugal and Chile, it was used by the French to familiarise their troops with 5.56mm weapons before the arrival of the FAMAS.

When the Swiss Army decided to go over to 5.56mm, the 540 was developed to become the SG550. To reduce weight, plastics and lightweight materials have been extensively used in the SG550, and the rifle sports a folding skeleton butt. The 20- or 30-round magazine is made from transparent plastic, and three can be clipped together side by side to provide a quick-change facility. A three-round burst selector is fitted, though this is independent of the rest of the firing mechanism and will not affect normal operation if it malfunctions. There is a SG551 short-barrelled version and a popular single-shot sporting model for the commercial market. SIG weapons are usually superbly engineered and assembled, and this successful series is no exception.

THE TRIUMPH OF 5.56MM

Spain was one of the first nations to enter the assault rifle business with the CETME Model 58, so it is no surprise that Spanish industry has continued to develop such weapons. The CETME Model L is a smaller and lighter 5.56mm version of the earlier design, which retains the roller-locked delayed blowback system that has proved so successful. Some 1.1kg ($2\frac{1}{2}$lb) lighter than its predecessor, it was originally fitted with a three-round burst system. However, experience showed that trained soldiers could fire controlled three-round bursts with the weapon set on full-automatic, so the facility was dropped.

Two NATO nations that have persevered with 7.62mm weapons for longer than most are Italy and Germany. Italian elite troops have the AR70, but other soldiers had to make do with the 7.62mm BM59 series. By the mid-1980s, the Italian Army decided to re-equip with a 5.56mm weapon, and it was planned to use an improved version of the AR70 series, to be known as the AR70/90. The main changes centre around a stronger receiver and detailed redesign to ease field stripping and maintenance. The AR70/90 uses a rotary gas-operated bolt, feeding from a NATO standard 30-round magazine. The trigger mechanism allows single shots, three-round bursts or full-automatic fire. The SC70/90 and its special carbine version have folding skeleton butts.

In the mid-1980s, the West German Army made a conscious decision not to convert to a 5.56mm assault rifle, but to stick with the 7.62mm G3. The extremely advanced G11 (described below) was under development and promised a dramatic increase in effectiveness over more conventional rifles, so the *Bundeswehr* embarked upon a risky strategy of skipping the next generation of weapons and awaiting the benefits of the new hi-tech arm.

German industry had not been resting on its laurels, however, and Heckler & Koch had continued to develop rifles based on its roller-delayed blowback system. The HK33E (E for export) is a successful design which is basically a G3 scaled down to 5.56mm. It uses exactly the same trigger, bolt and firing mechanism as the earlier weapon, but is somewhat shorter and lighter. It has the same sighting system and method of operation, and so a soldier trained on the G3 would have no difficulty maintaining and operating the lighter weapon. The HK33E is available with a fixed butt, with the H&K sliding butt, with a shorter carbine barrel, and in a sniping configuration. While it has not seen service with the *Bundeswehr*, the weapon has been exported to over 15 countries for use with both police and military forces.

The G41 is a further development of the HK33E, this time using the 5.56mm NATO round. A three-round burst facility has been added, and the weapon uses the NATO standard magazine interface and sight mounts. Other modifications include a bolt closure device, noise reduction measures and an ejection port cover. The G41 is also available with a shorter barrel and a fixed or extendable butt. With the combination of German reunification and associated economic problems, it is unlikely that the expensive G11 will fully replace the G3 in *Bundeswehr* service. Combat formations and support troops that do not receive the new weapon will probably be issued with the G41, and this finely engineered rifle should not be regarded as second best.

THE KALASHNIKOV CONTINUES

The Soviet Union had appreciated the advantages of lower-powered cartridges much earlier then most other countries, and in the AK-47 had produced probably the best rifle of modern times. They had also followed Western arguments concerning lighter 5.56mm cartridges, and in the early 1970s instigated their own research programme. The end product was a small calibre cartridge: 5.45mm x 39mm. This bullet has a soft jacket with an air gap in the nose and a mild steel core with a lead tip. The result is a bullet that deforms and tumbles on hitting the target, inflicting more serious damage than Western 5.56mm rounds. During the Soviet intervention in Afghanistan, Mujahedeen guerrillas referred to this round as the 'poison bullet', as few who were hit by one survived.

Rather than go to the expense and trouble of designing a completely new weapon to fire this round, the Soviets modified the existing AKM to come up with the AK-74. Most components are identical to those found on the earlier rifle, only the barrel and bolt piece requiring modification. The case of the new cartridge is the same length as that of the 7.62mm, so the magazine feed and the recoil distance also remain unchanged. The curved magazine holds 30 5.45mm bullets and is made from a steel core covered with plastic. The new weapon is as heavy as the AK-47, and the renowned simplicity, reliability and ruggedness of the earlier design have all been retained. An unusual addition is the fitting of a muzzle brake to the end of the barrel, which blows the muzzle gases against deflector plates then out to the side, reducing recoil. The combination of muzzle brake and reasonable weight make the AK-74 easier to control on automatic mode than most other rifles in current use. Apart from the muzzle brake, the only other identifying features that differentiate the 5.45mm weapon from its predecessors are the plastic-covered magazine and finger grooves cut into the solid wooden butt.

The AK-74 has formed the basis of a family of weapons, including the folding stock AKS-74 and the shorter AKSU-74 submachine gun. Instead of the stock folding underneath the body, as on the AKM, both wooden and metal stocks fold to the side. The AK-74 comes complete with a bayonet, and the BG15 40mm grenade launcher can also be attached under the barrel like the US M16/M203 combination. AK-74s have been seen with image intensifying night sights, and some were used by *spetsnaz* forces in Afghanistan equipped with suppressors and firing a special subsonic round. Like the AK-47, the later weapon has also been produced in large quantities in the former Warsaw Pact countries, and there have been copies produced in former Yugoslavia and China chambered for Western 5.56mm cartridges.

SNIPER RIFLES

The roles of a military sniper are varied. He may be tasked with killing specific officers and key individuals – missile operators, machine gunners, mortar crews, drivers or signallers – or his task may be that of harassment, pinning down an enemy unit with accurate fire. The thought that the next man to move is likely to be drilled through the forehead with a single shot can paralyse movement, both in the enemy frontline and farther to the rear. Snipers can also have an anti-materiel role: using heavy, large-calibre weapons with special ammunition they can damage or destroy high-value equipment such as aircraft, radars, missile launchers or fuel tanks. Special forces make extensive use of snipers, especially when operating behind enemy lines. Many special forces units also have an anti-terrorist role, as do paramilitary and police units. Here, the sniper is a vital and highly trained element in the anti-terrorist arsenal, especially for hostage-rescue operations.

Unlike the hostage-rescue sniper, absolute accuracy is not necessarily the main requirement for the military

Model SP 66

marksman, whose rifle must be sturdy enough to operate in extremes of temperature, and in varied terrain: sand, dust, mud, rain, salt spray or ice. His rifle must be able to withstand the daily knocks and bumps of field operations; it must be easy to maintain; and it must demand little in the way of care and attention. The highest levels of accuracy are an unnecessary luxury: the harassing and effect on morale of a near miss or a shot that only wounds can be just as great as a fatal shot to the head. Often, a wounded target is actually more desirable than a kill, as valuable enemy manpower and resources will be tied up in caring for the casualty.

Ammunition is a critical component in determining the accuracy of an individual weapon. Most civilian marksmen use specially designed match standard ammunition, optimised for target shooting. Many even hand load the propellant and projectile into the cartridge case, thereby achieving a more consistent performance than that given by factory-produced rounds. Such fine tuning is usually impossible for a military sniper in the field, who is often restricted to some version of the standard service ammunition, though he may often be supplied with a specially selected batch from the normal production line. Apart from counter-terrorist and police operations, it is usually impractical to have a frontline sniper firing bullets that are not readily available through the military supply chain.

A requirement sometimes demanded by special forces marksmen is the ability to silence or suppress the report of a shot. This can be useful in ambushes or at night, as it is much more difficult for the enemy to

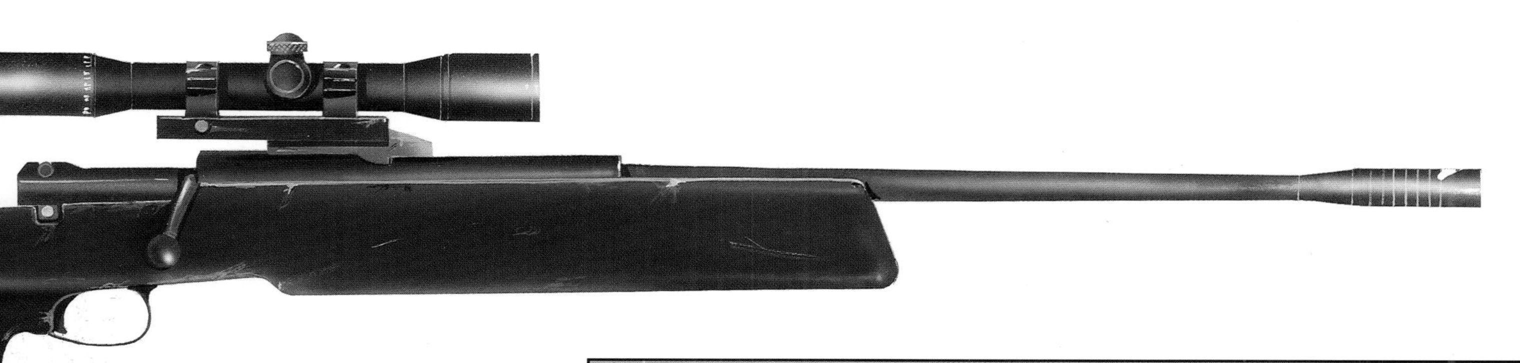

Calibre: 7.62mm
Weight: 6.12kg (13½lb)
Length: 1210mm (47½in)
Effective range: 800m (880yd)
Rate of fire: single shot
Feed: three-round magazine
Muzzle velocity: 868mps (2848fps)

■ RIGHT: The highly accurate Mauser 7.62mm SP 66 sniper rifle. It has been used by the German police, Spain's GEO and Israeli border guards.

know where the shot is coming from if all he can hear is a light popping noise rather than a loud crack. Absolute silencing is realistically impossible, though by building suppressors into the barrel the noise caused by the escaping gases can be greatly reduced. Most silenced rifles have a system of baffles that absorb much of the energy of these gases before they vent into the atmosphere. It is more difficult to suppress automatic weapons than bolt-action models because the noise of the mechanism clunking back and forward is still heard, as is the sound of gases escaping through the ejection port. It is possible to attach separate suppressors to the barrel of a standard rifle, though these are less effective than integral designs. They also tend to wear out quickly, as the corrosive effect of the hot gases attacks the baffles. The best suppressed weapons have usually been designed as such from the start.

As another major noise source is the crack produced by the supersonic flight of the rifle bullet, special low-powered subsonic ammunition should be used for maximum silencing. This, combined with the energy-absorbing effects of the suppressor, reduces the effective range of such a rifle when compared with its noisier counterparts. Most 7.62mm suppressed rifles are only accurate up to a range of 180m (196yd), compared to 550-730m (6-800yd) for a normal sniper's weapon.

All sniper rifles use magnifying optical sights, and there is a bewildering array of

PSG-1

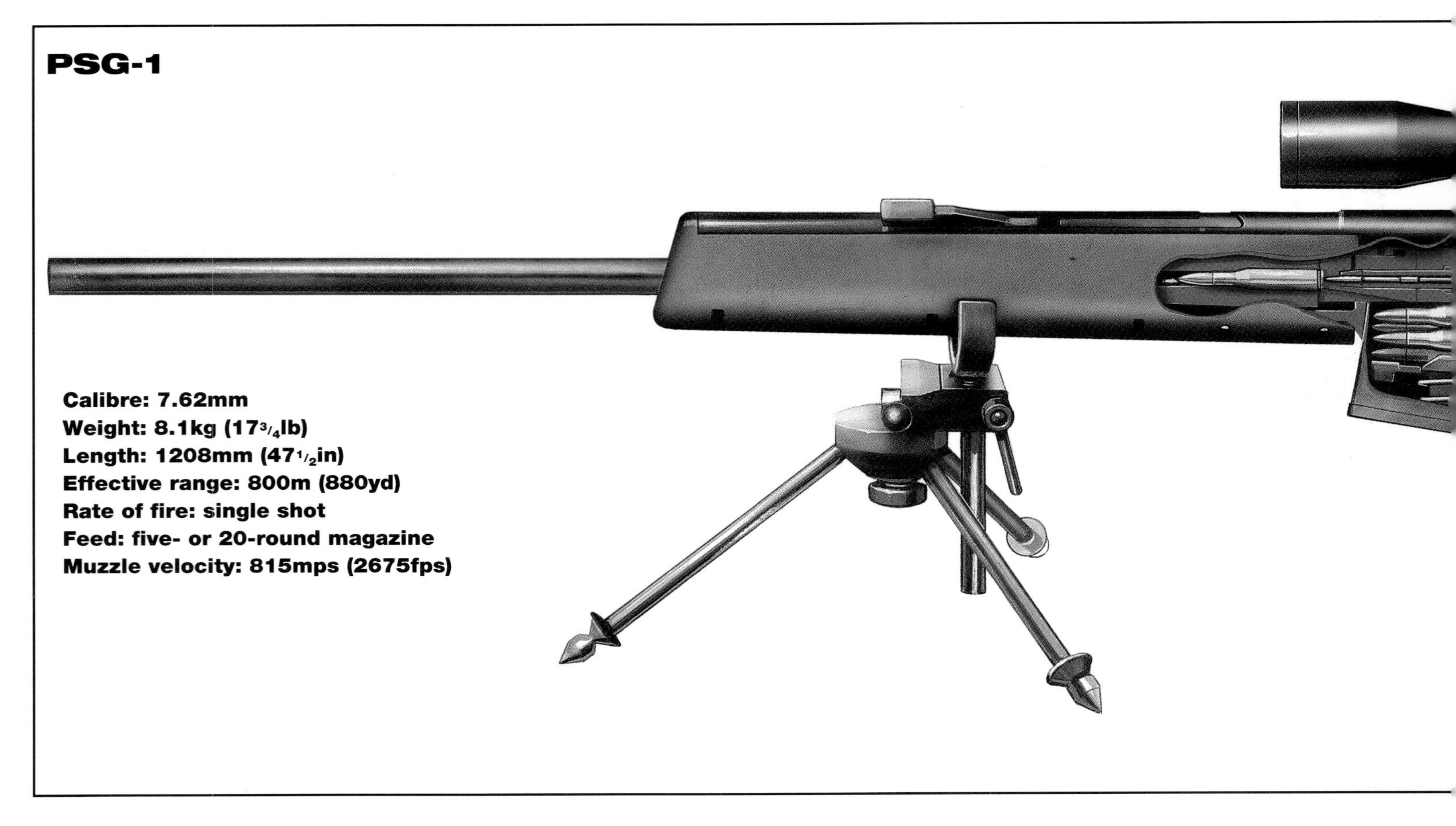

Calibre: 7.62mm
Weight: 8.1kg (17¾lb)
Length: 1208mm (47½in)
Effective range: 800m (880yd)
Rate of fire: single shot
Feed: five- or 20-round magazine
Muzzle velocity: 815mps (2675fps)

such devices to choose from. As might be expected, most military forces remain relatively conservative in their choices, requiring a reliable rifle which can be used in a wide range of lighting and environmental conditions. Night vision equipment such as image intensifiers are an essential addition to the sniper's armoury, having virtually totally replaced the obsolete active infrared lamps. Lasers are sometimes used to measure range or even show where a rifle is pointing, though these are often too bulky and fragile for field use.

Military snipers exist at many levels. Some, for example, are just ordinary infantrymen who have had some extra firearms training and who use standard service rifles fitted with telescopic sights. While these are not nearly as deadly as specially trained and equipped experts, they can provide a cheap and effective source of harassing fire. Most military snipers, however, use a specialised weapon adjusted for their own personal requirements.

The bolt-action rifle has retained its popularity for the sniping role. This is because first-shot accuracy from such a weapon is normally better than from a semi-automatic mechanism (though some of the newer designs are almost the equal of bolt-action systems). The disadvantage of the bolt-action rifle is that a second follow-up shot cannot be fired as quickly, and if the sniper has to fight his way out of trouble he may not have enough rapid firepower. In addition, the bolt must also be designed in such a way that the firer can operate the action without moving his head or the rifle from the aim position. Nevertheless, the bolt-action rifle is still widely used for sniping, and many armies remain firmly wedded to the concept.

THE OLD AND THE BOLD

Many sniping rifles are accurised versions of elderly service rifles. Typical of such conversions is the American Springfield M1903. Regarded as obsolete by the late 1930s, individual examples of this .30in calibre bolt-action rifle were equipped with Weaver scopes and designated the M1903A4, and served as sniper weapons throughout World War II and into the 1950s with the United States Army and the Marine Corps.

During World War II, the British also converted some specially selected No 4 rifles to sniper models, equipping them with telescopic sights and cheek rests. After 1945 sniping was largely ignored by the British, until experience in post-war colonial conflicts showed the need for such a capability. By then the Army was equipped with the L1A1, but it was felt that this semi-automatic weapon was not accurate enough, and that a bolt-action system was necessary. British designers returned to the ever-faithful Enfield rifle, taking some of the earlier No 4 sniper weapons and converting them to fire the 7.62mm x 51mm cartridge. The conversion involved a new barrel and ammunition feed, a new box magazine, and modifications to the bolt. The 'new' rifle was known as the L42A1, and is easily recognisable from the cut-down stock and the butt cheek piece. The earlier Telescopic Sight Mk32 was modified and issued as the Sight L1A1, though the same brackets on the rifle can be used to mount image intensifying sights for night operations. As a back-up, the standard folding rear sight and post foresight of the Enfield have been retained after being modified for the trajectory of the 7.62mm round. The L42 is perhaps not the last word in accuracy, but it is a tough and capable rifle. Having served successfully in boiling deserts, humid jungles and freezing arctic environments, it has proved itself to be reliable in all conditions. L42s were still in British use until the mid-1980s, and served with distinction during the 1982 Falklands War.

Once the US Army had converted to the M1 Garand, it was felt that a sniper version of this semi-automatic rifle should be designed. In 1944 the M1C was issued, to be followed by the M1D. These weapons

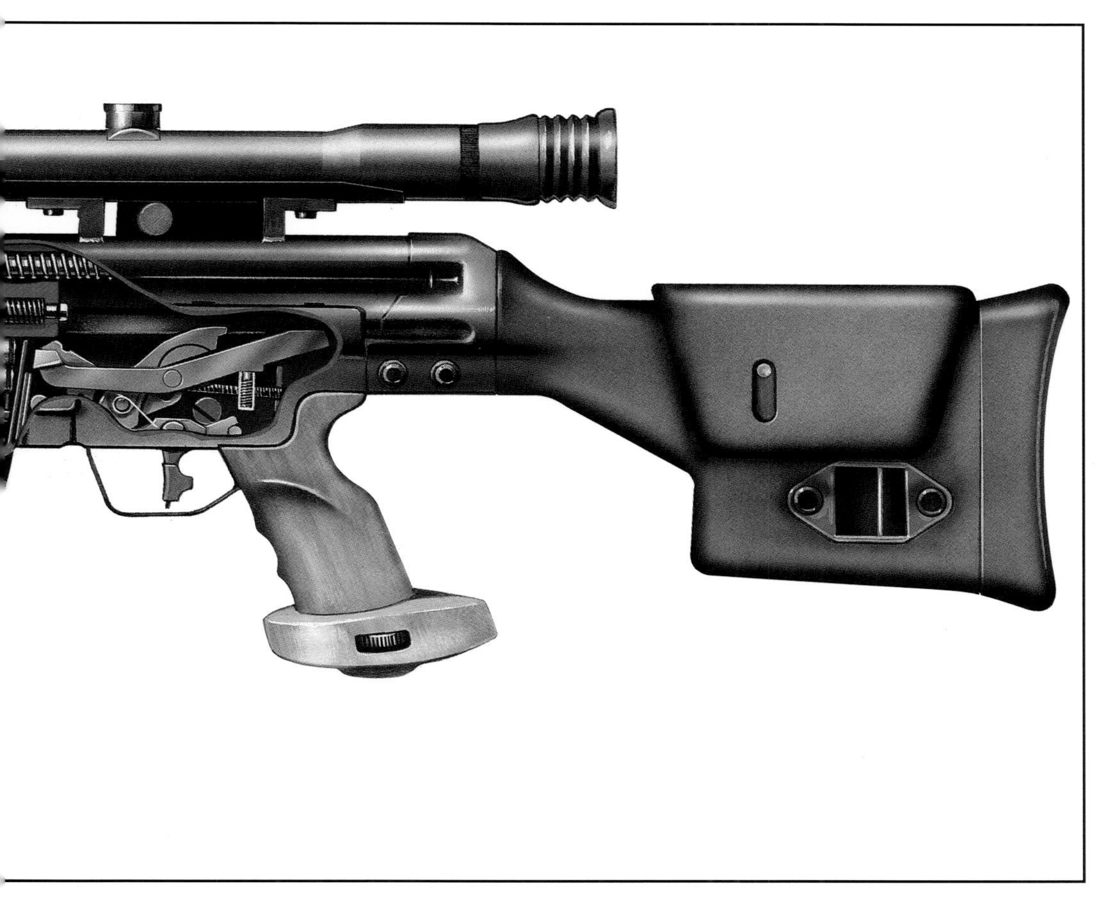

fired the same .30in M1906 round as the standard infantry model and were fitted with mounts for telescopic sights. The earlier model used either the Lyman M73 or the Weaver M73B1 scopes, and the later rifle used the Lyman in M81 or M82 form. The aiming mark was either a crosswire (on the M81) or a vertical post (on the M82). All sniper Garands had a detachable leather cheek piece and most were later fitted with flash suppressors. These rifles were a good compromise between the reliability of the standard service weapon and the accuracy of a scoped sniper rifle.

AMERICAN SNIPERS

When the 7.62mm M14 entered service in the 1950s, it also became necessary to devise a 7.62mm sniper weapon, and a version of the infantry rifle was the obvious choice. The M21 was eventually produced, which became the US Army's standard sniper weapon for many years. The M21 is manufactured to extremely high tolerances, using a much heavier barrel than that of the M14. The wooden stock is impregnated with epoxy resin to provide extra stiffness and improved stability in extreme environmental conditions. A fibreglass compound fixes the barrel to the stock, and the firing mechanism is carefully tuned and polished to provide a light but consistent trigger pull. Most other components are polished and fitted by hand, resulting in a weapon able to group 10 rounds within 15cm (6in) of the aiming point at 300m (370yd) range.

The M21 is limited to semi-automatic fire and has a conventional 20-round box magazine, albeit containing specially selected match standard ammunition. A Redfield variable magnification sight is used by the Army, and a bipod can be attached for steadiness. The sight has a cross-hair graticule, with two horizontal marks which are used for ranging. The magnification control on the telescope is adjusted until the two marks are correctly spaced to touch the helmet and waist of an upright man-sized target. A direct readout of the range is possible, but turning the magnification control also automatically adjusts the position of the aiming point for this range. The M21 has seen extensive service, and was used with great success in Vietnam and in most American actions since. Even with the advent of the M16 and its 5.56mm ammunition, the Army has kept the M21 for the sniper role. The smaller round is not really capable of the required degree of accuracy and stopping power, while the 7.62mm bullet is able to kill a man at a range of over 820m (897yd).

US Marine Corps (USMC) snipers returned to a bolt-action weapon in the shape of the M40A1, which is based on the Remington Model 700 commercial design. A wooden-stocked rifle with a heavy barrel, it has an integral magazine holding five 7.62mm x 51mm rounds. The M40 has no iron sights, being permanently fitted with a telescopic mount. The magazine is loaded using a charger, via the ejection port, and the bolt can be removed for cleaning without disturbing the scope. The USMC normally uses a times 10 magnification sight, though this can be replaced with night vision equipment if required.

In 1987, the first examples of the US Army's M24 sniper system were issued to combat units. The first Army rifle designed from the start as a sniper weapon, the M24 is to replace all other US military sniper rifles. Developed from Remington civilian designs, and having a common parentage with the M40, it is a conventional-looking bolt-action rifle with a six-shot integral magazine and a heavy barrel. In US service it will fire the M118 7.62mm x 51mm match standard ammunition, though the manufacturers are offering the weapon modified for the .30in Winchester Magnum cartridge. The stock has an adjustable butt plate and is made from synthetic composite materials with metal mounting components. The standard service sight is a Leupold Ultra M3 with a times 10 magnification, with iron sights as a back-up. A folding bipod is attached, and the complete system weighs 6.35kg (14lb). The M24 looks to be a good field sniper rifle, performing well with Rangers and Special Forces units during the 1991 Gulf war.

THE BRITISH TRADITION

The British firm of Parker Hale has always designed extremely accurate target rifles, and it is no surprise, therefore, that some highly effective sniper weapons have been manufactured by this company. The Model 82 is a bolt-action weapon of traditional appearance, with a wooden stock and an integral four-shot magazine. The rifle is chambered for NATO 7.62mm x 51mm ammunition, and uses a heavy, fully floating barrel which is embedded in the stock with an epoxy resin. The bolt is a modified Mauser design which locks at the front. A number of sights are usable with the Model 82, the most common being the Austrian Kahles scope with a times six magnification. The rifle is in service as the standard sniper weapon in Australia, Canada (as the C3) and New Zealand.

A later Parker Hale design is the Model 85, developed from the Model 82. The newer design uses the same ammunition but has a detachable 10-round box magazine. Tough and reliable, it has a stock

ABOVE: The French FR-F2 rifle was introduced in 1984. It is an improved version of the FR-F1: its fore-end is metal, its bipod more robust and the barrel is enclosed in a plastic sleeve.

made from fibreglass and a butt that can be adjusted by the addition or removal of extension pieces. The Model 85 is normally fitted with a bipod and conventional iron sights for emergency use. The standard sight is a Schmidt & Bender times six magnification scope, though many others can be used. The sight mount includes brackets for the Simrad KN250 image intensifier sight, which projects its image through the normal telescopic sight, thus demanding no adjustment in aiming position from the firer. A dovetail mount allows the sights to be removed and remounted without disturbing the zero. The M85 design requirement was to achieve a 100 per cent first round hit capability up to a range of 600m (660yd), which it fulfils very handsomely.

The current British Army sniper weapon is not a Parker Hale design, however, but the Accuracy International PM, designated L96A1 in service use. Designed from the start as a military sniper weapon, the L96 is a bolt-action rifle firing match standard 7.62mm x 51mm ammunition. A heavy, free-floating barrel is supported by an aluminium frame, and the whole assembly is held in a high-impact plastic stock. To help control any muzzle jump, the barrel and butt are in a straight line, with the butt length being adjustable by the addition or removal of extension pieces. There is a thumb hole through the stock, behind the grip, and a 10-round detachable box magazine protrudes below the body.

The choice of a bolt-action system when there are now so many superb semi-automatic weapons available may seem reactionary, but the British remain convinced that the critical first-shot accuracy from a manual system is superior. The L96 employs a short-throw bolt, enabling the firer to keep his head in the aiming position between shots. The normal sight is a Schmidt & Bender times six magnification scope, but the PM has fully adjustable iron sights as a back-up, calibrated to 700m (770yd). A light folding bipod is attached to the front of the stock, and the whole system is capable of a guaranteed first round hit at over 600m (660yd).

Accuracy International also offers a counter-terrorist model with an adjustable power sight, a flash hider and a monopod to help keep the rifle on target for long periods without tiring the firer. A version with a specially designed suppressor barrel is also manufactured which, with the correct type of subsonic ammunition, is effective up to a range of 300m (330yd). Accuracy International has also developed the weapon to use other ammunition, including .30in Winchester Magnum and 7mm Remington Magnum for extremely long-range work.

The Israeli armed forces are firmly committed to a semi-automatic sniper weapon, using a development of the Galil assault rifle. Chambered for 7.62mm ammunition, the Galil sniper has a heavier barrel than the infantry rifle, a muzzle brake, and a heavy bipod attached to the receiver, behind the foregrip. The normal Galil mechanism and ammunition feed (from a 20-round detachable box) is retained, though careful attention is given to the fit and finish of the components. An adjustable folding butt cheek piece is standard, as is the rugged Nimrod times six magnification scope. The standard iron sights are kept for emergency use. The Galil is a tough, soldier's weapon, and while not as accurate as the best bolt-action systems,

it is a combat-proved weapon effective for most military sniping purposes.

EUROPEAN RIFLES

In Germany, manufacturers have produced both bolt-action and semi-automatic sniper weapons. The Mauser SP66 has been selected by the police and military forces of over 12 countries, and is a superbly accurate bolt-action rifle. Again chambered for specially selected 7.62mm x 51mm ammunition, the SP66 feeds from a three-round integral box magazine. The finely finished stock stops half way down the heavy barrel, and is moulded with a cheek piece and thumb hole behind the grip. Extension pieces can be attached to the butt to suit individual firers. The Mauser bolt system uses an extremely short action, reducing the length of the body slightly and helping the firer to keep on the point of aim while operating the mechanism. The barrel has a combined muzzle brake and flash hider, supposedly improving accuracy by reducing the recoil and dispersing muzzle flash, which can be a problem when using telescopic sights. The standard model employs a Zeiss one to times six magnification adjustable sight, though many other sights and night-vision devices can be employed.

Heckler & Koch has continually developed its roller-delayed blowback system, using it on a successful range of semi-automatic sniper weapons, for example the PSG-1. A semi-automatic weapon firing specially selected 7.62mm ammunition (normally Lapua Winchester match grade) from either a 20- or five-round detachable magazine, its parentage from the G3 is obvious. The PSG-1 has a completely different design of barrel, however, employing an extremely heavy, precision-made item with a polygonal bore. This shape prevents the escape of the tiny quantities of gas that normally leak past the bullet in conventional rifling, thus removing another source of minor inconsistencies in trajectory.

The plastic butt is fully adjustable, as is the angle of the butt plate and the position of the cheek piece. Normal sighting is through a times six magnification telescope with illuminated cross-hairs, and there are no iron sights fitted. A separate tripod rest is often used by police and anti-terrorist snipers, though this comparatively heavy item is often too cumbersome to be carried by their military counterparts. The PSG-1 has a system for silent bolt closing, and the trigger has an adjustable shoe to change its width to suit individual preferences. The rifle has proved popular with police, military and special forces as a reliable and superbly accurate weapon, and Heckler & Koch has developed the MSG90 as a further improvement on the basic design.

France, like Britain, has stayed with bolt-action sniper systems, and in the late 1960s deployed the FR-F1 with specialist troops. A finely finished, competent design based on a popular competition target rifle, it has proved to be an extremely effective weapon. Early models were chambered for the French 7.5mm x 54mm M1929 round, but most have entered service designed for the NATO 7.62mm round. Firing from a 10-round detachable magazine, the weapon has a high-quality wooden stock and a wooden pistol grip behind the trigger. The butt length can be adjusted by attaching extension pieces, and there is an adjustable cheek piece made from plastic.

GALLIC SNIPER

In French Army service the FR-F1 is fitted with a Modèle 53b times four magnification telescope, though night sights are also available. Iron sights are fitted, but to use them involves the scope being removed and the back-up sights folded. Once the scope is zeroed, it can be removed and replaced without further adjustment. The whole weapon is a robust and simple design which has given many years of effective service to French snipers. A replacement was introduced in 1984, known as the FR-F2. It is an improved version of the earlier weapon, having the same basic dimensions and mechanism as before. Again chambered for NATO 7.62mm ammunition, the FR-F2 has a thermal sleeve protecting the barrel, a forestock made from plastic-covered metal, and a bipod shifted rearwards to the front edge of the receiver.

Other Western nations keeping to bolt-action systems for their snipers include Switzerland with the specially produced SSG2000, Italy with the Beretta sniper rifle, and Austria with the Steyr SSG69. The Swiss have also developed a sniper version of the SG550 assault rifle, though this seems to be aimed more at the civilian market. The Finns have the conventional bolt-action 7.62mm Sako TRG21 sniping rifle in service, but have also devised the unusual Vaime series of weapons.

Vaime rifles are specially designed as silenced arms, having a heavy integral suppressor built around the barrel. The

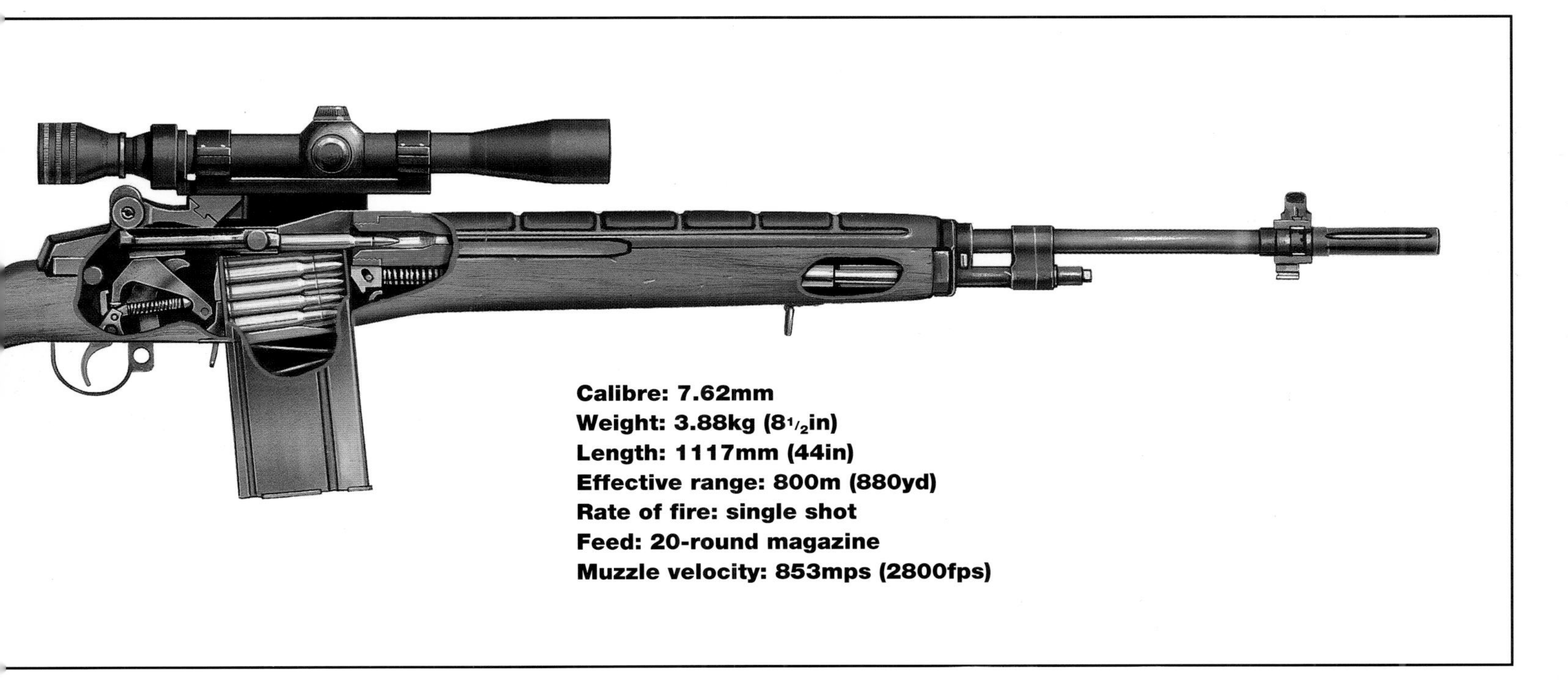

Calibre: 7.62mm
Weight: 3.88kg (8½in)
Length: 1117mm (44in)
Effective range: 800m (880yd)
Rate of fire: single shot
Feed: 20-round magazine
Muzzle velocity: 853mps (2800fps)

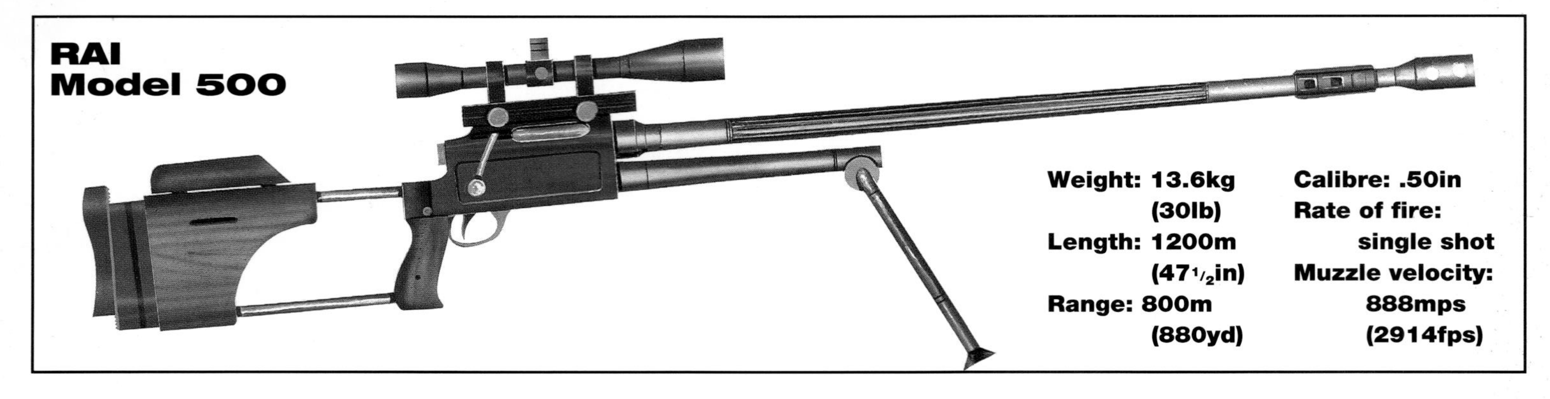

conventional bolt-action mechanism fires subsonic 7.62mm NATO ammunition from an integral 10-round box magazine, while the butt and stock are made from high stability non-reflective plastic. A folding bipod is normally fitted to the front of the stock, and any telescopic or night vision sight can be accommodated. The silencer is extremely effective, reducing the report to about the same loudness as a suppressed .22in calibre rifle, though the subsonic ammunition is only accurate up to a range of 2-300m (220-330yd). The Vaime is used by a number of special forces units and also by the US Secret Service.

THE DRAGUNOV

Experience in both World Wars convinced the Red Army of the need for large numbers of snipers in its sub-units, and the nations of the Commonwealth of Independent States (CIS) have kept the sniper as a vital part of their military capabilities, with a sniper attached to every platoon in most motorised infantry units. Soviet designers have produced a highly effective weapon for these men, striking a careful balance between ruggedness, ease of use, maintainability and accuracy.

The Dragunov SVD has been in service since the mid-1960s, and has proved itself in combat in Afghanistan and elsewhere. It is a semi-automatic single-shot weapon which employs a modified Kalashnikov mechanism and a 10-round box magazine. The round fired is a full-powered 7.62mm x 54mm cartridge, based on the Russian design used in World War I. The gas-operated mechanism is modified to use a short-stroke piston, reducing the mass of the moving components and making it easier to keep the rifle on the aim point. The rifle has a wooden foregrip and a wooden butt, with cutouts to reduce weight. The SVD is long – 1225mm (48½in) – though this is compensated for by its lightness (4.31kg/9½lb). It shares the same simplicity and reliability as the Kalashnikov series, but is extremely accurate, having a 90 per cent chance of hitting a man-sized target at 300m (330yd).

A PSO-1 times four magnification scope is normally used, and this is also a tough item designed to survive the rigours of field use. An image intensifier sight can also be fitted, the standard Russian design being the NSP-3. While not as effective at longer ranges as the latest bolt-action rifles, the SVD is easy to shoot and maintain, and is well designed for use in the rigours of extended combat operations. It will remain in service with the CIS armies, the ex-Warsaw Pact nations and ex-Soviet client states for many years to come.

HEAVY METAL

An unusual recent addition to the battlefield is the extremely large-calibre anti-materiel rifle. Generally long and heavy, it is used to destroy key targets such as parked aircraft, helicopters, light vehicles, signalling and radar equipment, logistics kit, larger weapons and their crews, and key personnel.

Perhaps the best known of these monsters are the series of rifles produced in the United States by Barrett Firearms Manufacturing, Inc. The M82A1 'Light Fifty' makes use of the Browning .50in (12.7mm) cartridge, normally used in the M2 heavy machine gun. This large, powerful round comes in ball, armour-piercing (AP), tracer and incendiary configurations, and the AP round will penetrate most light armour at ranges up to 1000m (1100yd) – a useful attribute on the modern battlefield. Such a cartridge provides an immense kick, and so the M82 uses a muzzle brake to dissipate much of the energy from the gases. The rest is used to drive the barrel and bolt mechanism back against the return spring and recoil buffer. After 13mm (.5in) of travel, the barrel is stopped by retaining lugs, and the bolt and carrier unlock to continue rearwards, ejecting the empty case and returning to feed a new one. By this time the barrel has returned to the firing position.

The M82 is a semi-automatic weapon which has an 11-round detachable box magazine. The rifle has an overall length of 1550mm (61in), and the Light Fifty weighs in at 14.7kg (32¼lb). A heavy folding bipod is an essential fitting, and in US service the M82 has a times 10 telescopic sight. While the usefulness of such a weapon may be restricted to certain special situations, a US Special Forces sniper during the 1991 Gulf War achieved a confirmed kill at over 1000m (1100yd) with a Light Fifty. Barrett also offer a bolt-action and bullpup version of this mighty beast.

The Austrian firm Steyr has designed an even more fearsome weapon in 15mm calibre: the AMR (Anti-Material Rifle). A massive crew-served weapon over 2m (78¾in) long and weighing in at 20kg (44lb), it fires specially developed tungsten flechette (arrow) ammunition, said to be effective up to 2000m (2200yd) and able to penetrate 40mm (1½in) of armour up to a range of 800m (880yd). Recoil is absorbed by a hydro-pnuematic buffer system, and a heavy bipod is an essential component. It will be interesting to see if this deadly but cumbersome weapon ever enters service.

THE FUTURE

Most of the current crop of assault rifles use ammunition and principles dating from the 1960s and 1970s, and many will still be in service in the early years of the next century at the very least. However, engineers and designers are continually trying to improve the accuracy and lethality of the standard infantry weapon, and a number of ammunition and rifle concepts are currently being investigated.

A pointer to the future can be seen in the Heckler & Koch G11 combat rifle, now entering service with German special

■ RIGHT: A French Foreign Legion sniper takes aim with an FR-F1 rifle. The gun fires match standard 7.5mm ammunition. The use of tracer or armour-piercing can damage the bore, and is discouraged.

SSG69

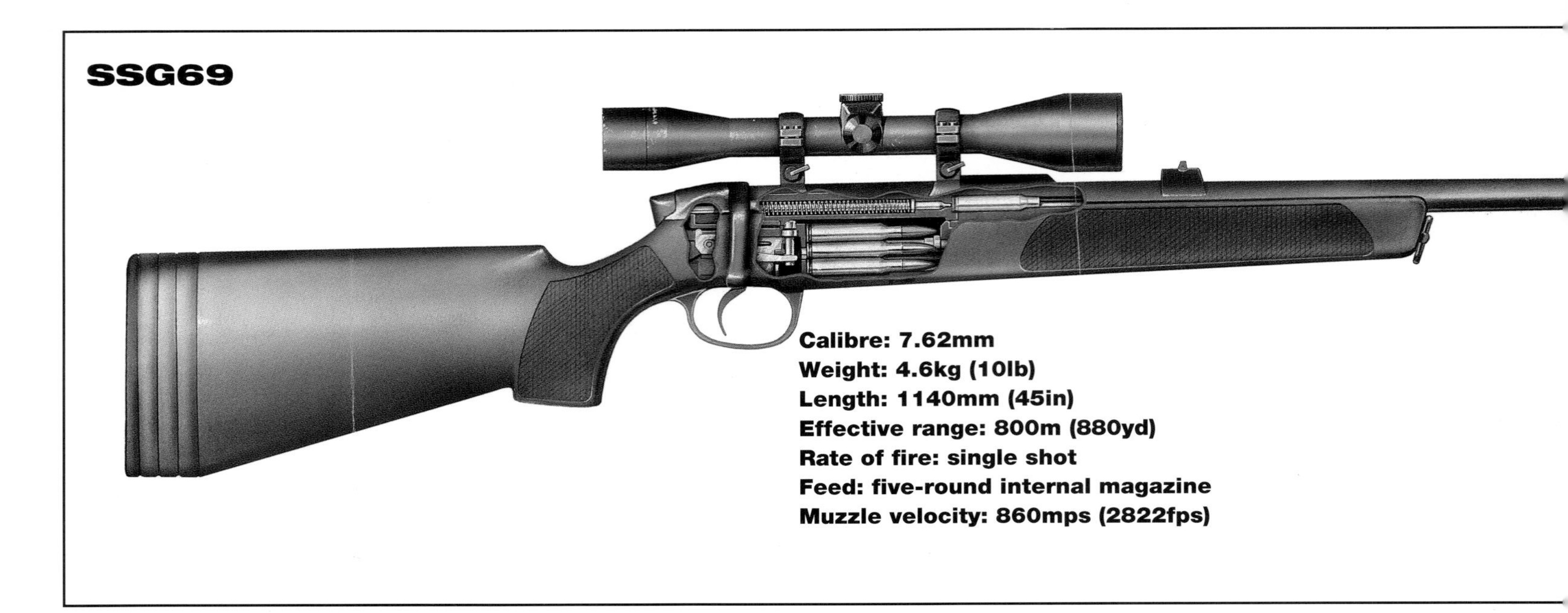

Calibre: 7.62mm
Weight: 4.6kg (10lb)
Length: 1140mm (45in)
Effective range: 800m (880yd)
Rate of fire: single shot
Feed: five-round internal magazine
Muzzle velocity: 860mps (2822fps)

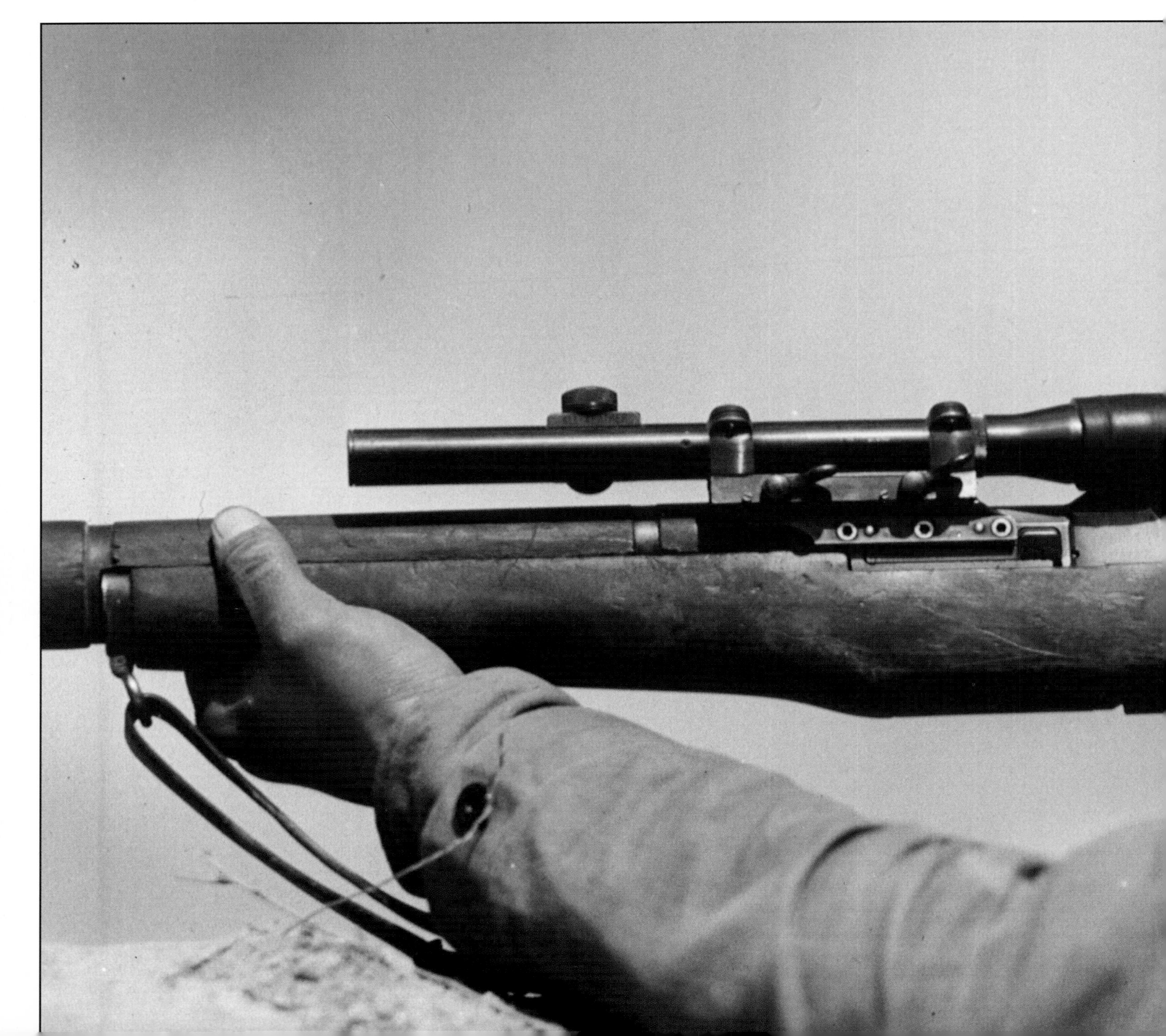

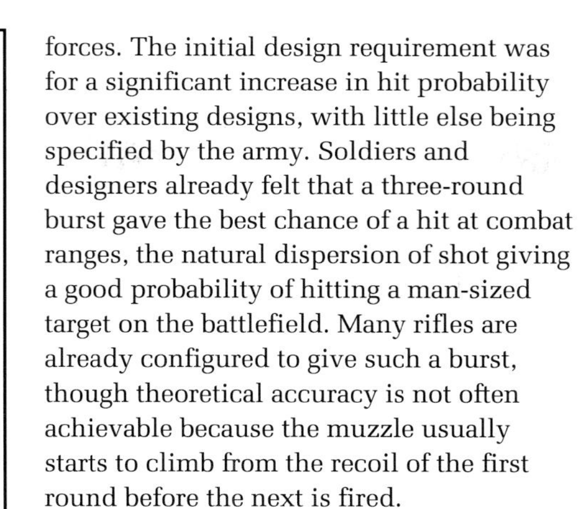

forces. The initial design requirement was for a significant increase in hit probability over existing designs, with little else being specified by the army. Soldiers and designers already felt that a three-round burst gave the best chance of a hit at combat ranges, the natural dispersion of shot giving a good probability of hitting a man-sized target on the battlefield. Many rifles are already configured to give such a burst, though theoretical accuracy is not often achievable because the muzzle usually starts to climb from the recoil of the first round before the next is fired.

■ BELOW: A firearms legend with a telescopic sight on top – an M1 Garand in the sniper configuration. The sight is an M82 scope, and the weapon is also equipped with a flash hider.

Heckler & Koch's studies indicated that the best solution would be to find some way of firing all three rounds before the recoil affected aim. The plan was to have some form of external casing, within which the barrel, breech, firing mechanism and magazine all recoil against a buffer. The challenge was to have a sufficiently high rate of fire to shoot three rounds before this assembly hit the buffer and caused the weapon to jump with the recoil. The end result, after years of careful development and testing, is the G11, probably the strangest looking weapon in military service today.

The rate of fire needed to be around 2000 rounds per minute, some three times faster than the 600 or so typical of a conventional assault rifle. To achieve this, the G11 makes use of specially developed caseless

ammunition and a unique rotating breech. The ammunition propellant is a rigid block, rectangular in outline, with the 4.7mm calibre bullet sunk into it and not protruding. The advantage of caseless ammunition is that there is no need for an extraction cycle, and the next round can be loaded immediately after the first is fired. Long development was needed to ensure that the unprotected propellant was immune to water, grease and solvents, and that without the protection of a brass case was not susceptible to accidental detonation ('cook-off') if left in the hot breech. Other problems which had to be overcome were the lack of a gas seal normally provided by the case, and the tendency to leave residue in the chamber after firing, but the Dynamit Nobel propellant design team seems to have solved all these problems.

The ammunition sits pointing vertically downwards, in a horizontal row inside the 50-round magazine that sits above the barrel. Chargers holding 10 rounds apiece are normally clipped to the outer casing and can be loaded into the magazine when needed. The precise details of the mechanism have not been revealed, but certain principles are known. A round is fed downwards into the chamber, which at this point is pointing vertically downwards. The chamber is actually in the centre of a vertical disc-shaped unit, which now rotates through 90 degrees around a horizontal axis and aligns the chamber and cartridge with the barrel. When the trigger is pulled the round is fired, and the barrel, chamber and feed assembly start to recoil to the rear. The chamber rotates again to align vertically with the next round. There is no case to extract, so the next bullet is fed straight into the chamber, which rotates again to align with the barrel and fire once more. This cycle is repeated one more time before the recoil assembly runs up against the buffer and the firer feels the recoil force. The whole three-round burst is so fast that it sounds like one continuous explosion.

THE ACR PROGRAMME

The G11 may look rather cumbersome, with its large, squarish outer casing, but it is reported to give a dramatically improved hit probability to even an average shot. It is an expensive weapon, however, and with the break-up of the Warsaw Pact and the costs of German reunification, its widespread issue to the German armed forces is in doubt. It may be that only certain elite units are equipped with the new sytem, with the others receiving something cheaper and more conventional, such as the G41.

The United States Army also spent some time and money in the late 1980s and early 1990s developing concepts for a new infantry weapon. Four contestants were considered in the Advanced Combat Rifle (ACR) programme, ranging from a highly modified and improved design based on the the M16, to a development of the G11. While some of the rifles may have been recognisable developments of existing technology, great attention was being paid to new forms of ammunition.

Colt put forward a proposal based on a much improved M16, with greatly reduced recoil and a new optical sight. It would fire standard 5.56mm ammunition or a new design of duplex cartridge. The duplex was optimised for close ranges, and consists of a normal brass case containing two bullets, one behind the other. The theory is that the first bullet flies to the aim point, while the second gives an amount of random dispersion, helping to compensate for human error in aiming.

The Steyr competitor was a plastic-shrouded bullpup design based on the AUG system. This also fires unusual ammunition. A steel arrow or flechette is held inside a plastic case by plastic sabots or spacers. When fired, the flechette flies very

BELOW: Is it a rifle or anti-tank weapon? In fact, the Barrett 'Light Fifty' is a long-range sniper rifle firing the 0.5in Browning heavy machine gun cartridge.

Dragunov

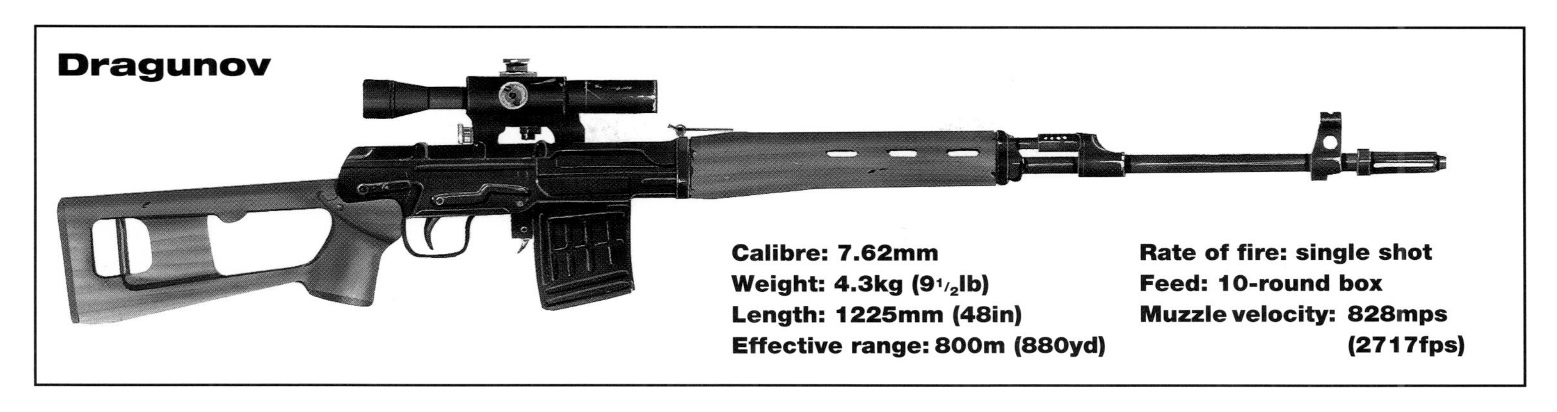

Calibre: 7.62mm
Weight: 4.3kg (9½lb)
Length: 1225mm (48in)
Effective range: 800m (880yd)
Rate of fire: single shot
Feed: 10-round box
Muzzle velocity: 828mps (2717fps)

G11

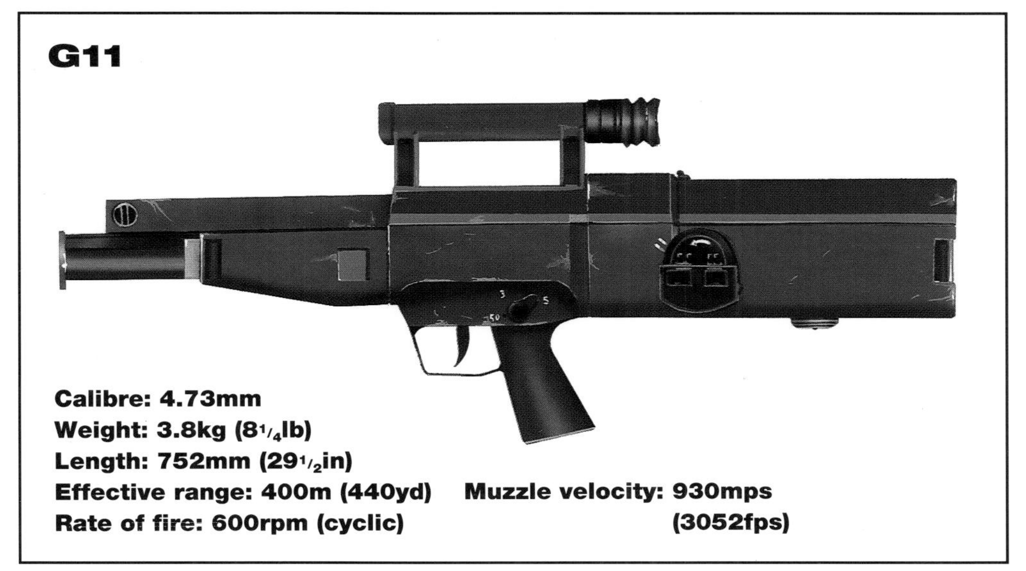

Calibre: 4.73mm
Weight: 3.8kg (8¼lb)
Length: 752mm (29½in)
Effective range: 400m (440yd)
Rate of fire: 600rpm (cyclic)
Muzzle velocity: 930mps (3052fps)

fast and on such a straight trajectory that virtually no drop is encountered over normal ranges, so no sight adjustment is necessary. The flechette is supposedly better at penetrating cover and body armour than a conventional bullet, though a disadvantage is the hazard caused to friendly troops by the sabots flying out of the mouth of the barrel.

Heckler & Koch put forward a derivative of the G11, and the fourth competitor was an AAI gas-operated weapon, also firing a flechette round. With the ending of the Cold War and the voters' demand for a 'peace dividend', US military chiefs had to look hard at new items of military expenditure, and in 1992 it was announced that the ACR programme was to be dropped, as none of the candidates showed sufficient improvement over the M16A2. US troops will enter the next century equipped with the M16A3, a further modified version of Eugene Stoner's 1957 design.

However, designers in many countries are still looking at increasing the lethality of the infantryman's rifle. Special grenade launchers, large-calibre weapons, enhanced cartridges and multi-shot devices are all being considered. A promising area of development is in the field of combat shotguns, and it is here that many new types of ammunition are being examined. It may be that the infantryman of the future will be equipped with something different from the rifles that have been used up till now, but only time will tell.

BELOW: The SIG SSG550 sniper rifle, a development of the SG550 rifle. This model is fitted with a night vision sight.

CHAPTER 2
MACHINE GUNS

Since the development of the first firearms, soldiers and engineers have continually looked for ways to improve their killing power. An obvious way was to increase the quantity of projectiles fired, and in the second half of the nineteenth century a number of designers created weapons which used multiple barrels to give a salvo fire effect. Gatling's hand-cranked revolving cannon of the early 1860s is the best known example of this type of weapon.

ENTER THE MAXIM

In 1884, the first of a new breed of rapid fire guns was being demonstrated in London. Developed by an American engineer, Hiram Maxim, the new design was the first to make use of the energy contained in the recoil caused by firing a bullet. Assuming a continuous supply of ammunition was available, Maxim's gun would repeatedly load and fire as long as the trigger was held back. This self-powered device was the first real 'machine' gun. Other engineers were working on similar concepts, and Maxim's development was to be followed by designs in the United States and France. Maxim's design was quickly snapped up by armies, and became a mainstay of British colonial expeditions in Africa. Other countries also saw the value of this device, and guns based on Maxim's principles were to appear in the armies of both Germany and Russia. The weapons that were to pour out such devastating swathes of fire on the battlefields of World War I were, in the main, direct descendants of the first Maxim design.

It took some time for armies to work out the best tactical employment for these new devices. The British initially mounted them on large wheeled carriages, to be used rather like light field guns: deployed in the open to fire at massed formations of enemy troops. The problem with this was that skilled riflemen equipped with modern bolt-action weapons were able to bring the machine-gun crews under effective fire, and casualties among the crews were high.

LEFT: The German MG3 entered service in 1968. It is based on the 1930s-vintage MG42 design, the main difference being the change to 7.62mm calibre.

By the time of World War I, however, the machine gun was firmly established as an infantry weapon, firing from protected positions and mounted on a tripod or a small, hand-towed wheeled carriage.

Machine guns were still relatively static and essentially defensive, though. Once emplaced, it was difficult for the crews to move, especially over the shell-torn landscape of a World War I battlefield. What was required was a much lighter weapon, perhaps carrying its ammunition in a box or drum magazine. Light machine guns (LMGs) were therefore developed to meet such needs. Appearing during the latter years of World War I, they could be carried forward with the infantry to provide mobile fire support. The larger weapons became known as medium machine guns (MMGs). In an effort to simplify ammunition supply, most machine guns were designed to fire rifle rounds. As the war progressed, however, there emerged a requirement for large machine guns firing a heavy, long-range bullet for anti-aircraft and anti-armour roles. A number of such guns were produced, and this class of weapon became known as the heavy machine gun (HMG).

THE VICKERS MACHINE GUN

The main task of the medium machine gun – which is a comparatively large and immobile device – is to lay down continuous fire beyond the range of the infantry's rifles. Barrels and other components are relatively heavy in order to withstand the high temperatures and constant wear of such use. Whether in attack or defence, medium machine-gun teams usually provide the main source of infantry combat firepower, and so reliability and ruggedness in the weapon are essential. If a rifle jams it may get the user killed; if the machine gun jams, however, the whole unit may be wiped out.

The best of the early medium machine guns was the Vickers, developed in Britain from a licensed-built Maxim. The Vickers was one of the toughest and most reliable weapons to see service in World War I, and was to be the British Army's main machine gun in World War II, Korea, and well into the mid-1960s. Designed to fire the .303in

Vickers .303in

Calibre: .303in
Weight: 18.1kg (39lb)
Length: 1155mm ($45\frac{1}{2}$in)
Effective range: 1000m (1100yd)
Rate of fire: 450rpm
Feed: 250-round fabric belt
Muzzle velocity: 745mps (2445fps)

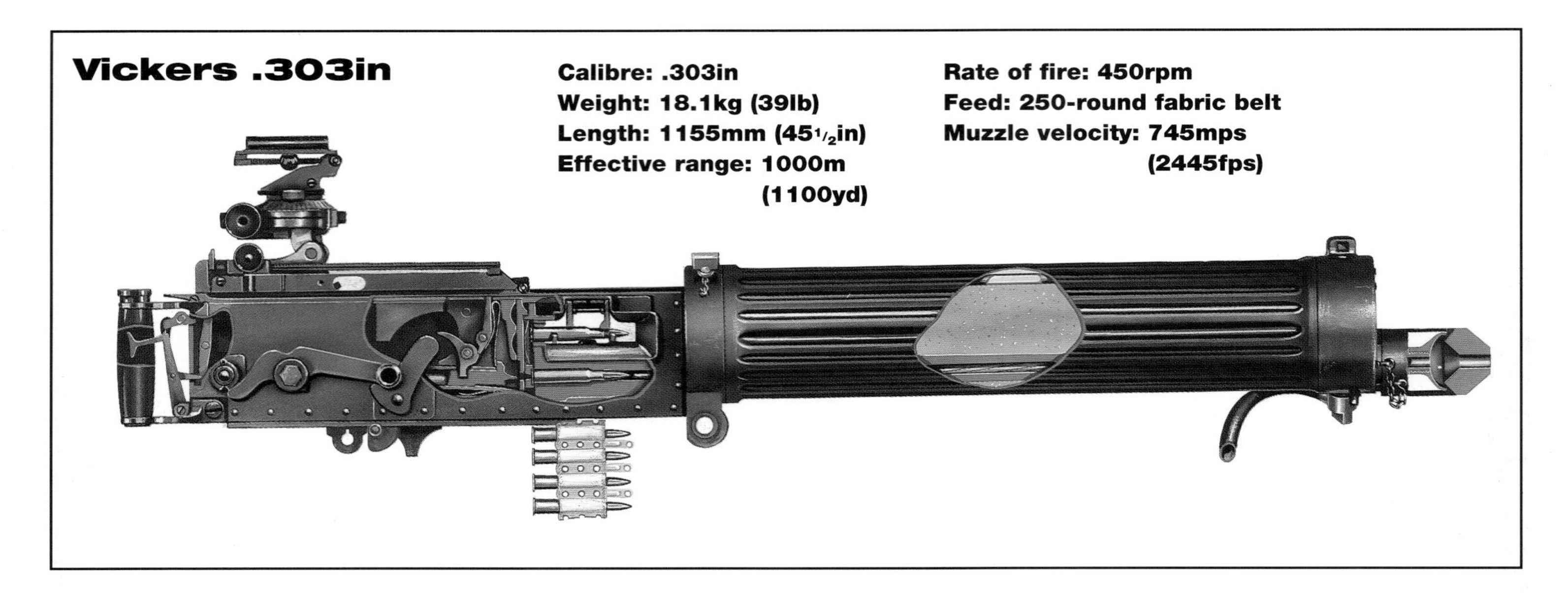

ammunition used by British Lee-Enfield rifles, the Vickers was stronger and more reliable than its Maxim predecessor. Although lighter than the parent design, the gun still weighed in at a hefty 14.97kg (33lb). It was normally mounted on a folding tripod, which added another 22.7kg (50lb), and with sights, cooling water and a few thousand rounds of ammunition, it is easy to see why machine-gun teams found tactical movement difficult when in action.

The Vickers works on the short-recoil principle, whereby the recoil impulse pushes back the barrel and bolt together. Behind the bolt is a horizontal locking toggle which holds the bolt to the barrel. The barrel only moves for a short distance – 18mm ($\frac{3}{4}$in) – before it is stopped by lugs on the receiver. At the same time, the locking toggle hinges in its centre and bends upwards, unlocking the bolt and allowing it to continue its rearward travel. During this time, the bolt extracts the empty case and catches the next round, pulling it rearwards from the cartridge belt. A 'fuzee' spring, attached to the bolt, is in a casing running along the side of the gun, and is extended by its travel to the rear. Once the bolt has finished moving, this spring propels it forward, giving enough impulse to feed the next round into the barrel. While this is happening, the barrel runs forward into the firing position, and as the bolt slams home, its locking toggle snaps straight, holding the bolt in place. If the trigger lever is still depressed, the weapon will continue to fire until the ammunition runs out.

The Vickers has a distinctive outline: a large rectangular box receiver attached to the thick water casing around the barrel. A deflector cap is fixed to the front of this casing, which uses some of the gases blown out at the muzzle to push back on the barrel and help the recoil system to operate. While there are simple iron sights fitted, the main system is a complex dial sight, where the range and deflection for wind (windage) is set before aiming. The gunner then fixes the weapon onto the target, using a sighting tube above the dials.

Browning M1919A4

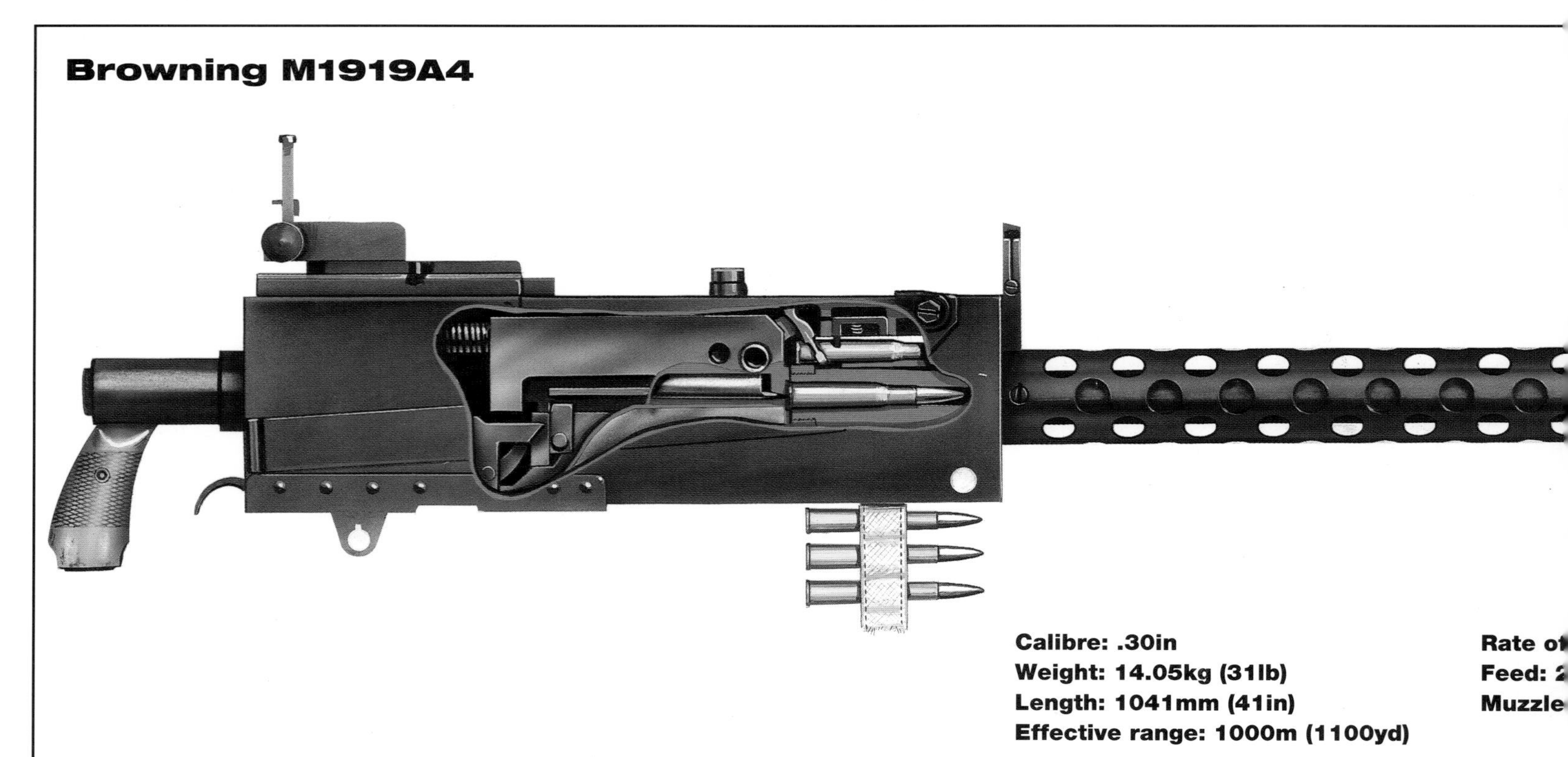

Calibre: .30in
Weight: 14.05kg (31lb)
Length: 1041mm (41in)
Effective range: 1000m (1100yd)
Rate o
Feed: 2
Muzzle

■ ABOVE: A Lewis machine gun in action in France, July 1916. The gun was made in large numbers during World War I. It was used by infantry and also fitted to aircraft.

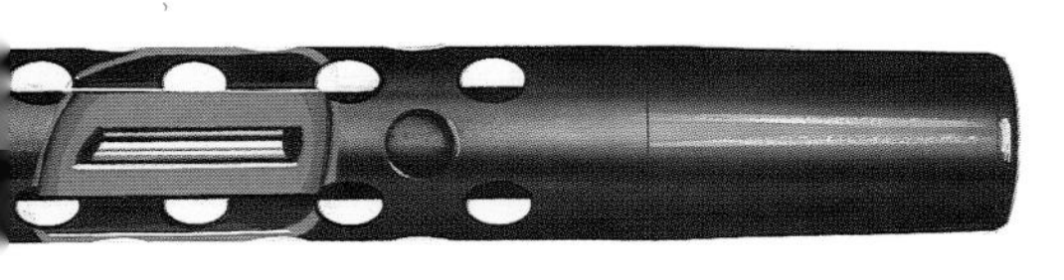

: 500rpm (cyclic)
ound fabric belt
city: 853mps (2800fps)

Fine adjustment is possible by turning elevation and azimuth screws on the tripod. In action, the firer holds two handle grips at the rear of the receiver, with a spring-loaded, thumb-operated trigger lever in between. Ammunition is fed from the right from a canvas belt holding 250 rounds.

DESIGNED TO FIRE FOR HOURS

As the gun was expected to fire continuously for long periods of time, a water-cooling jacket was fitted around the barrel. Machine gun barrels heat up quickly, and extended fire will result in the barrel glowing red (one tried and tested way of stopping a barrel getting too hot is to urinate on it when firing). Operating at such temperatures quickly wears out the rifling and the barrel lining, so most machine guns employ a quick-change system, whereby a replacement barrel can be fitted in a matter of seconds. The Vickers has a quick-change barrel, but extra cooling was still felt to be necessary for sustained fire. Therefore, a steel jacket containing four litres of water surrounds the barrel. After about 3000 rounds of continuous fire, the water starts to boil, losing around one litre for every thousand rounds fired. The gun is normally fitted with a rubber condenser tube leading from the jacket to a tin can containing cold water. Steam and vapour from the hot jacket are fed into this can to condense, thus retrieving most of the water lost. Heavy fire will eventually demand a replenishment of the water supply, and there are many tales of machine-gun teams using up all the water around their positions and having to collect urine from the troops nearby.

In the sustained fire (SF) role, the Vickers would often fire as part of a machine-gun platoon, with each weapon being locked onto an axis of fire and used to spray rounds continually along this bearing. Such a platoon could deny a large area of ground to enemy movement, even when the target area was not visible to the gunners. A well-known example of this occurred during a British attack on High Wood in August 1918. A machine-gun detachment was given the task of preventing enemy movement in a large area behind the German frontline, at a range of over 1800m (1970yd). The 10 Vickers guns fired an amazing total of one million rounds in 12 hours, with only short stoppages for reloading, barrel changing, oiling and cleaning. Over 200 infantrymen were used to collect water and carry ammunition, and the detachment exacted a fearful slaughter in the target area.

The Vickers was popular with the troops, as it was extremely reliable. Minor problems included a tendency for the canvas ammunition belts to swell when wet, sometimes jamming the mechanism, and the weight was also a minus point. A number of air-cooled versions were mounted on aircraft, and modifications were also made to allow variants to be mounted on armoured vehicles. The basic infantry gun remained almost unchanged throughout its life, and a few are still to be found around the world in reserve stocks.

Other countries developed their versions of the Maxim, including Germany with the MG08 (firing the 7.92mm x 57mm Mauser round) and Russia with the PM1910 (firing the 7.62mm x 54mm cartridge). The MG08 saw service throughout the 1930s, but was replaced by the MG34 general purpose machine gun (GPMG) just before World War II. The Russian design had a longevity of service similar to that of the Vickers, and this weapon with its distinctive turntable mount and small-wheeled carriage was still in Soviet frontline use in the early 1960s.

Not all first-generation machine guns were derived from the Maxim. The French Army, for example, operated a series of gas-operated weapons designed by the Hotchkiss Company, the best known being the Modèle 1914. This air-cooled weapon fired 8mm ammunition loaded in 30-round metal strips, and while heavy and awkward to load, was reliable enough to see widespread service in World War I and World War II.

AMERICAN MEDIUMS

One of the most prolific weapons designers during the early years of this century was the American John Browning, who was to create a series of machine guns that would

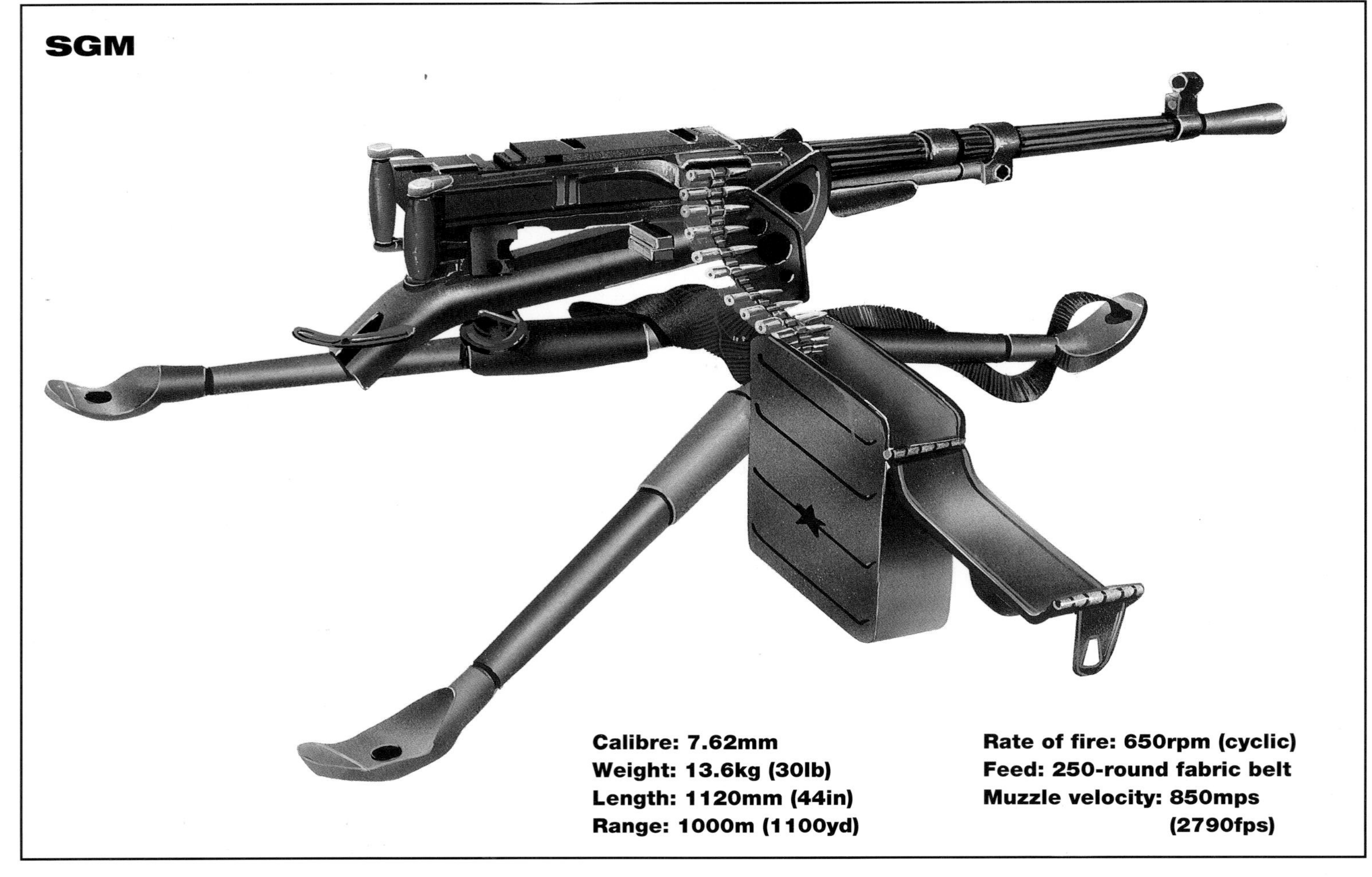

SGM

Calibre: 7.62mm
Weight: 13.6kg (30lb)
Length: 1120mm (44in)
Range: 1000m (1100yd)
Rate of fire: 650rpm (cyclic)
Feed: 250-round fabric belt
Muzzle velocity: 850mps (2790fps)

■ **ABOVE: French troops with a Browning M1917 machine gun. Some 68,000 had been made by the end of World War I.**

serve around the world up to the present day. During World War I, the United States Army had had to obtain most of its machine guns from its European allies. John Browning, however, had designed and built a number of his own models, and in 1910 had developed an effective recoil-operated gun. At that time, the US Army had insufficient funds and little interest in the new weapon, and it wasn't until 1917 and the entry of the United States into the European war that the Army procured Browning's design. This late decision meant that American troops went into battle with foreign weapons while American industry tooled up to produce indigenous designs.

The Browning M1917 was a superb gun that closely resembled its contemporaries, having a large cylindrical water jacket and a rectangular receiver. It also worked using the recoil system, though the mechanism was slightly simpler and lighter than in the Vickers. A 250-round canvas belt fed .30in M1906 rifle ammunition into the side of the gun, and the whole weapon was altogether more effective, reliable and lighter than its contemporaries. Browning developed the design into the M1919, the A4 version of which was to become the standard United States medium machine gun throughout World War II and into the 1960s. It has been used as a platoon and company level infantry weapon, and has been mounted on tanks, armoured cars, jeeps, trucks, boats and aircraft.

The M1919A4 retains the long rectangular receiver of the M1917, but the barrel is replaced by a much heavier item. There is no water jacket; instead a narrow outer casing is heavily perforated to allow air cooling. At first sight, this method of cooling appears to reduce the amount of time it can fire continuously. However, by using a heavy barrel the M1919 can easily cope with firing over 60 rounds a minute for at least 30 minutes (the M1919A4 also uses a 250-shot canvas ammunition belt). The Browning employs a similar recoil system to that of the Vickers, although in the A4's case the bolt is locked to the barrel extension by a spring-loaded catch attached to the bolt.

A simple pistol grip is attached below the short buffer tube at the rear of the gun, and the weapon is fired by pressing a curved trigger lever. A straight cocking handle protrudes from the right side of the receiver, and is pulled back rather like a rifle bolt. A folding leaf rear sight is used for most tasks, although a more sophisticated dial unit can be attached for long-range sustained fire. The M1919 weighs 14kg (30¾lb) and is usually mounted on a light (6.35kg/14lb) tripod. At one time there was a version with a rifle-style butt and other modifications for the LMG role, though the gun was really too bulky for this. Nevertheless, as an infantry MMG the Browning has been an outstanding success. Surprisingly light for the capabilities bestowed, the M1919 is a tough and reliable weapon, and thousands are still in service around the world.

MEDIUM RED

Development of the tripod-mounted medium machine gun continued throughout World War II and after, and one of the best new designs was the Russian SG series. The Russians were looking for a lighter, simpler and easier-to-manufacture replacement for their sturdy M1910 Maxims, and so the designer Stankovyi Goryunova came up with the SG43. This saw only limited service during World War II, but mass production continued, and the SG series was widely used by the Red Army, their allies and their 'client' states in

BREN GUN

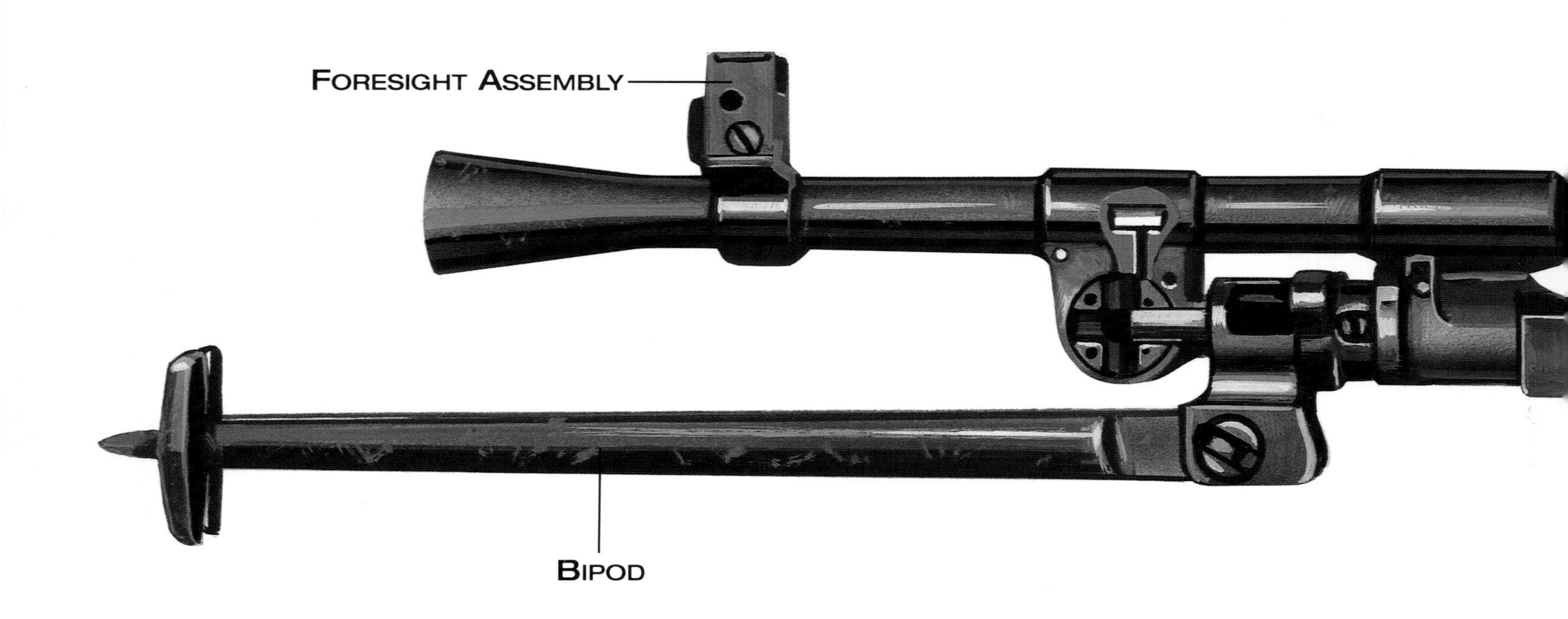

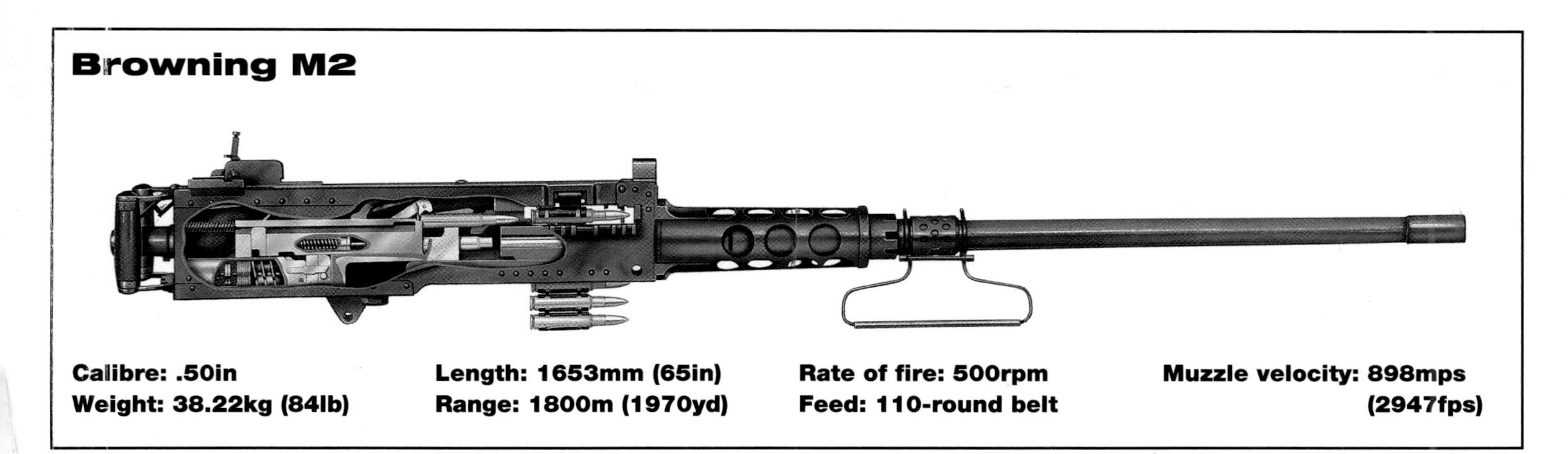

Browning M2

Calibre: .50in
Weight: 38.22kg (84lb)
Length: 1653mm (65in)
Range: 1800m (1970yd)
Rate of fire: 500rpm
Feed: 110-round belt
Muzzle velocity: 898mps (2947fps)

the post-war period. An improved version of the design was introduced as the SGM, and this also saw widespread service. Wherever Soviet and Soviet-backed troops fought throughout the 1950s, 60s and 70s, the SGM would be accompanying them. Hundreds were used against US and South Vietnamese troops in Vietnam, and this reliable and effective weapon is still in widespread service around the world.

THE SOVIET SGM

Goryunova's design is gas operated, with the gases being bled off from the barrel and used to propel a piston backwards to operate the firing mechanism. The piston and cylinder lie below the heavy barrel, which on the SGM has lateral flutes engraved to ease cooling. The gun is fed from a metal belt and fires the Soviet 7.62mm x 54mm rimmed cartridge, which has been in service as a rifle cartridge since World War I. The firer has two grips at the rear of the gun, and the cocking handle is on the right of the receiver. A handle extends from the side of the barrel to help when changing this item, and the sights are a fixed-post foresight combined with a fold-up leaf rear sight.

The piston extends into the receiver, where a shaped block or post extends upwards from the end of the piston into a large slot in the bolt. The bolt travels back when the cocking handle is pulled to the rear, and a cartridge gripper simultaneously pulls a round rearwards out of the cartridge belt. As the bolt moves, the piston post (and hence the piston) is also pulled backwards, compressing the return spring. The gun fires from an open bolt, so the mechanism locks to the rear until the trigger is pulled. When this is done, the piston is flung forward by the compressed return spring, pulling the bolt with it. The fresh round has already dropped into the lower feed cover, and the bolt picks this up and pushes it into the chamber. As the mechanism moves forward it drives the feed slide, which pulls the next round in the belt into the upper feed position.

Once the bolt presses against the chamber, the piston post continues to move forward in its slot. The shape of the slot causes the rear of the bolt to be slid sideways, pushing it into a locking shoulder in the receiver (this mechanism has similarities to the tipping bolt found on the FN FAL rifle, though here the movement is horizontal rather than vertical). Once the bolt is in place, the piston post continues forward, striking the firing pin and firing the round. The high-pressure gases in the barrel are tapped into the pressure cylinder and they start to move the piston to the rear. The piston post also moves rearward in its slot, and there is about 6mm of travel before the rear of the bolt is forced back to the centre and the bolt is free to move back, by which time the gas pressure in the barrel has dropped to a safe level. The bolt is now pulled back by the piston and piston post, taking the empty case with it for extraction. As the bolt reaches the rearmost limit of its travel, the empty case is flipped out of the gun and the next round is pulled backwards out of the ammunition belt. There is no selector lever for fire modes – the SGM only works on full-automatic.

Though the SGM system sounds complex, and hence prone to jamming, the weapon has proved itself to be extremely reliable and robust in all conditions, even in the hands of partially trained troops. However, it is heavy – 13.6kg (30lb) – and is normally mounted on a wheeled carriage, similar to the Sokolov mount on the M1910. The SGM carriage has a small steel shield around the gun and a single trailing arm for stability. The mount has adjusting knobs to aim the gun precisely in azimuth and elevation, and the gun can be unlocked for all-round fire. The mount is easily converted to the anti-aircraft role by removing the gun then tipping the mount forward until the top edge of the shield rests on the ground and the trailing arm sticks vertically upwards. The gun is then attached to the bracket on the rear of the trailing arm. Other mounts associated with the SG series include a wheeled chassis with a tubular steel U-shaped trail, and a more conventional folding tripod.

Versions of this gun have been manufactured in China, Hungary and several other communist countries, and it has been used on many types of armoured vehicle, in both pintle and co-axial mountings. The SGM is still in service around the world, though the Russian Army has now replaced it with the PK series of GPMGs.

BROWNING'S HEAVY

During the second half of World War I, battlefield defences became more and more elaborate, with earth, wood and even steel plates being used to shield positions from enemy small-arms fire. Primitive armoured vehicles had also made an appearance, with their crews being protected by steel plate. While medium machine guns were devastating when engaging infantry in the open, something heavier was required to attack static and moving 'hardened' targets.

A number of designs were therefore put forward for a gun firing larger, heavier bullets, and the best known of these was to come from the fertile brain of John Browning. His MMG design, in the shape of the M1917, had proved itself to be effective and reliable, so he simply scaled the design up to create a water-cooled gun firing the French 11mm round. The bullet was found to be ineffective, but by the end of the war the Americans had captured some German Mauser anti-tank rifles. These fired a .50in (12.7mm) round which had a high muzzle velocity and excellent anti-armour characteristics. An American version of this round was quickly designed

FAR LEFT: A British Bren gun team in action in Korea in 1950. The Bren is undoubtedly the finest light machine gun ever built. Its mechanical components are easily understood, and it can be stripped and reassembled very quickly.

LEFT: The modern version of the Bren, the L4, which fires the 7.62mm NATO round instead of the .303in bullet.

RIGHT: A Bren in the anti-aircraft role. The weapon was originally a Czech gun that had been designed to fire the German 7.92mm rimless cartridge. It therefore had to be redesigned to fire the British .303in rimmed round, and this is the reason why the Bren has a distinctive curved magazine.

Calibre	.303in
Weight	10.15kg (22¼lb)
Length	1150mm (45in)
Effective range	800m (880yd)
Rate of fire	500rpm (cyclic)
Feed	30-round magazine
Muzzle velocity	731mps (2400fps)

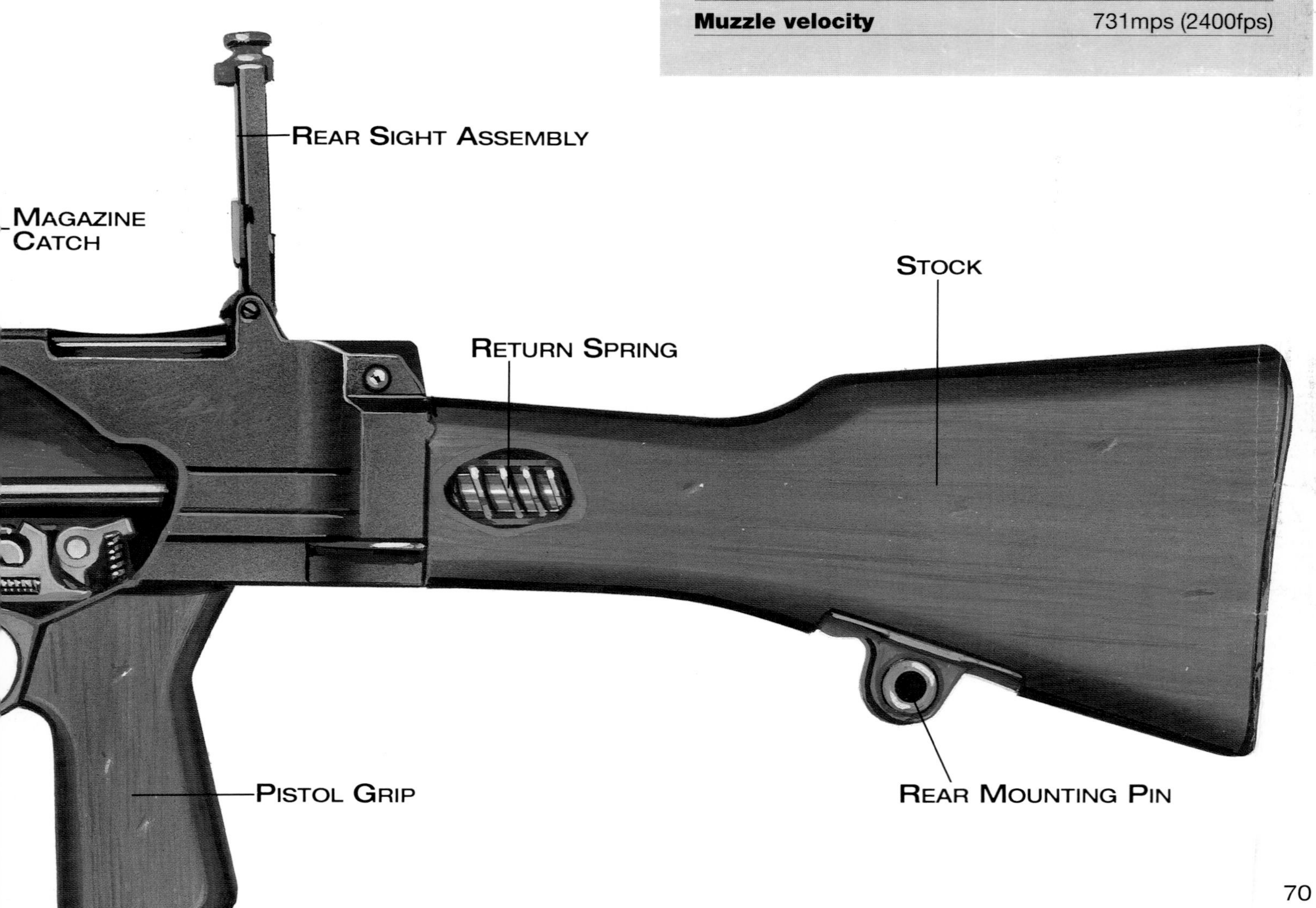

Magazine
Carrying Handle
Gas Cylinder
Forward Mount Pin for Tripod
Trigger

as the .50in (12.7mm x 99mm) M2 cartridge, with Browning's heavy machine gun being modified to fire it. The new weapon was too late for the war, not entering service until the 1920s, when it was designated the M1921. The .50in round had an extremely flat trajectory and long range, which made it effective as an anti-aircraft round, and it was in this role that the M1921 first saw service.

By 1933 the gun had been redesignated M2, and had appeared with an air-cooled barrel, originally developed for aircraft use. The barrel would overheat quickly after only a few rounds, so a much heavier item was soon introduced. This gun became known as the M2HB (Heavy Barrel). In this form, the M2 became the standard heavy machine gun of the US Army and other armed forces around the world. Air crews fired them from turrets on bombers, fighter pilots had fixed batteries of them on the wings of their aircraft, tanks used them as co-axial guns, all sorts of vehicles used them for anti-aircraft defence, and the infantry mounted them on tripods for anti-aircraft, anti-vehicle and long-range anti-personnel duties. The M2HB, or 'fifty-cal', has seen service in World War II, Korea, Vietnam, Panama, Grenada and the 1991 Gulf War, and in virtually every other conflict during the last 50 years. Over 20 countries have M2s of various types currently in service.

The .50in round is capable of penetrating over 40mm (1½in) of armour at ranges of over 800m (880yd). This firepower demands a sturdy construction, and the gun weighs some 38.22kg (84lb), with another 19.86kg (43lb) for the tripod. It looks similar to the M1919A4, although it does not have the perforated jacket surrounding the barrel. The same short-recoil mechanism is used in both guns, however, with the ammunition being fed

■ **ABOVE: The Browning M2 heavy machine gun, seen here with American troops in the Mekong Delta during the Vietnam War. The M2 was originally designed for aircraft use, but has proved to be outstanding in the ground role.**

into the M2 via a 110-round link belt. When the gun is mounted on vehicles, the ammunition belt is usually held in a steel box which is clipped to the side of the gun mount. The M2 has two handle grips behind the receiver, with the trigger lever in between. A large cocking handle protrudes from the right-hand side of the receiver, and the spring buffer compresses into a tube protruding at the rear. Normal sights are a shrouded post and folding leaf type at the front and rear of the receiver respectively. More sophisticated sights are used for SF roles, and night sights can be fitted if required. The M2 also has a number of specialised sights for the anti-aircraft role.

There is normally a tiny gap between the bolt face and the rear of the barrel when the bolt is closed. This 'headspace' is present in virtually all firearms, and must be set precisely to match the characteristics of the weapon and ammunition combination. On the M2HB, when the barrel is changed the headspace has to be reset for the new barrel, a time-consuming and awkward task in the field. As the heavy barrel is supposedly much more heat-absorbent than before, it was felt that rapid barrel changes would be unnecessary in combat. In recent years, however, modified M2s have appeared with the facility to change barrels quickly, without needing to adjust the headspace. Such Quick-Change Barrel (QCB) kits have been produced by a number of manufacturers and can be retro-fitted to earlier models. The modified guns are usually known as the M2HB (QCB).

THE AGELESS 'FIFTY-CAL'

The M2HB has a surprisingly slow rate of fire, and its steady thud makes a distinctive sound on the battlefield. Still used against aircraft and light armour, the 12.7mm round is effective against infantry and other unprotected targets at ranges up to 2000m (2200yd). It also has good penetrative power against brickwork and masonry, a useful attribute for urban combat. 'Fifty-cals' are mounted in pods on helicopters and light counter-insurgency aircraft, and the round is used by the Barrett 'Light Fifty' series of sniper rifles.

The death of the 'fifty-cal' has been announced on a number of occasions, with pundits proclaiming its obsolescence in the face of competition from rapid-firing cannon of 25mm calibre and above. However, the complexity, cost and weight of such weapons has made their use less widespread than originally expected. At the other end of the calibre spectrum, the latest rifles and light machine guns has largely moved to 5.56mm, reducing their capability for long-range fire. The gap in calibres that has appeared between these extremes has ensured there is still a place for weapons such as the M2, and it seems that Browning's World War I concept will still be in service into the next century.

The Soviet equivalent of the Browning is the DShKM, a heavy machine gun firing 12.7mm x 108mm ammunition. The performance of this gun is similar to that of the M2HB, though it is a lighter weapon at 35.5kg (78lb). The original weapon, the DShK38, saw extensive service in World War II. This gun used a complex feed mechanism to extract rounds from the 50-round metallic belt, a system which proved fragile and somewhat unreliable in combat. The design was modified in 1946, and the DShKM has been the main heavy machine gun of pro-Soviet forces ever since.

THE RED ARMY'S HEAVY

Tough and capable, the DShKM (nick-named 'Dushka' by Russian troops) has cooling fins along most of the barrel and a flat, disc-shaped muzzle brake at the end of the barrel. It is gas operated, with the bolt being locked by two hinged flaps which are pushed out to the side as the firing pin moves forward. These flaps lock into shoulders in the receiver, and hold the bolt in place immediately after a round is fired. By the time the gas pressure has dropped to a safe level, the firing pin has moved backwards, pulling the flaps back into the side of the bolt and releasing it to start the recoil, extraction and reloading cycle. Ammunition types include ball, armour-piercing, tracer and incendiary. The Dushka is no longer used in the ground role by the Russian Army, but many are still to be found around the world. It was in the anti-aircraft role in the Vietnam War that American airmen learned to treat this weapon with great respect, diverting many flight hours to hunt down individual guns. Dushkas are also mounted on almost all Russian-designed tanks, and were used by both sides during the painful Afghanistan conflict (1979-89).

A replacement heavy gun, known as the NSV, was deployed in the early 1970s. Named from the initials of the designers (Nikitin, Sokolov and Volkhov), it fires the same 12.7mm ammunition as the Dushka and has a faster rate of fire. Gas operated, it uses a two-piece rotating bolt which resembles that used in the Kalashnikov rifle. The NSV is fed from a 50-round metal belt, and is employed as the main anti-aircraft gun on later Russian tanks. The NSV is also issued to ground troops as a heavy support weapon. It is mounted on a new design of tripod and equipped with an optical sight. The gun is effective against low-flying helicopters and aircraft up to 1560m (1700yd) away, and ground targets up to a range of 2000m (2200yd).

Stoner 63 medium machine gun

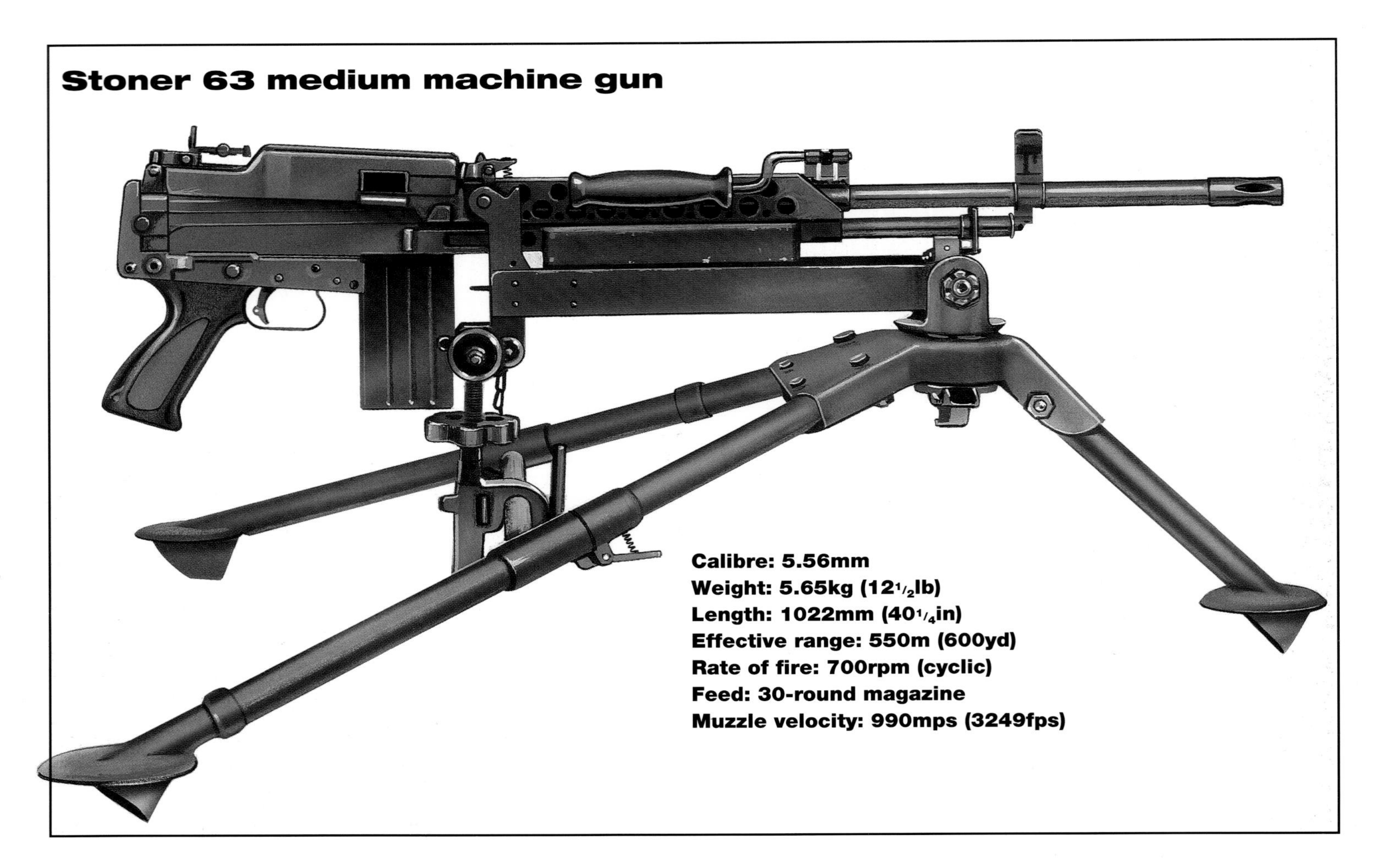

Calibre: 5.56mm
Weight: 5.65kg (12½lb)
Length: 1022mm (40¼in)
Effective range: 550m (600yd)
Rate of fire: 700rpm (cyclic)
Feed: 30-round magazine
Muzzle velocity: 990mps (3249fps)

EARLY LIGHT MACHINE GUNS

The heavy and medium weapons described above have all been designed to provide maximum firepower on the battlefield, with ease of mobility being low on the list of design priorities. Combat experience in World War I, however, emphasised the need for a machine gun that could be carried forward with the infantry, even over the shell-blasted mud of Flanders. The first such weapons to enter service were a lighter version of the German MG08, the drum-fed Lewis gun, the disastrous French Chauchat, and the American Browning Automatic Rifle (BAR). The Lewis was actually an American design, but only entered widespread service in the British Army. The weapon has a wooden rifle butt and pistol grip, and is supported by a folding bipod, The distinctive feature of the Lewis is a large diameter outer casing that surrounds the barrel. This covers a radial array of cooling fins that run down the length of the barrel. By 1918 the Lewis was issued to British infantry platoons and was put to great use in the final 1918 offensives. Lewis detachments could move forward with the infantry and engage enemy strongpoints; they could even stalk medium machine-gun posts. The gun also served as an anti-aircraft weapon, was mounted on early aircraft, and was still in second-line infantry use during the early years of World War II.

The United States Army was to be issued with yet another Browning design: the BAR. This weapon resembles a rather large assault rifle, although it was issued as a squad-level light machine gun. It was designed for the United States doctrine of 'walking fire', whereby a continuous barrage of rounds was sprayed ahead of the advancing troops. With this concept, light automatic weapons were essential to produce sufficient firepower to keep the defenders pinned down. The BAR turned out to be rather too heavy – 8.85kg (19½lb) with bipod – to be fired from the shoulder as a rifle, and it also lacked the firepower of a true light machine gun.

The weapon has a long, relatively light barrel, a horizontal wooden foregrip and a wooden rifle butt. There is a folding bipod at the front of the barrel. Twenty rounds of .30in ammunition are held in a detachable box magazine, necessitating frequent changes in action. The original models fired both single-shot and full-automatic, but later versions were modified to fire automatic fire only, though two rates of fire were selectable. A gas-operated weapon with a bolt locking piece which tipped upwards into a recess in the receiver, the BAR was extremely well made, incredibly strong and totally reliable. These features endeared the weapon to the troops, and although it was too late to see much service in World War I, the BAR became the standard squad light machine gun in all theatres during World War II, and remained in service throughout the Korean War and up until the late 1950s.

FG42

THE BRITISH CZECH

By World War II, the British had replaced their Lewis guns with an LMG that was to become one of the most famous of all such weapons. When the Army carried out trials in the 1930s to find a replacement for the Lewis, one of the guns examined was the Czech ZB26. As it was superbly accurate and reliable, the British decided to introduce a version of this gun, modified to fire their .303in cartridge, as their new LMG. The gun was manufactured in Britain and was named by combining the first two letters from the original Czech factory (Brno) with those of the British factory (Enfield). The Bren gun was born.

The Bren is a rugged gas-operated design, firing with a distinctive slow rate of fire (500 rpm). Some 10.2kg (22½lb) in weight, it is easily handled by one man, though normal procedure includes a second man to carry and load magazines. The gun has a long silhouette, with a wooden rifle butt and pistol grip, but the most distinctive recognition feature is the large 30-shot curved box magazine sticking

■ ABOVE: A heavy machine gun in the service of Allah, albeit one captured from the infidel. A Mujahedeen DShK gun.

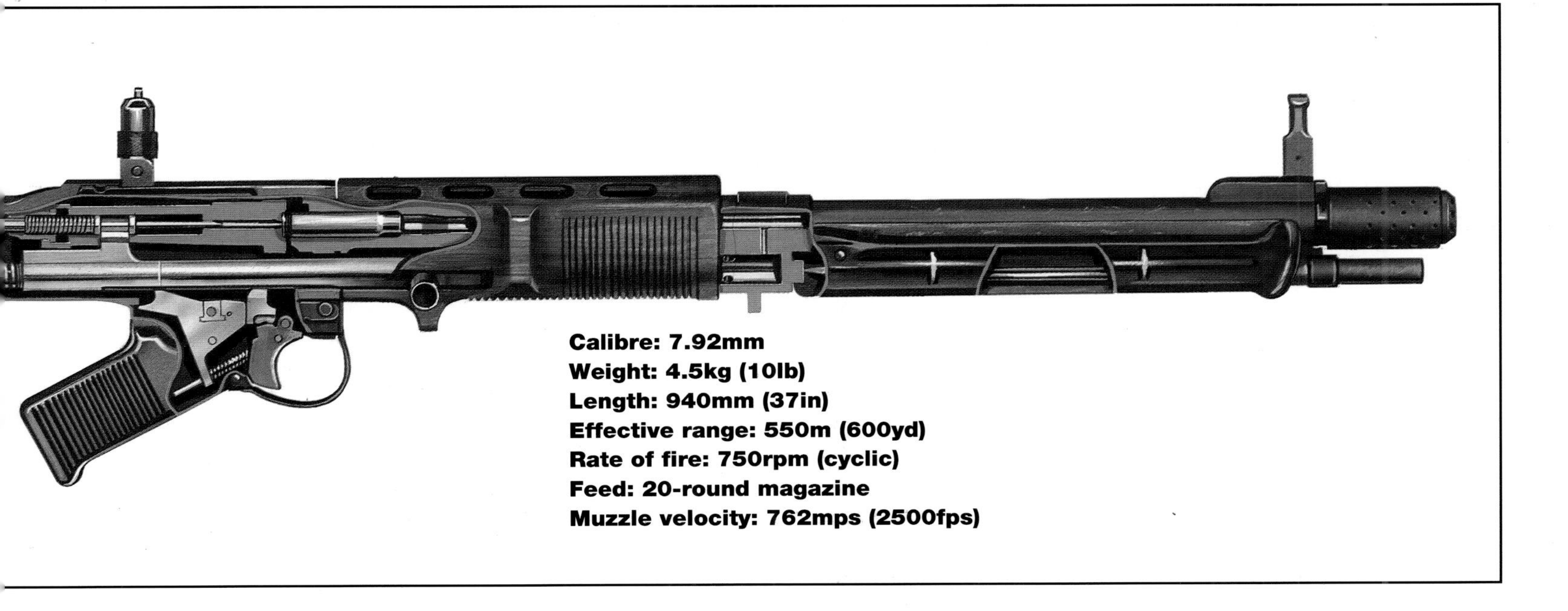

Calibre: 7.92mm
Weight: 4.5kg (10lb)
Length: 940mm (37in)
Effective range: 550m (600yd)
Rate of fire: 750rpm (cyclic)
Feed: 20-round magazine
Muzzle velocity: 762mps (2500fps)

vertically upwards from the receiver. The Bren uses the gas cylinder and piston method of operation, with the cylinder lying beneath the barrel. The piston is connected to an extension piece that holds a piston post, which extends upwards into a slot cut in the bolt. When the weapon is cocked – by pulling back the handle on the right of the receiver – the piston post and bolt are moved to the rear, compressing the return spring. The gun fires from an open bolt, so the whole assembly stays locked to the rear until the trigger is pulled. Once this happens, the piston extension is released and the return spring sends it forward, pulling the bolt with it. The bolt catches the next round from the magazine and takes it forward, pushing it into the chamber. As the bolt slams home, the piston extension continues forward. Two small ramps force the bolt to tip upwards at the rear, and a vertical lug at the rear of the bolt locks into a recess in the receiver. The piston post continues to move forward in

RPD

Calibre: 7.62mm
Weight: 7kg (15½lb)
Length: 1041mm (41in)
Effective range: 800m (880yd)
Rate of fire: 700rpm (cyclic)
Feed: 100-round metal belt
Muzzle velocity: 735mps (2412fps)

■ BELOW: An early example of the Soviet SG43 medium machine gun. This model has a finned barrel, whereas later ones had smooth barrels.

its slot, striking the rear of the firing pin and firing the cartridge. As the bullet flies down the barrel, gas is bled off into the cylinder to start the piston movement to the rear. The piston extension and piston post move back until the sloping rear edge of the piston post hits the rear of its slot within the bolt, pulling the bolt down from its locked position. Once it is released, the bolt, together with the piston extension, moves to the rear, compressing the return spring and the soft buffer. The empty case is ejected below the gun, while the next round drops into place.

The Bren only fires bursts, although the rate of fire is slow enough to allow a skilled operator to pick single shots with the trigger. Barrels can be changed quickly and easily, and are normally swapped after 3-400 rounds of sustained fire. The sights are a folding leaf rear sight and a simple post at the front, although they are offset slightly to the left to clear the large vertical magazine. A folding bipod is attached to the front of the gas cylinder which, in a neat design feature, can be used to clear carbon fouling by giving the bipod a sharp twist. A prominent carrying handle is just in front of the magazine, with a cone-shaped flash hider at the muzzle.

The Bren is one of the best light machine guns ever – it is reliable and accurate in all conditions. Light enough to be fired from a standing position, it has been used by British soldiers throughout World War II and beyond. When the Army changed to 7.62mm x 51mm ammunition and the SLR rifle, its Brens were modified to the new calibre. The updated gun, known as the L4, is easily recognisable by the almost straight magazine and slotted flash eliminator. The L4 saw service into the late 1970s, though mostly with rear-echelon and support troops.

THE LIGHT PARA

By the beginning of World War II, the German Army had little use for light machine guns, having moved almost completely to the concept of the general purpose gun and the MG34 (see page 79). *Luftwaffe* paratroop forces, however, were of the opinion that these weapons were rather heavy for squad level use, and that something lighter was needed. Paratroopers usually fight without heavy support, so any weapon that could increase the firepower of the ordinary para once he hit the ground was welcome. The FG42 was designed in the middle of the war and, like the BAR, can be regarded as a halfway house between the assault rifle and the light machine gun.

A light (4.5kg/10lb) gas-operated weapon, the FG42 looks like a straightline assault rifle, with its metal butt and pistol grip, and wooden foregrip. The gun fires from an open bolt when firing bursts, and a closed one when firing single shots. The selector lever is on the left, and the cocking handle is in front of the trigger, on the right side of the receiver. A 20-round magazine protrudes to the left of the receiver, and there is a folding bipod and integral bayonet under the front of the barrel. The weapon fires full-powered 7.92mm x 57mm rifle cartridges, and this, combined with a light weight, makes it rather a handful when firing on full-automatic. The FG42 was expensive and difficult to produce, which combined with a lack of sustained firepower ensured that it was only ever issued to paratroopers.

RUSSIAN LIGHTWEIGHTS

In the Soviet Union, Degtyarev had produced the DP, a drum-fed weapon that was to be the Soviet Army's main LMG throughout World War II and into the post-war era. Adopted in 1928, the DP fired the then standard Russian 7.62mm x 54mm rimmed cartridge. The detachable flat drum magazine held 47 rounds, which were fed into position by a clockwork spring system. Gas operated, with a standard piston and cylinder arrangement, the DP fires from an open bolt to aid cooling between bursts.

■ ABOVE: A German machine-gun team in action during World War II. The weapon is an MG34, one of the deadliest machine guns of the war. It had a tendency to jam in dust, dirt and snow, however.

The bolt is locked in place by two hinged flaps, which are forced outwards into recesses in the receiver by a cammed surface on the firing pin as it slides forward. The DP gave good overall service to the Soviets, but did have problems with the fragile tin drum magazine and the rimmed ammunition. It was an accurate and effective LMG, however, and saw continuous service throughout the 1950s, and saw service in both Korea and Vietnam. An improved DPM was issued in 1945 with a pistol grip and changeable barrel, and the DT variant was used on armoured vehicles.

When the intermediate 7.62mm x 39mm cartridge was developed, Degtyarev created a new light machine gun to fire this round. The RPD appeared in 1953, and quickly became the standard squad automatic weapon for the Red Army and Soviet client states. It has seen service all around the world, especially in Southeast Asia, and has been built in a number of countries, including China. The RPD is long and looks rather thin, with a wooden rifle butt, pistol grip and foregrip. It is fed from a 50-round metal belt, although belts can be linked together for continuous fire. The ammunition is usually coiled in a metal drum belt container which is attached beneath the gun. The gun is light – 7.0kg ($15\frac{1}{2}$lb) – but has a high rate of fire (700rpm). A folding bipod is attached to the barrel, but stability when firing has always been a problem with this weapon. The mechanism is similar to that found in the DPM and SGM, ie the hinged flap method of locking the bolt. The barrel is not changeable, however, so the gunner has to be trained to allow time to cool between periods of sustained fire. It has taken four versions of the RPD before minor design flaws have been eradicated, but the later models are fine, reliable weapons which give a high level of firepower to infantry squads. As with most Soviet designs, the RPD is rugged and reliable. It is still used by many armies and guerrilla forces around the world, although it has been superseded in Russian frontline service by the Kalashnikov-derived RPK and PKM.

MG42

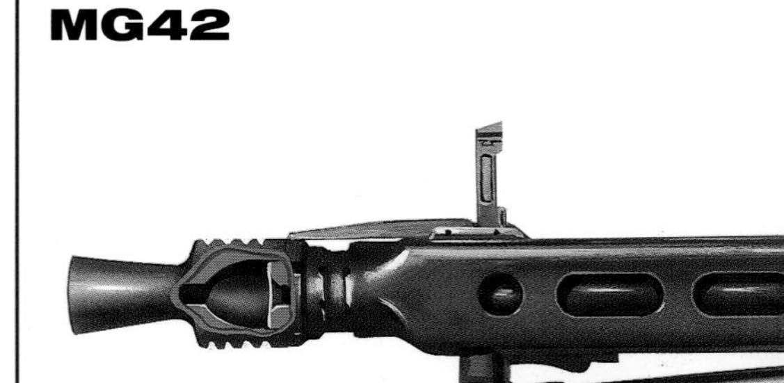

Calibre: 7.92m
Weight: 11.5kg
Length: 1219m
Range: 1000m

MG34

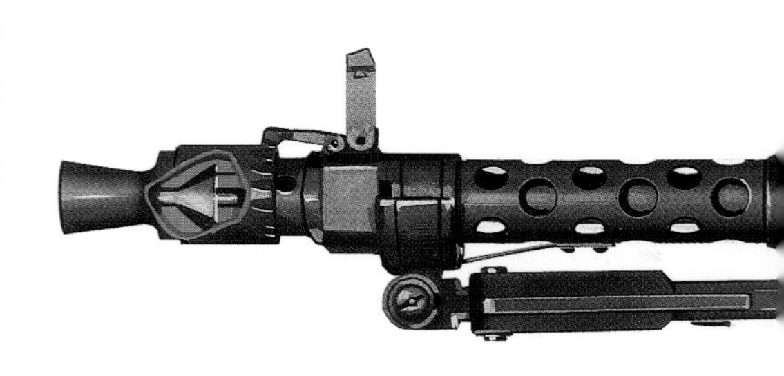

Calibre: 7.92mm
Weight: 12.1kg (
Length: 1219mm
Range: 1000m (1

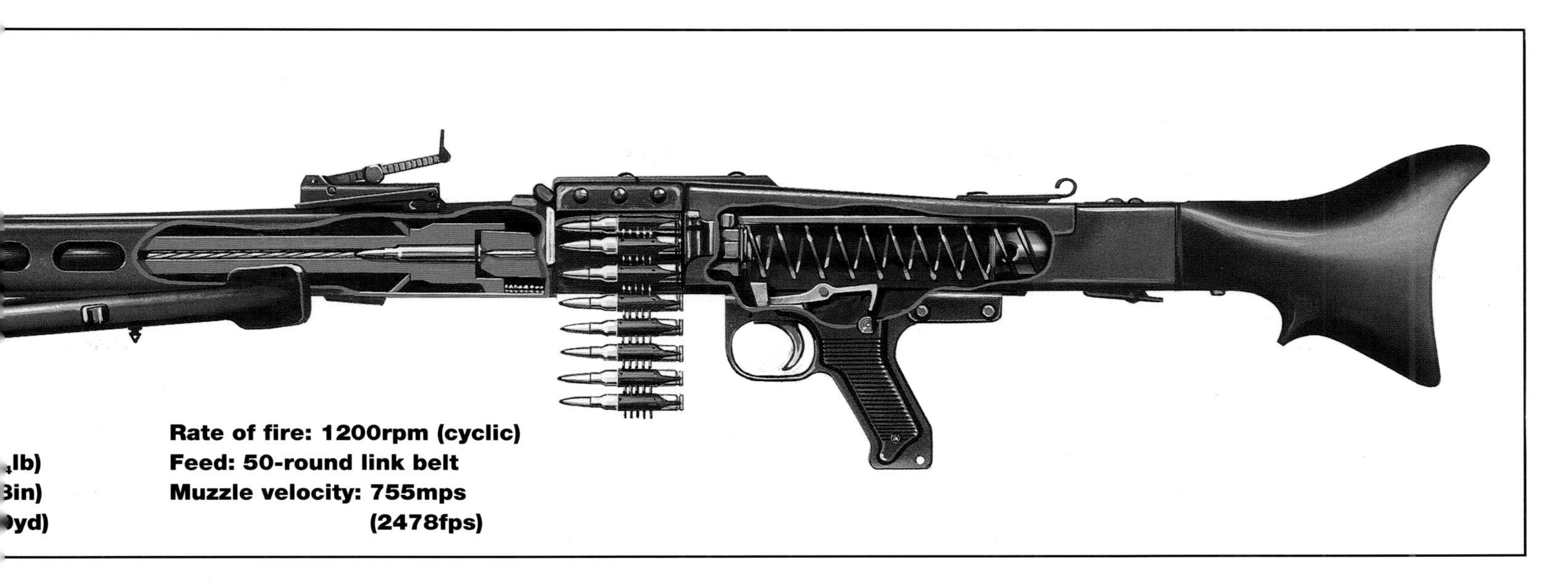

A GUN FOR ALL SEASONS

In the 1930s, the reconstituted German Army was open to many new ideas while developing and refining their *Blitzkrieg* concept of fast-moving offensive operations. The traditional MMG was too heavy and immobile for this style of warfare, so the Germans decided to do away with distinctive medium and light machine guns. Instead they were to develop a new concept, one which virtually every manufacturer and designer was to copy in the years ahead. The general purpose machine gun (GPMG) was to be a weapon that would carry out all the roles of the earlier weapons. Mounted on a bipod, with ammunition held in drum magazines or belt boxes, it would be the squad and platoon level LMG. Attached to a tripod, and with the ammunition fed in continuous belts, it would double as an MMG. Equipped with extra barrels and a dial sight, the GPMG would carry out SF tasks. The same gun could also be used on vehicles, aircraft and in an anti-aircraft role. Training and supply would be much simpler than before, and the lighter weapons and their modern tripods would be much easier to break down into reasonable man-portable loads for movement.

THE RADICAL MG34

The initial German attempt to meet this demanding requirement was the MG34. Developed from the earlier MG30, this was the first 'modern' machine gun, and was to be the forerunner of a completely new class of weapon. The MG34 is a long and slender weapon, with no gas cylinder alongside the barrel. Operation is by a combination of gas and recoil. When a round is fired, the barrel recoils a short distance, the recoil being helped by gas pressure on a deflector at the muzzle. The bolt is locked at its face by an interrupted screw, and the initial movement of the barrel causes it to rotate and unlock. When the barrel ends its movement, the bolt continues to the rear, extracting the empty case and flipping it beneath the gun, while pulling the next round from the belt. As the return spring sends it forward, the bolt takes the next round and guides it down into the chamber. The MG34 fires standard 7.92mm x 57mm Mauser ammunition, and can be fed either from a 50-round belt or from a 75-round twin drum unit which sits across the top of the gun like a saddle.

High-impact plastics are used on the butt and pistol grip, and there is a folding bipod permanently attached. The barrel is air-cooled, and has a cylindrical perforated jacket surrounding it. It can be changed for a cool one in seconds when operating in the SF role. There is no fire selector. If the trigger is pulled to the first pressure, one shot is fired, and if it is pulled further, a continuous burst ensues. The gun can be quickly attached to a light tripod, and dial sights can be easily fitted. When mounted on a tripod the trigger is obscured, so a remote firing mechanism is used, operated

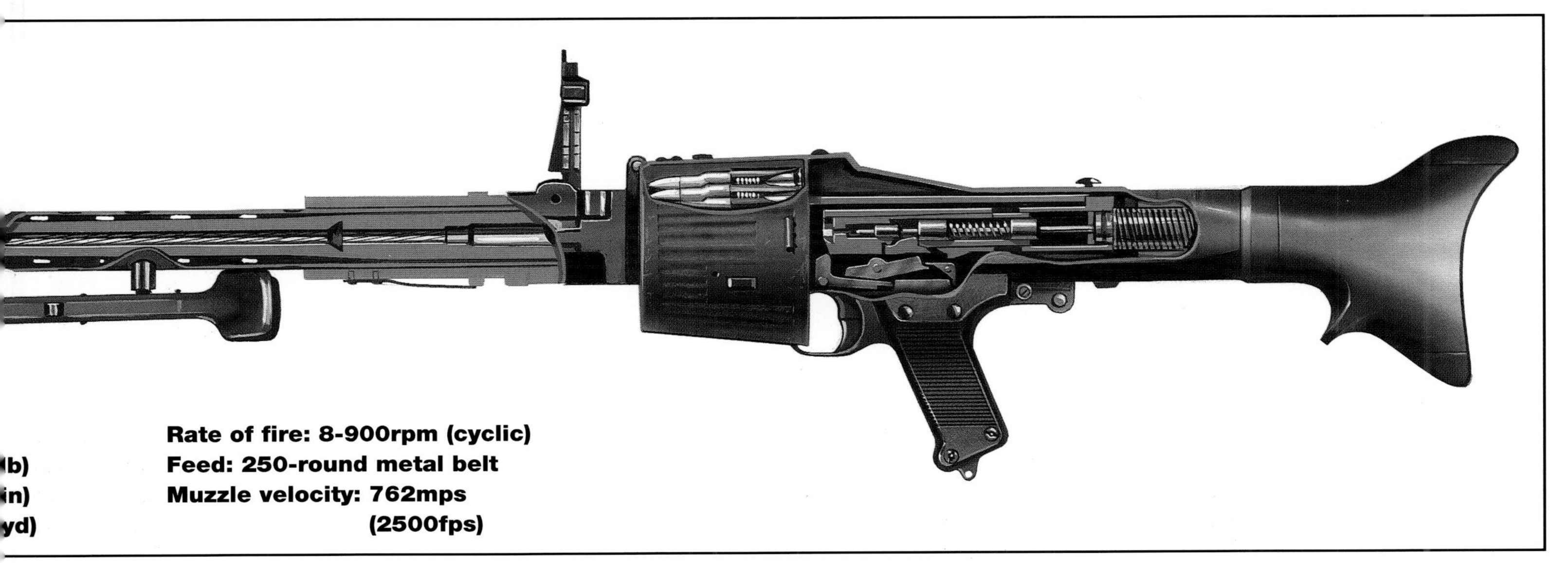

Stoner 63 Multi-Purpose Machine Gun

(see page 74 for specifications)

by a grip on the right of the mounting. The gun can be quickly dismounted for the LMG role, and the complete package splits up into man-portable loads.

Entering service in 1934, the MG34 quickly proved its worth in the early years of World War II. It was superbly engineered, which led to problems with achieving high wartime production rates. The fine tolerances also meant that the gun was vulnerable to poor conditions, and would quickly seize up if dust or sand was present. Nevertheless, if carefully looked after, it was a fine gun, and saw frontline service throughout the war.

As the war progressed, the Germans needed a machine gun that could be easily built in large quantities, and one which could withstand combat better than the MG34. Mauser consulted a Dr Grunow, an industrialist who specialised in the technology of mass production. A new gun was devised, incorporating lessons from the first years of the war, and being specifically designed for quick and cheap manufacture. The ensuing MG42 was made from steel stampings and pressings rather than machined from solid blocks. It was riveted and spot-welded together, and the design was functional rather than finely finished.

LEFT: One of the finest medium machine guns of the post-war era: the British GPMG, called 'Gimpy' by the troops.
RIGHT: The German MG3. Basically this is the same weapon as the MG42, and is in current German service.

FN MAG

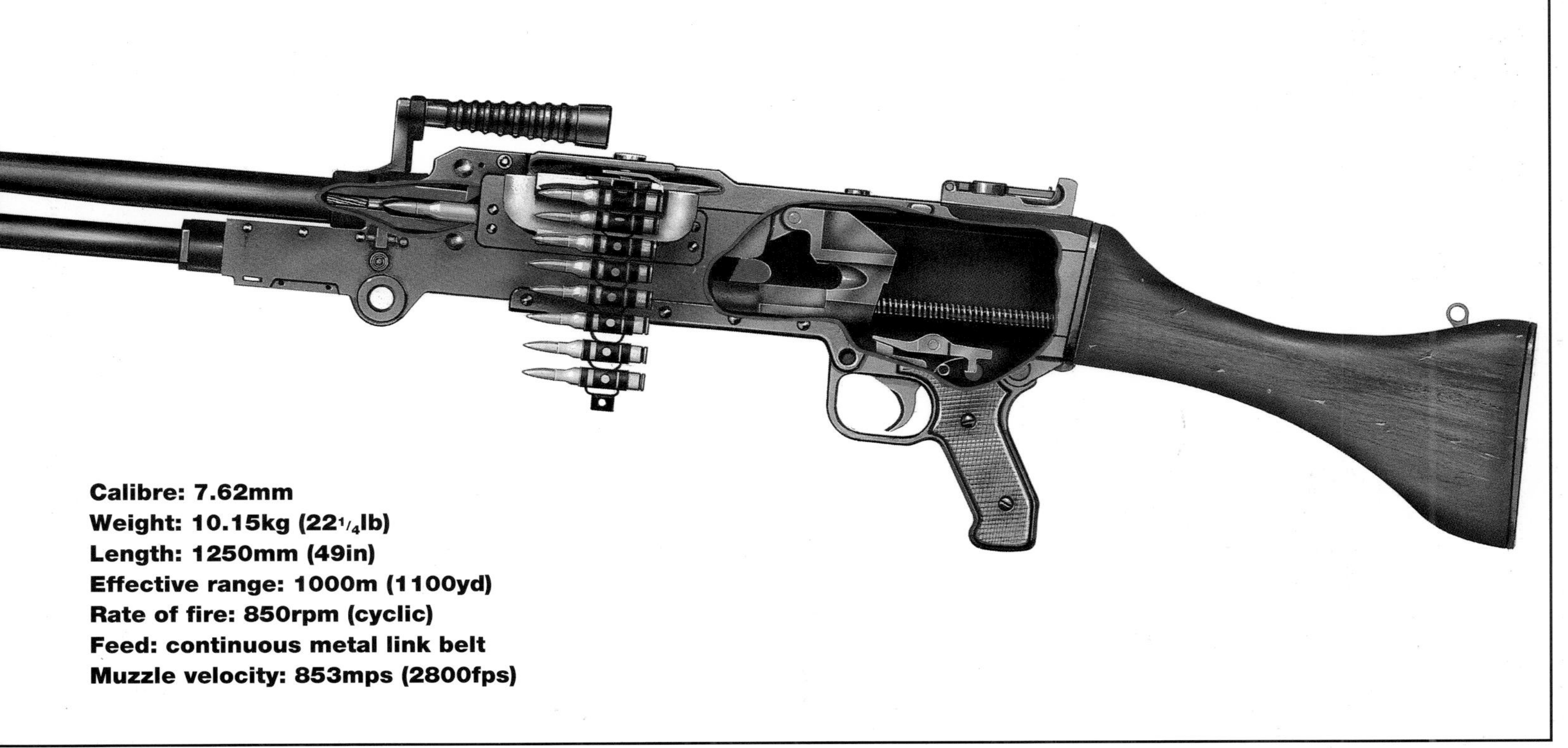

Calibre: 7.62mm
Weight: 10.15kg ($22\frac{1}{4}$lb)
Length: 1250mm (49in)
Effective range: 1000m (1100yd)
Rate of fire: 850rpm (cyclic)
Feed: continuous metal link belt
Muzzle velocity: 853mps (2800fps)

M60 GPMG

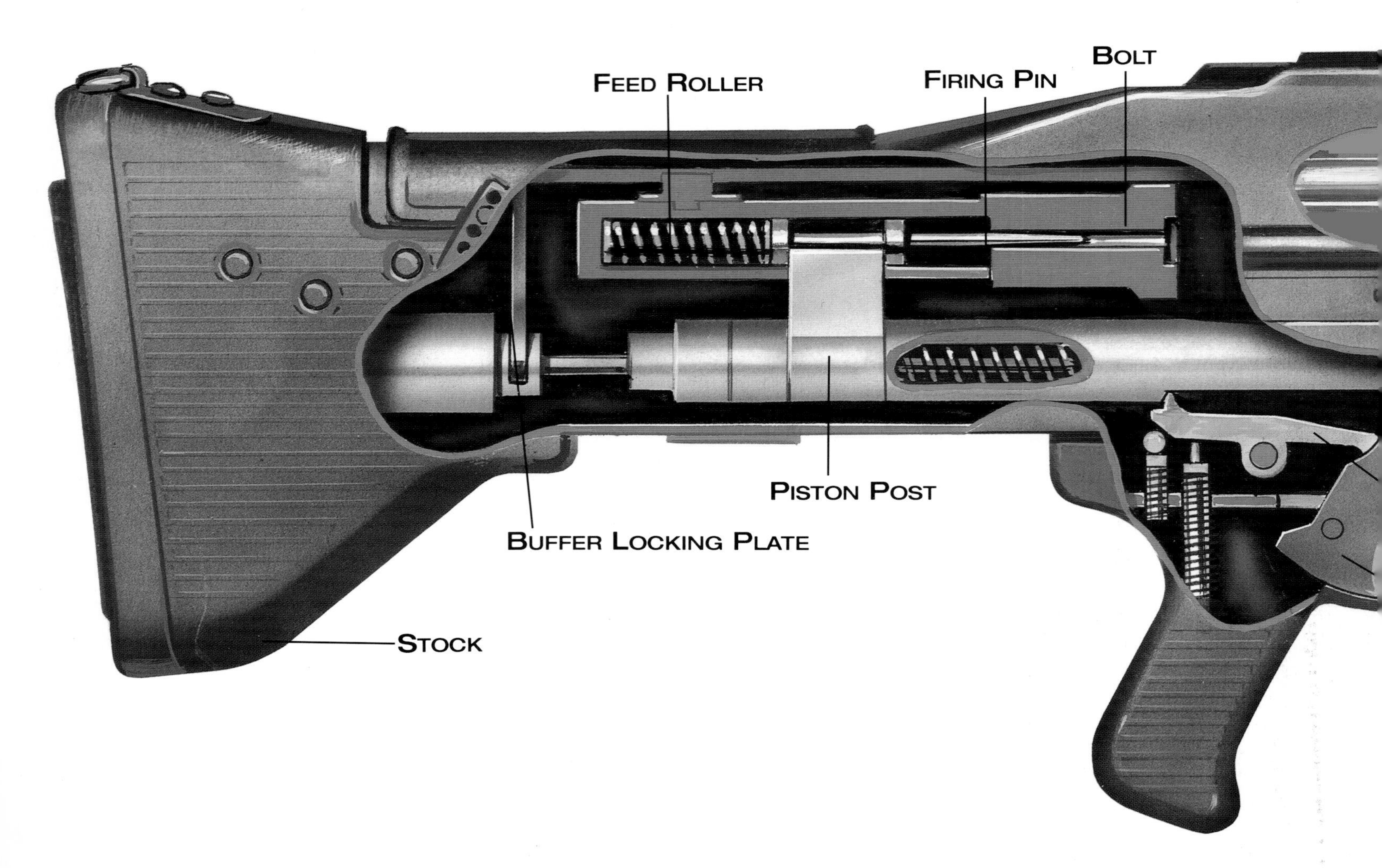
Feed Roller
Firing Pin
Bolt
Piston Post
Buffer Locking Plate
Stock

■ **LEFT: The M60 is an attractive weapon to terrorist organisations such as the IRA (shown here) because it can be fired from the hip – excellent for hit-and-run tactics.**

Notwithstanding wartime manufacturing standards, the MG42 was to become one of the finest machine guns of all time, adding reliability and ruggedness to the excellent firepower of the MG34. The new weapon used a completely different mechanism: a new form of delayed blowback. Already described in the Rifles chapter (see the CETME and G3), the new mechanism was developed from a Polish design, obtained when that country was overrun in 1939.

The bolt is in two pieces, with the rear piece holding the firing pin in a sloping-faced striker sleeve. When the bolt is pushed home, shoving a new cartridge case into the chamber, the striker sleeve slides in behind it, forcing two rollers out to the side, where they lock in recesses on the barrel extension. When the round is fired, the barrel and bolt initially travel rearwards together until the rollers are forced inwards by a sloped cam surface on the barrel extension. This movement unlocks the bolt, which then continues rearwards through the extraction and reloading cycle. A similar system is used in CETME weapons and Heckler & Koch's series of machine guns, submachine guns and assault rifles.

The MG42 also incorporates a much-copied feed system, where movement of the bolt causes feed pawls to advance the 50-round belt, ready for the next round. The gun has a plastic butt and pistol grip, and the barrel is shrouded by a square-sectioned cover, with wide slots cut in it for cooling. A quick change barrel system is fitted, where the barrel is unlocked and removed through a long slot in the right side of the cover. The gun has a phenomenal rate of fire – over 1200rpm – which reduces accuracy when firing from a bipod. The German Army were prepared to accept this, however, as the sheer quantity of fire was more than compensation. The effect on morale was also considerable, and Allied soldiers who faced the MG42 will always remember the terrifying sound, 'like ripping canvas', made by this weapon. There are those who argue that the whole concept of a GPMG is mistaken, and that such a weapon falls between two stools: too light for real sustained fire, too heavy and cumbersome for use as a squad LMG. There is some validity to this argument, but to the soldiers who had to face the fast-firing German guns (mistakenly nicknamed 'Spandau' by the British), they were a deadly and effective threat.

THE MG42 LIVES AGAIN

When the West German Army was reconstituted in the 1950s, it needed a machine gun to operate alongside its G3 assault rifles. After looking at available weapons, the Germans felt that none were better than their wartime MG42, and so decided to reintroduce this gun into production. The detailed engineering drawings had disappeared in the chaos at the end of the war, so new specifications had to be copied from a wartime weapon. The first version of this new gun was almost identical to the MG42, but later models were modified to fire the NATO 7.62mm x 51mm ammunition. Other changes include an externally tapered chrome-lined barrel and modifications to the trigger, bipod and feed mechanism. The current weapon, known as the MG3, is in service with the *Bundeswehr* and the armies of 12 other nations. It retains the high rate of fire of the wartime model, although this can be reduced by fitting an alternative bolt and buffer. It is made under licence in Spain, Italy, Greece and Switzerland. The MG42/MG3 is one of the greatest machine guns of all time, and will remain in service for many years to come.

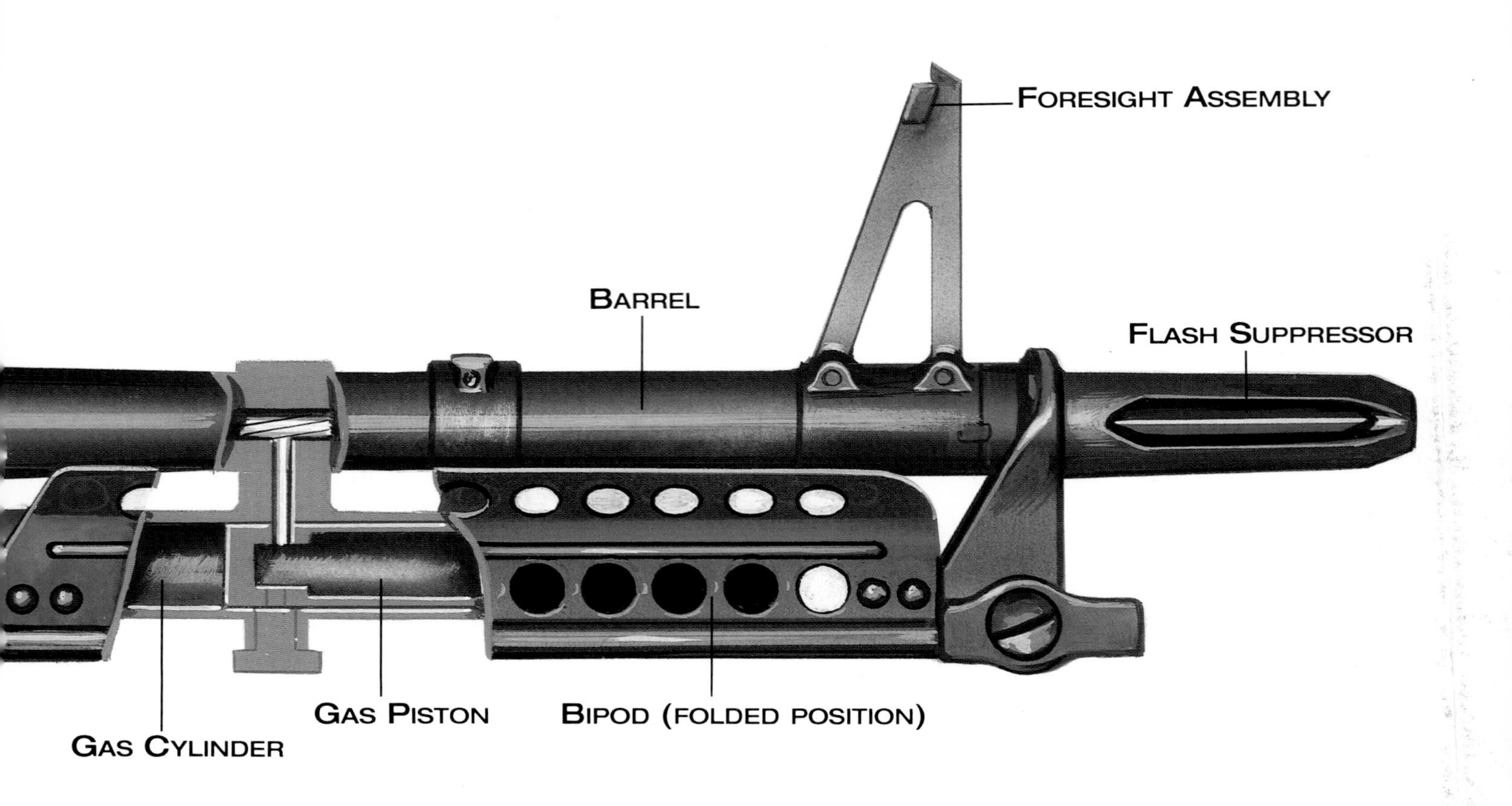
Foresight Assembly
Barrel
Flash Suppressor
Gas Piston
Bipod (folded position)
Gas Cylinder

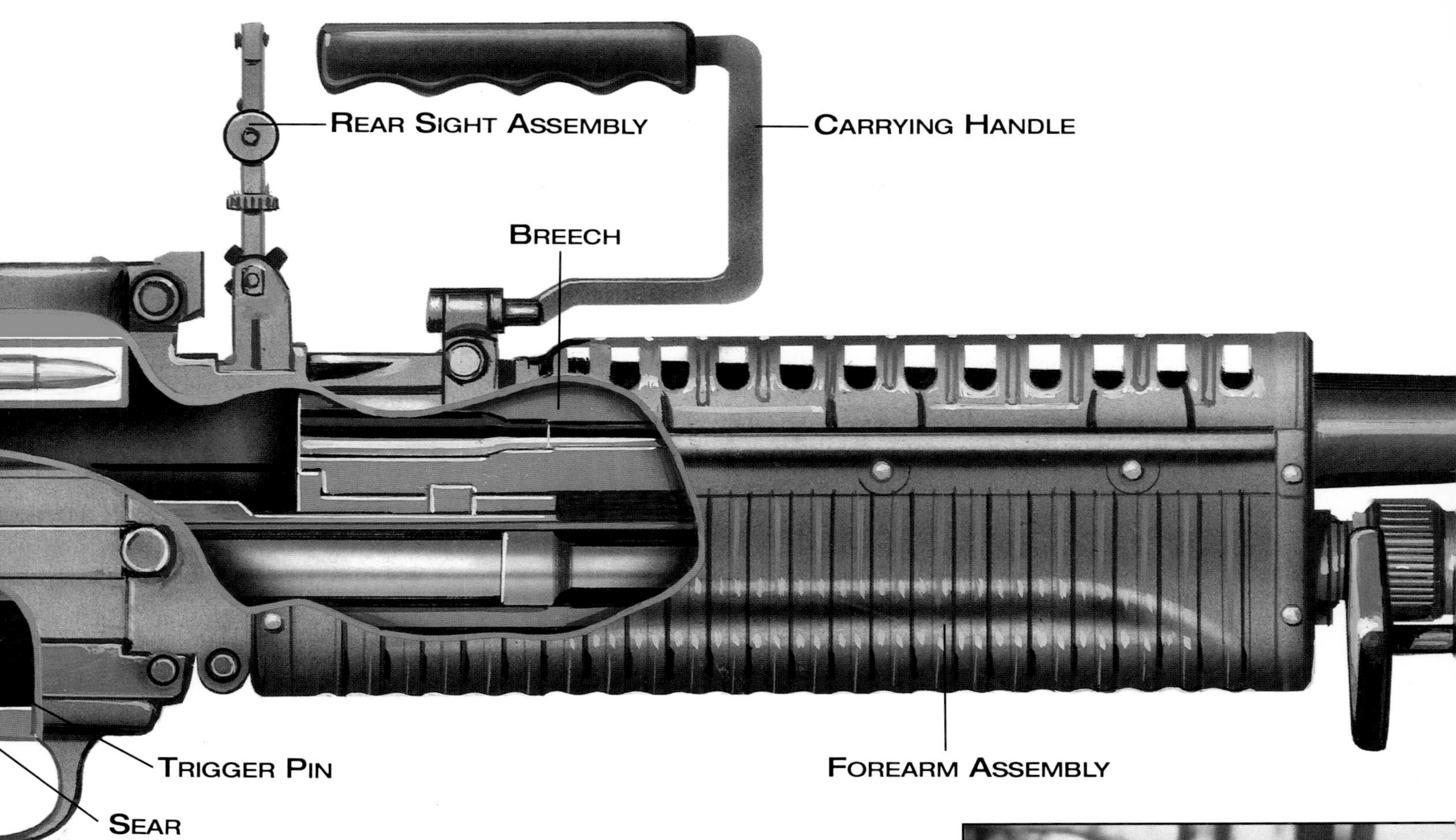

Calibre	7.62mm
Weight	10.5kg (23lb)
Length	1100mm (43in)
Effective range	1000m (1100yd)
Rate of fire	550rpm (cyclic)
Feed	metal belt
Muzzle velocity	855mps (2805fps)

■ LEFT: The M60 machine gun. Though the latest versions seem to work adequately, the initial models were far from satisfactory. For example, changing a hot barrel was ridiculously complicated. Nevertheless, the Americans have stuck with it, and the current E version of the gun is the best yet.

■ RIGHT: An M60 and firer in warlike pose. All M60s have stellite-lined barrels, which means they last longer than those lined with ordinary steel.

AAT 52

THE BELGIAN GPMG

After World War II, the victorious armies looked long and hard at their infantry equipment, and decided to replace many of the weapons that had fought the war. The soldiers who had faced the German machine guns were impressed with their effectiveness, and many countries looked at acquiring similar weapons. It was an attractive concept to have one weapon to carry out the squad LMG, platoon and company fire support, sustained fire, light anti-aircraft and vehicle defence tasks. Costs would be fewer, ammunition supply simplified and training made easier. The downside would be that the soldiers could end up with a weapon that was too much of a compromise: mediocre in every task but excellent in none. Nevertheless, most nations embraced the GPMG concept, and a range of guns was manufactured to meet these requirements, with mixed results.

The Belgian company FN had close links with John Browning and, by incorporating elements of his designs with certain features of the MG42, they came up with an extremely effective general purpose gun. The FN MAG (*Mitrailleuse à Gaz*) is gas operated, and fires NATO 7.62mm ammunition from a disintegrating link belt. A box-shaped receiver made from steel pressings riveted and welded together holds the gas cylinder and the quick-change barrel. The gas piston sits inside the cylinder and is connected to an extension piece and a piston post. There is a slot in the extension piece to allow empty cases to pass through and be ejected beneath the gun. The piston post extends upwards to line up behind the bolt, which is connecte to it by two pivoted levers: a short locking lever connected to the piston post, and a longer locking lever link which connects t the shorter lever at one end and to a point underneath the bolt at the other. When the assembly is in the gun, the bolt is held horizontally by guide ribs which extend into slots in the receiver.

When the gun is cocked, the piston and piston post are pulled back against the

■ RIGHT: The Heckler & Koch 21A machine gun on a field mount. The A version is belt-fed only, whereas the orginal variant could use magazines if required.

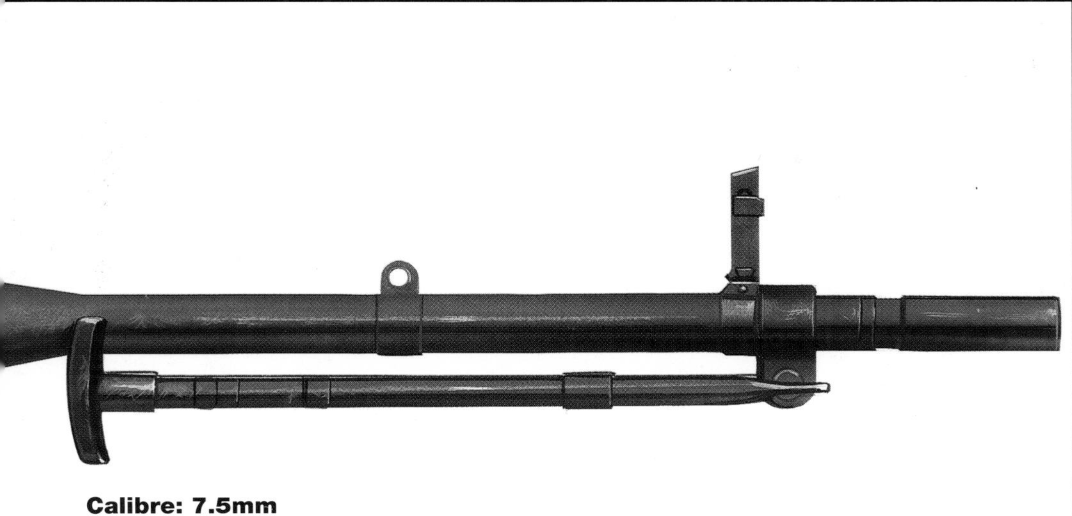

Calibre: 7.5mm
Weight: 9.97kg (21lb)
Length: 1145mm (45in) – butt extended; 980mm (38½in) – butt retracted
Effective range: 1000m (1100yd)
Rate of fire: 7-900rpm (cyclic)
Feed: continuous metal link
Muzzle velocity: 840mps (2757fps)

return spring, pulling the bolt with them. They then fly forwards, and the bolt takes the next round from the ammunition belt. A roller on top of the bolt moves an angled feed arm to one side, pulling the next round into position as the links that hold the first round are ejected to the left of the gun. The bolt pushes the cartridge into the chamber then stops. The piston and piston post continue forwards, and guides in the receiver cause the hinged locking lever and lever guide to pivot downwards. The levers lock against another protrusion on the receiver as the piston post continues forward to strike the firing pin. Once the round is fired, gas is tapped off the barrel into the cylinder, which forces the piston to the rear, causing the piston post to move, unlocking the bolt and starting the extraction cycle.

The MAG can be fitted with a wooden or plastic butt for the LMG role, or can be mounted on a tripod for medium tasks. The barrel is air-cooled, although there is no protective shroud. However, by turning a carrying handle through 90 degrees it can be quickly unlocked for removal and replacement with a cool one. Originally it was planned to have a heavier barrel lined with hard-wearing stellite for the SF role, but this idea was abandoned owing to manufacturing difficulties. The gun has a folding bipod underneath the adjustable gas regulator, and a plastic pistol grip with the trigger. Normal sights are a leaf rear sight, which is folded upright for long ranges, but laid down as a sight for short- and medium-range actions. An adjustable post foresight is at the end of the barrel. Night vision sights and dial units are available for SF tasks, along with a tripod.

THE BRITISH GPMG

The MAG is reasonably light for such a gun (10.15kg/22lb), although it makes a hefty package for a squad support weapon. Used as a bipod-mounted LMG it is effective out to 800m (880yd), and tripod-mounted in the SF role to over 1200m (1300yd). It is tough and reliable, and has proved itself in service with over 75 countries, being licence-built in India, Israel, Sweden, the USA and the UK. The British version is known as the L7A2 GPMG. Known to the troops as the 'Gimpy', the L7A2 has been the standard British infantry machine gun since the early 1960s, replacing both the medium Vickers and the light Bren. It has seen service in all kinds of terrain, from the cold of the Falkland Islands to the heat of the Arabian desert. It is carried as a LMG by rifle sections, mounted on tripods as platoon- and company-level SF guns, strapped to light helicopters in both flexible and fixed mounts, and mounted on vehicles as an anti-personnel and anti-aircraft weapon.

HK21E

Calibre: 7.62mm
Weight: 7.92kg (17½lb)
Length: 1021mm (40in)
Range: 1000m (1100yd)
Rate of fire: 900rpm
Feed: metal link
Muzzle velocity: 800mps (2625fps)

RPK

Calibre: 7.62mm
Weight: 4.76kg (10½lb)
Length: 1041mm (41in)
Effective range: 600m (660yd)
Rate of fire: 600rpm (cyclic)
Feed: 30- or 40-round magazine
Muzzle velocity: 732mps (2400fps)

■ RIGHT: **The Soviet RPK-74.**

PKM

Calibre: 7.62mm
Weight: 8.4kg (18½lb)
Length: 1160mm (45½in)
Effective range: 800m (880yd)
Rate of fire: 710rpm (cyclic)
Feed: 100-, 200- or 250-round belt
Muzzle velocity: 825mps (2700fps)

THE AMERICAN EXPERIENCE

The United States Army chose an indigenous design for its GPMG, which eventually entered service in 1960 as the M60. Employing features copied from the MG42, the M60 is made from stampings and pressings, with a rubber-coated metal butt and a plastic hand guard and pistol grip. It is a bulky weapon, rather awkward to handle, although at 10.5kg (23lb) it is not especially heavy. The M60 is gas operated and has an unusual hollow piston, the front of which extends forward of the gas port. High-pressure gases are tapped into the cylinder and through tiny holes drilled in the side of the hollow piston, to impinge upon the piston head inside the hollow tube. Once the piston starts to move backwards, the tiny holes are moved out of line with the gas port, cutting off the supply of gas to the piston. This mechanism is supposed to deliver the correct impulse from the gas even if the gas port is badly fouled, obviating the need for a gas regulator (in actual practice, of course, dirt, sand and grit will eventually jam an M60, which demands regular cleaning to stay serviceable).

The piston extends into a piston post, which protrudes upwards into a cammed slot in the bolt. Once the piston is moved to the rear, the return spring sends it forwards, taking the bolt with it. The next

HK11E

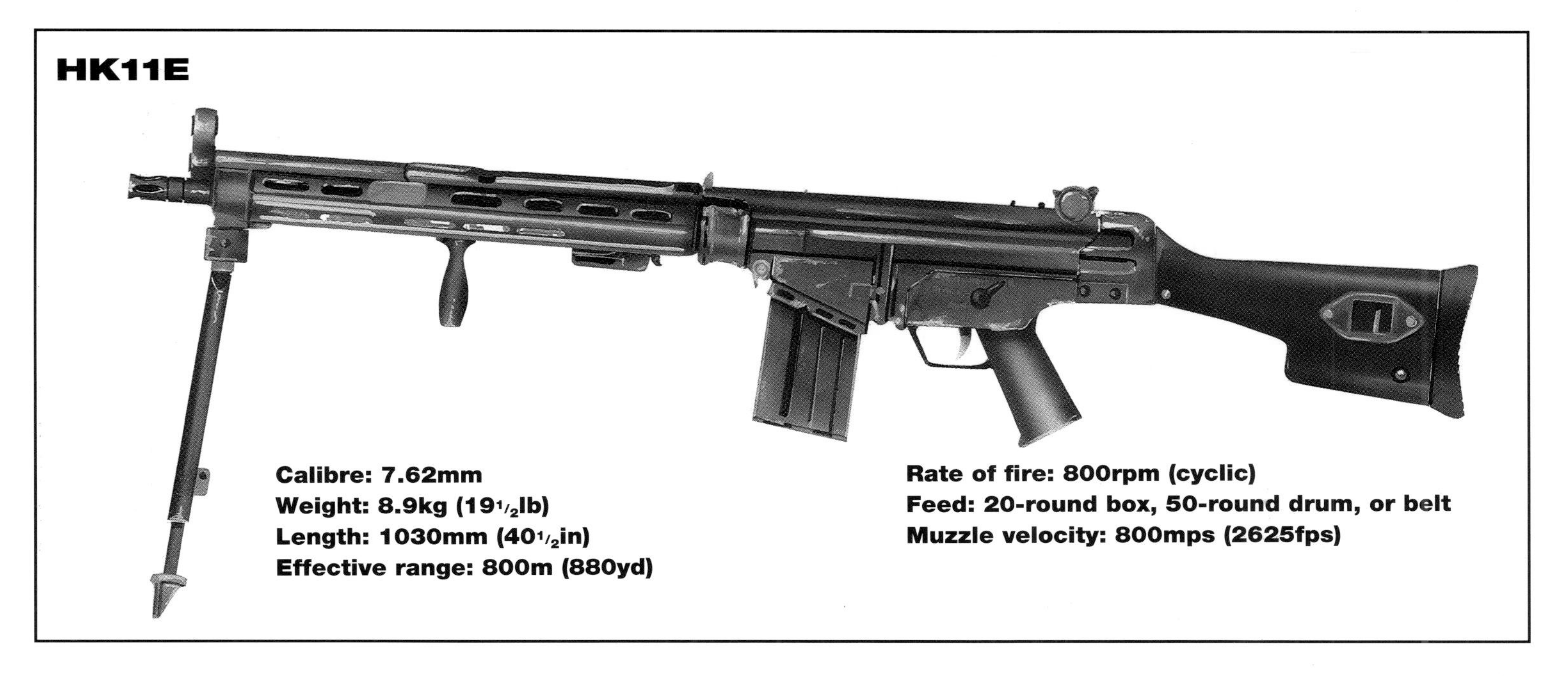

Calibre: 7.62mm
Weight: 8.9kg (19½lb)
Length: 1030mm (40½in)
Effective range: 800m (880yd)
Rate of fire: 800rpm (cyclic)
Feed: 20-round box, 50-round drum, or belt
Muzzle velocity: 800mps (2625fps)

round is fed from the disintegrating link belt and slammed into the chamber. When the bolt stops against the end of the barrel, the piston post continues forward within its slot, the shape of which causes the bolt to rotate and lock in place. The M60 only fires bursts, although a skilled gunner can control single shots using the trigger. The barrel is lined with stellite, a hard-wearing, heat-resistant alloy which prolongs barrel life, although it demands great precision in the manufacturing process. The barrel is still relatively light, and thus needs to be changed frequently when sustained fire is required. Unusually, the gas cylinder and piston are attached to the barrel, and are also replaced when this is changed. The carrying handle is attached to the receiver, which means that there is no easy way for the second gunner to remove the red-hot barrel without scorching his hands. Asbestos gloves are issued as part of the gun kit, but these tend to get lost or mislaid, and so makeshift substitutes such as rags, caps or towels have to be used. To make life even more challenging, the folding bipod is attached to the barrel, so when the latter is being changed there is nothing to support the front of the gun, which has to be cradled by the gunner or rested on the ground. In addition, there is a rather complex and fiddly folding rear sight, though the foresight is a simple, non-adjustable post fixed to the end of the barrel. Most guns with changeable barrels have adjustable foresights to allow each barrel to be individually zero'd before combat, thus requiring no further adjustment in action. M60 gunners are supposed to zero each barrel using only the rear sight, which then needs to be adjusted when barrels are changed. In practice, most crews set the rear sight to an average figure, accepting the loss of accuracy as a penalty for simpler and quicker barrel changes.

The original M60 had a disastrous introduction into service, with reliability and operating problems abounding. A number of modifications were incorporated, and the gun has since seen extensive use in Vietnam and in every US conflict since. The M60D variant is mounted on APCs, trucks, reconnaissance vehicles and helicopters. The M60E2 is designed for internal mounting in armoured vehicles, and the M60C was modified for remote controlled fire from helicopter weapon pylons. An improved version was introduced as the M60E1, which has the gas cylinder and bipod fixed to the gun body, a carrying handle fitted to the barrel, and changes to the feed system and rear sight.

THE UNHAPPY M60

Sasco International has also developed a much lighter gun, the M60E3, which has a smaller forward hand guard, a pistol foregrip, a simplified gas system and an adjustable foresight. This weapon is used by the US Marine Corps, the Navy and the Air Force, although the Army has not yet decided to procure it. The M60 suffers from the same problems as all GPMGs: too light for the squad role, but not heavy enough for platoon/company level SF tasks. The M60 design adds to these problems with some unique quirks of its own, and the US experience with this gun has not been an unqualified success. The E3 version finally overcomes most of these problems, however, and is the weapon that the M60 should have been at the outset.

FRANCE'S LIGHTWEIGHT GPMG

When the French Army was being reconstructed after World War II, great efforts were made to equip the soldiers with indigenous designs of small arms. In 1952, they were issued with a lightweight GPMG known as the AAT 52 (*Arme Automatique Transformable Modèle* 52). This is a belt-fed weapon that weighs only 10kg (22lb) and comes complete with a folding bipod attached to the end of the barrel. The gun has no gas system; instead, it uses a form of delayed blowback originally designed by the Hungarian engineer, Kiraly, and used since on the FAMAS assault rifle (see the Rifles chapter). A light bolt head is connected by pivoting levers to a much larger and heavier bolt body. When a round is fired the bolt head tries to move back, but is held in place by the pivoting levers. They are locked at one end by lugs in the receiver, so they rotate around the pivot, levering the large bolt body to the rear. The force needed for this absorbs much of the initial energy from the gas pressure in the barrel, and only when the bolt body has started to move are the levers unlocked and the whole assembly free to recoil. Flutes engraved around the walls of the firing chamber allow some gas to pass around the empty cartridge case, enabling the case to 'float' free of the chamber when being extracted.

The gun feeds from a metal continuous disintegrating link belt, employing some elements of the MG42 feed system. When operating in the LMG role, there is an extending skeleton stock and extendable butt monopod which can be used to support the weapon at the aim position. Barrel change is awkward, as the bipod

■ **ABOVE: The LSW, the 5.56mm light machine gun in use with the British Army.**

comes off with the barrel, leaving the gunner to support the weapon in some way while the replacement is fitted. When operating in the SF role, a heavier barrel can be used and the whole gun mounted on a light tripod, modified from a US design. The gun is fitted with a hinged block foresight, which has a slot in it for day use and tritium markers for night shooting. The rear sight is a sliding ramp.

Originally chambered for the French 7.5mm x 54mm M1929 round, the AAT 52 was redesigned in the 1960s to take the NATO 7.62mm x 51mm cartridge. Renamed the AA 7.62 NF1, this is otherwise almost identical to the earlier weapon. Made from light pressings welded and riveted together, it has a relatively slender shape and is easier to carry than many other GPMGs. By using a delayed blowback system on such full-powered cartridges, the French gun operates near the limits of cartridge case strength. If the headspace is not precisely adjusted, the cartridge will rupture, jamming the gun and causing a dangerous escape of high-pressure gases to the rear. The receiver, bolt and barrel have to be made to the highest manufacturing tolerances, though even then bulged and deformed cases are not uncommon, especially when firing for long periods. However, as long as the weapon is looked after and well

Light Support Weapon

Calibre: 5.56mm
Weight: 5.4kg ($11\frac{3}{4}$lb)
Length: 900mm (35in)
Effective range: 500m (550yd)
Rate of fire:7-850rpm
Feed 30-round magazine
Muzzle velocity: 970mps (3183fps)

maintained, it has proved to be as reliable and effective as any other machine gun.

HECKLER & KOCH'S GPMG

Even though the German Army had standardised on the MG3, this didn't stop Heckler & Koch developing its own range of GPMGs. The HK21, for example, is a belt-fed 7.62mm weapon which resembles a slightly heavier G3 rifle. Using the same roller-delayed blowback system as all the HK weapons, it feeds from a continuous disintegrating link metal belt. The heavy barrel is easily changed, and a folding bipod is fitted to the front hand guard. A plastic rifle butt is fitted, and the gun can fire single shots or bursts. On the light side (7.92kg/$17\frac{1}{2}$lb) for sustained fire, it can nevertheless be attached to a tripod for the SF role. Heckler & Koch has designed an almost modular series of weapons, and this is no exception. By replacing the barrel, feed plate and bolt, it can be converted to fire NATO 5.56mm or even the Soviet 7.62mm x 39mm ammunition, and by removing the feed mechanism and fitting an adaptor, any Heckler & Koch 7.62mm magazine can be used. The HK21 never entered German service, though it is in use in Africa and Southeast Asia. A licence-built model is produced in Portugal.

A later development is the HK21A1, which removes the magazine feed option. Instead, the belt feed system can be hinged downwards to allow rapid, easy insertion of the new belt. A belt-carrying box can also be clipped underneath the weapon for mobility in the squad LMG role. The most recent modification is the HK21E, in which the results of extensive experience have been incorporated. The receiver, for example, has been extended by 94mm ($3\frac{3}{4}$in), which reduces the recoil and lengthens the sight radius, thus improving overall accuracy. The trigger mechanism has also been modified to allow three-round bursts, and the quick-change grip on the barrel is improved. A hand grip under the barrel is now fitted, which makes the gun easier to control when firing from a standing position in the assault. An adjustable drum-type rear sight is also fitted. Modifications have been made to the feed system, in that the belt is pulled forward to feed the next round in two stages rather than one, reducing the stress on the belt and the feed system.

Stoner 63 LMG

(for specifications see page 74)

ABOVE: The Heckler & Koch 11A1, the belt-fed version of the HK21A1.

The Soviet Union remained unconvinced by the concept of one gun for all roles, and had thus kept the excellent SG series for SF tasks and the RPD as the squad LMG. However, these fine weapons were approaching obsolescence, so two new designs were produced. The magazine-fed RPK was an uncompromising section LMG, and is described below. The belt-fed PK series was the first Russian GPMG, though tactical employment was more in fire support roles than as a squad weapon. The PK uses the old-fashioned Russian 7.62mm x 54mm full-powered rimmed cartridge fed from a 250-round metal belt. There are a number of variants: the PKS for mounting on a tripod, the PKT vehicle-mounted coaxial gun, the improved PKM, the PKMS tripod-mounted gun, and the pintle-mounted PKMB vehicle gun.

RUSSIA'S GPMG

The most common infantry variant is the PKM, which is remarkably light at 9kg (20lb). This makes use of the gas system and two-piece rotating bolt of the AK series, resulting in a tough and reliable mechanism. The feed system is based on that of the SG, and the receiver is a light assembly made from stampings riveted together. It has a metal butt with a large weight-reducing cutout in its centre. A simple plastic pistol grip and trigger are beneath the receiver, and only automatic fire is possible. A folding bipod is attached to the front of the gas cylinder, and the barrel has an AK-style blade foresight. As the bipod comes off with the barrel, the gun has to be supported while a barrel change takes place.

Light metal boxes holding 250-round or 100-round belts can be clipped to the weapon for the assault role, and there is also a 7.5kg tripod for use in SF roles. The PKM has a shorter effective range than the M60: able to hit area targets at up to 1000m (1100yd). It is much simpler to use and maintain, however, and has very little recoil and muzzle jump when firing. American troops who fired the PKM in tests at Fort Benning found the Russian gun to be easier to use and much more reliable than their own M60s.

THE LMG SURVIVES

Not everyone wholeheartedly subscribed to the post-war fashion for general purpose guns, and a number of squad-level LMGs were produced and operated throughout the 1960s and 1970s. These weapons were normally beefed-up versions of the infantry assault rifle, firing the same ammunition from box magazines. Terminology advanced, however, and many of these light weapons were now referred to as light support weapons (LSWs). The precise definition of the difference between an LMG and an LSW depends upon which army is doing the defining, but in general the LSW is lighter and usually developed from an assault rifle. The Russians were the first to follow the LSW concept with their RPK, which entered service in 1960 (although it can be argued that the original BAR was the first LSW). Designed to complement the AK rifles, the RPK is basically an AKM with a longer and heavier barrel and fitted with a folding bipod. At 4.76kg (10½lb) it is only about .45kg (1lb) heavier, and it fires the same 7.62mm x 39mm intermediate round as the rifle. The mechanism is virtually identical, and components can actually be swapped from the rifle and the LSW without affecting operation. Ammunition is fed from a 40-round curved magazine, and there is a 75-round drum which can be clipped into the same feed recess. In an emergency, standard 30-round AK magazines can be used.

There is no changeable barrel, so the gunner must be sufficiently well disciplined to avoid overheating and excessive barrel wear. The gun largely replaced the belt-fed RPD in the infantry section, and two are normally issued to each mechanised squad. When the squad is carried in the BMP series of infantry fighting vehicles, the RPKs are fired through the forward firing ports in the infantry compartment. Sharing the good and bad points of the AK, the RPK is light, tough and simple to use, and is an ideal support weapon for use in a fast-moving infantry assault. However, the intermediate round, box magazine and fixed barrel contribute to a lack of sustained firepower, so in some situations the squad's weapons are supplemented by the PKM GPMG.

OTHER HECKLER & KOCHS

In Germany, Heckler & Koch developed a similar variant of its 7.62mm x 51mm G3 assault rifle, again using the same roller-delayed system as its rifles, general purpose machine guns and submachine guns. The HK11 was produced especially for police, anti-terrorist and security forces, where accuracy is more important than the heavy suppressive fire normally required in conventional warfare. At 8.15kg (18lb) it is significantly heavier than the rifle, although it is almost exactly the same length. A heavy quick-change barrel is fitted, with a folding bipod at the end of the barrel guard. The bolt system and mechanism are standard H&K designs, almost identical to those found in the G3, HK21 and others. A plastic butt is fitted, shaped to allow the left hand to grip from underneath – a common machine gunner's technique. A selector lever above the pistol grip and trigger allows for semi-automatic, full-automatic and three-round bursts to be fired. Feed is from a standard 20-round box magazine or from a 50-round drum. A conversion kit is available to change the gun to use continuous belts, although in this configuration it is virtually indistinguishable from the HK21 (see above). The weapon is a precise and accurate support weapon, almost the machine gun equivalent of the sniper rifle. It is used by many police and security agencies, including Germany's elite GSG9 anti-terrorist unit. In German service, the HK11 is designated the G8.

Apart from these weapons and a few others (such as the belt-fed Valmet LMG), the future for the lightweight squad-level

HK13

Calibre: 5.56mm
Weight: 8kg (17½lb)
Length: 1030mm (40in)
Range: 500m (550yd)
Fed: 20- or 30-round magazine
Rate of fire: 750rpm
Muzzle velocity: 925mps (3035fps)

LMG seemed bleak throughout the 1960s and 1970s. With the change to 5.56mm ammunition for the infantry, however, new problems and new opportunities confronted the soldiers. The effective range of the ordinary rifle was being reduced, and if the infantry squad retained its 7.62mm GPMGs it would have to carry two calibres of ammunition. There was also a feeling that perhaps these guns were not ideal squad-level weapons anyway, being really too heavy and cumbersome for this task. Many armies felt that it was time to reappraise their squad fire support requirements, and out of this came a whole new range of lighter support weapons.

ABOVE: The Heckler & Koch 23 machine gun. A direct descendant of the HK13, it fires the 5.56 x 45mm round.

THE 5.56MM LSW

The British chose to standardise on their L85 Individual Weapons System, and in 1985 introduced the L86A1 LSW. The receiver, bolt, trigger and other components are almost identical to those of the L85A1 rifle, although the support weapon has a much longer and heavier barrel. The gun is some 114mm (4½in) longer and .45kg (1lb) heavier than the standard rifle, and has a hand grip under the butt and a metal shoulder support strap at the rear. A metal guard extends forward from the plastic foregrip under the barrel, and at the end of this is a folding bipod. The same SUSAT optical sight used by the squad's riflemen is normally fitted, although alternative optical and night vision sights can be used.

Unlike the rifle, the bolt is held open between bursts, allowing a flow of cooling air into the chamber. The same 5.56mm x 45mm NATO ammunition as the rifle is used, fed from an identical 30-round box. The only advantage the operator of this weapon has over his rifle-armed comrades is the ability to fire longer bursts without overheating, and the increased accuracy and effective range bestowed by the longer barrel. Previously, British infantry squads (or 'sections') formed two groups: a gun group, with the two-man L7A1 GPMG crew and section second-in-command, and a rifle group, which comprised all other members of the squad. With the advent of the LSW, things changed. Two were issued to each squad, which is now made up of two four-man fireteams. In a concept adapted from American practice, each fire-team operates as a semi-independent unit with its own support weapon. Experience has shown that the 5.56mm box-fed LSW sometimes provides insufficient firepower, so many squads now form a 'gun group' from both weapons. The 7.62mm 'Gimpy' is still held at platoon and company level to provide long-range fire support. The LSW has also suffered from the early problems experienced with the L85 rifle, and early users had similar problems with reliability and manufacturing quality control. However, it is a superbly accurate 5.56mm weapon, especially when used with the SUSAT optical sight, and it is to be hoped that the teething problems encountered by this weapons system will soon be a thing of the past.

MORE LIGHT MACHINE GUNS

Heckler & Koch also developed a box-fed 5.56mm LSW, based on its HK33E rifle. Known as the HK13, it is the 5.56mm equivalent of the HK11. Fitted with a heavier barrel and bipod, it is somewhat heavier than the HK33 at 5.4kg (12lb) and some 52mm (2in) longer at 980mm (38½in). It feeds from the standard H&K 25-round magazine and was originally chambered for the 5.56mm x 45mm M193 round. Like the other H&K machine guns, the weapon has been improved in the light of experience, and the current model is the HK13E. As in

■ **LEFT: The Minimi machine gun. It can accept either a magazine or a belt feed.**

the HK21E, this modification includes a longer receiver, which reduces recoil and gives a greater sight radius. There is also a new design of drum rear sight, a hand grip under the barrel guard, an improved trigger unit, and a three-round burst facility. The gun has also been modified to fire the 5.56mm NATO SS109 round, and has a NATO standard (M16) magazine feed to allow a wide range of box and drum magazines to be used. The gun also meets NATO standards for sight mounts, and most military optical and night vision sights can be used. By changing the feed components, the gun can be converted to belt feed, although users that require this capability would normally procure the HK23 (see page 95). The gun is a light but effective LSW, using a reliable and well-proved mechanism. It has not entered service with the German armed forces, although it has met export success in Southeast Asia.

Other box-fed 5.56mm weapons include a version of the M16A2 fitted with a heavy barrel, folding bipod and larger front handguards. Developed by Colt and the Canadian company Diemaco, it uses the same ammunition and mechanism as the M16, although it has been modified to fire from an open bolt. Any M16 magazine will fit, including the special C-MAG 100-round twin-drum unit. The standard M16 sights are retained, although optical and night vision equipment can be fitted to the carrying handle if required. Anyone familiar with the M16A2 rifle can fire this LSW, and it is in service with Canada (as the C7), the US Marine Corps and some South American armies.

The highly successful Austrian Steyr AUG system has an LSW variant, which has a longer, heavier barrel and folding bipod. Known as the HBAR (Heavy Barrelled Automatic Rifle), it uses the same plastic receiver and grip, together with the same mechanism as the AUG rifle. Ammunition is fed from a transparent 42-round plastic box, although the standard AUG 30-round magazine can also be used. Like most box-fed LSWs, the barrel is not a quick-change item so the temperature has to be controlled by good fire discipline. By changing a few components, the gun can be converted to fire from an open bolt, which helps keep the chamber and bolt cool. The standard HBAR has the optical sight and carrying handle of the AUG, while the HBAR-T uses a receiver with a flat mounting rail for any other optical or night vision sights. As with Heckler & Koch's series of weapons, the AUG system is so constructed that once a soldier is trained to operate the rifle, he can easily fire the LSW and submachine gun versions with little extra training.

The Italians also decided to take advantage of their assault rifle designs, and have developed LSWs based on the Beretta AR70 and AR70/90 weapons. Heavier quick-change barrels and folding bipods are the main additions, together with modifications to allow fire from an open bolt. The same principle has been followed by the Russians. Ever economical, when they converted their successful AK design to fire 5.45mm ammunition, they also decided to do likewise with the RPK LSW. The RPK-74 uses the same receiver and mechanism as the AK-74, but has a fixed, longer and heavier barrel, without the rifle's muzzle brake. It looks almost identical to the 7.62m RPK, the only obvious identifying feature being the orange- or brown-coloured magazine.

THE BUZZ-SAW

Many nations feel that the box-fed LSW doesn't provide enough firepower even for a squad-level weapon, and that something with a better sustained fire capability is needed. The change to lighter 5.56mm ammunition meant that designers could pack the firepower of a belt-fed weapon into a lighter and handier package, and a number of new weapons have been developed. These 'mini-GPMGs' are usually known as SAWs (squad automatic weapons). They look similar to their 7.62mm predecessors, although they are lighter, and the 5.56mm ammunition has a shorter effective range. While some can be fitted to tripods, the ammunition is not effective enough for the medium role.

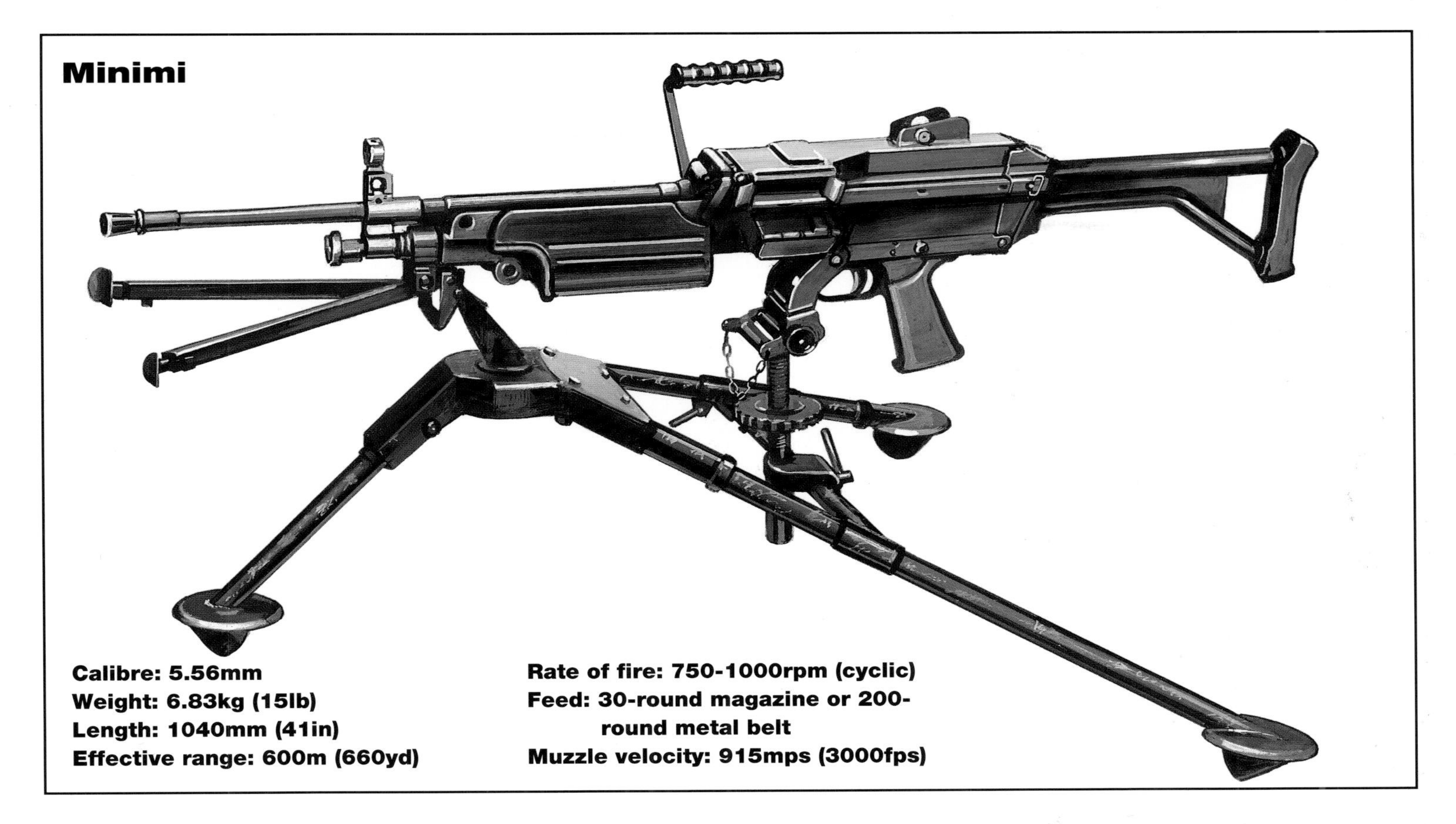

Unlike the GPMG, the SAW is optimised for fire support within the infantry squad, with no design compromises to try to fulfil other roles.

One of the earliest of these 5.56mm belt-fed weapons was the German HK23. This is basically the 7.62mm HK21 with some components changed to suit the new calibre. It operates in exactly the same manner as the other HK machine guns, and shares many identical components. The current version is the HK23E, which weighs 8.75kg (19 1/4lb) and has the same lengthened receiver as the HK21E, HK11E and HK13E. This gun also sports the three-round selector mechanism, and has a folding bipod and front hand grip. With the addition of this weapon, Heckler & Koch has a complete range of rifles, and machine guns in both 7.62mm and 5.56mm calibres. In 7.62mm there is the G3 rifle, the HK11/G8 box-fed LSW, and the HK21 SAW. In 5.56mm there is the HK33E and G41 rifles, the HK13 LSW and the HK32 SAW. If a soldier is trained on any one of these guns, he will find it easy to use any of the others.

BELGIAN MINIMALISTS

Probably the most popular of this new breed is the Minimi, again from the Belgian company of FN. Significantly lighter than the earlier 7.62mm FN MAG, which weighs 10kg (22lb), the Minimi weighs some 6.8kg (15lb). It is made from stampings welded and riveted together, with a plastic butt, pistol grip and large plastic hand guard. There is a tubular metal stock available, and there is also a para version of the gun which has a shorter barrel and telescopic stock. The gun uses a conventional piston and cylinder gas system, with the cylinder underneath the barrel. The gas plug and regulator are modified from the MAG, and have two basic settings, one for when the gun is clean and another to overcome fouling. The bolt is a two-piece model, with the bolt face locking into the barrel extension by means of locking lugs. A cam system on the bolt carrier causes the bolt to unlock, in a similar manner to the methods used in the M16 and many assault rifles.

An unusual feature of the Minimi is the ability to use either a box magazine or belt feed without modification. In normal use, a 200-round metal disintegrating link belt is carried in a plastic box clipped underneath the weapon. This feeds into a slot on the left of the receiver, and a feed horn on the top of the bolt strips the round from the belt, positioning it so that the bolt rams it home into the chamber. A second feed slot below the first is blocked by a folding plastic flap. If no belt is fitted, any M16-type magazine can be fitted into this second feed slot, with the plastic flap folding up to block the belt feed. A second set of feed horns is on the underside of the bolt, so no modification is required from the operator. When firing from a magazine, the cyclic rate of fire is much faster than from a belt, as the mechanism does not need to lift the weight of the 200-round belt. Magazine feed is really only a secondary option, although it could be useful in an emergency.

THE VERSATILE MINIMI

The gun has a heavy, quick-change barrel, and a neat folding bipod is attached behind the gas regulator. A folding carrying handle extends above the barrel, and normal sights are an adjustable post foresight on the barrel and a simple adjustable aperture rear sight above the receiver. The Minimi will fit most standard tripod and vehicle mounts, although it is really too light for this role. The 5.56mm anmmunition is effective out to a range of 600m (660yd), and provides an effective source of firepower for the squad. It has proved to be extremely reliable in both trials and actual combat. The Minimi was chosen by the United States Army as a squad support weapon, and in US service has been designated the M249 SAW. Changes were minor, mainly to suit American manufacturing methods, and the gun has proved very popular with the troops. While there are those that would prefer the extra punch of a 7.62mm cartridge, most US troops have found the M249 to be much more reliable

■ ABOVE: The Spanish Ameli, a weapon that uses a delayed blowback system.

and easier to handle than the M60. The Minimi has also been adopted by many other countries besides the USA: Italy, Australia, Belgium, Canada and Indonesia.

THE AMELI

CETME in Spain has also produced the Ameli: a 5.56mm SAW using the same roller-delayed blowback system found in its 5.56mm and 7.62mm rifles (and also most Heckler & Koch weapons). Looking like a scaled-down MG42 or MG3, the Ameli has a similar perforated casing around the quick-change barrel and a bipod beneath it. First seen in 1982, the gun weighed 6.35kg (14lb), but a lighter version has since been introduced. It is a compact handy SAW, firing NATO 5.56mm ammunition from a metal disintegrating link belt. A plastic 100- or 200-round belt box can be attached beneath the receiver, and a neat carrying handle is positioned above the rear of the barrel. An unusual and useful feature is the ability to change the rate of fire from 800 to 1200rpm, just by changing one component. Conventional aperture and post sights are fitted, although a night sight is easily attached to the receiver. The gun can be vehicle or tripod mounted, and it is in service with the Spanish Army as the standard squad fire support weapon.

Chartered Industries of Singapore has developed a SAW in which low weight has been a prime design consideration. The Ultimax 100 weighs a remarkable 4.9kg (10¾lb), and is designed to be operated by one man. It uses a two-piece rotary bolt and a gas and piston system, similar to those in the M16 and many other assault rifles. It has a plastic butt and pistol grip, with a similar grip under the front barrel guard. There is a folding bipod in front of this grip, and the barrel is quickly changed by using a prominent folding carrying handle. The gun fires 5.56mm NATO ammunition from a 100-round drum magazine, and the recoil forces are so low that full-automatic fire is easily controlled, even when firing from the hip. At first glance, the Ultimax looks too light and fragile to be a battlefield SAW, but the manufacturer's trials have proved its capability to withstand sustained fire and rough handling. To date, this light and effective weapon is only in service in Singapore.

Israel's isolation has prompted an indigenous design of SAW, one which complements the Galil series of assault rifles. The Negev is very close in concept to the Minimi, is almost exactly the same length, and weighs only 7.2kg (15¾lb). It fires NATO 5.56mm ammunition, although a replacement barrel can be fitted to take the US M193 round. The mechanism uses a conventional gas and piston method of operating, with a two-piece rotary bolt. Either semi- or full-automatic fire is selectable, and by adjusting the gas plug the rate of fire can be adjusted from 650 to 900rpm. There is a quick-change barrel and the folding bipod sits beneath the front hand guard. The standard gun has a folding tubular metal stock, and there is a variant with a shorter barrel for paratroopers and vehicle troops. The designers have made the weapon as flexible as possible, and it will feed from Galil or M16 box magazines, drum magazines or continuous belts. The magazine feed is from below, and in this way the gun becomes a heavy assault rifle or LSW. Alternatively, a metal disintegrating link belt feeds into the left side of the receiver top cover. Instead of clipping a plastic belt box beneath the gun, the Israelis use an unusual zippered canvas drum-shaped bag to hold a 200-round belt. This allows a soldier to move silently, without the sound of the ammunition rattling inside a box. Only in service with Israel, the Negev is proving to be tough and reliable, and is an effective source of firepower for the infantry squad.

ABOVE: The Israeli Negev 5.56mm light machine gun with belt-feed unit.

THE MACHINE GUN'S FUTURE

In the immediate future, it seems that most armies will be using some form of 5.56mm machine gun at squad level, whether a box-fed LSW or a belt-fed SAW. However, 7.62mm guns will still have a role, as the smaller calibre is not sufficiently powerful for longer ranges or for penetrating cover and light armour. Future designs will probable stray from the GPMG concept, with weapons being optimised for heavier tasks. Some of the ammunition developments projected for future rifles may well be seen in fire support weapons. For example, Heckler & Koch is known to be working on a machine gun derived from its G11 rifle and its caseless ammunition. Special flechette rounds could be useful for squad-level weapons, although they may lack the punch for long-range medium machine gun tasks. High explosive rounds are often considered for machine guns, although in the past these have been the province of large-calibre cannon mounted on vehicles and aircraft. In recent years, however, the automatic grenade launcher has greatly increased in popularity. Firing bursts of high explosive fragmentation projectiles of around 40mm calibre, they are sometimes used to provide a lethal and fearsome suppression capability in lieu of a tripod-mounted machine gun. Weapons such as the American Mk 19 or the Russian AGS-17 are fully described in the chapter on grenades.

THE BRG AND THE TARG

There is also a surprising amount of work being done to find a replacement for the heavy Browning M2. As infantry machine guns reduce their calibre, and as vehicle-mounted cannons become larger and heavier, there still seems to be place for the heavy machine gun, firing ammunition of around 12.7mm calibre. Two examples of potential future designs are the Belgian FN BRG-15 and the United States' ARES TARG. The Belgian design uses a reasonably conventional gas system, and is a hefty beast at 60kg (132lb). It has a dual-feed system, whereby two belts of ammunition can be fed into the gun simultaneously from both sides of the weapon. The firer can select which one to fire by moving a simple lever. One belt can hold armour-piercing and the standard ball, or there can be a combination of ball and incendiary, or any other pairing desired. The ammunition is a specially designed 15.5mm x 106mm type with a plastic driving band which engages the rifling and reduces barrel wear. This gun may well be selected as a battalion/company level support weapon, although its weight must be a drawback to tactical use.

The ARES weapon is also gas operated, but uses a special revolving four-chambered cylinder, rather like a giant revolver. The 12.7mm ammunition is telescoped, ie the round is contained completely within the casing and surrounded by the propellant. An initial small charge pushes the bullet forward out of the casing before the main propellant charge ignites, sending the round down the barrel. This technique makes for a completely cylindrical cartridge, which allows the case to be ejected forward as the next is fed in from the rear. There is no belt – rounds are fed into the gun from the ammunition box by a feed rotor. The revolving cylinder allows for ejecting and feeding to happen while the next round lines up with the barrel to be fired. TARG (Telescoped Ammunition Revolver Gun) is significantly lighter than any other heavy gun at 20.4kg (44¾lb), although it remains to be seen if the concept can be made reliable enough for service.

The soldier will always need some form of fire support weapon, whether to suppress enemy defences in the assault or to break up an attack, but whether the machine gun will remain in its present form is debatable. With the advent of new technology ammunition, it may be that some form of automatic shotgun or grenade launcher may take over as the dominant infantry weapon on the battlefield of the future. But the grandsons of today's soldiers could well go into battle accompanied by a trusty LMG, and still (judging by its record so far) with the reassuring clunk of the Browning M2 heavy machine gun in the background.

CHAPTER 3
HANDGUNS

The hand-held pistol has been used by soldiers on the battlefield for some 400 years. Curiously, in all this time the weapon has had little military significance. Effective at only the shortest of ranges, and extremely difficult to shoot accurately, the handgun has proved itself to be largely irrelevant in battle. During the twentieth century, the demise of the handgun as a military weapon has been predicted by numerous pundits, most of whom cite the utility of the submachine gun and various new types of self-defence weapon. In what appears to be a defiance of logic, however, millions of pistols are still in use, and development of handgun technology continues in dozens of countries.

THE ENDURING HANDGUN

The handgun is more significant as a firearm for non-military roles. Many law enforcement agencies, for example, equip their men and women with handguns, and security personnel and bodyguards often have a need for small, portable, reliable firearms. Until the early years of this century, the requirements of the civilian sports user were also a driving force in firearms development. However, since most countries have introduced tight restrictions on weapons ownership, this market is now of marginal interest. A major exception is the United States, where liberal gun laws ensure a thriving firearms industry.

Military handgun users are largely confined to officers, military policemen, rear area security personnel and those whose duties preclude the carrying of a large, heavy rifle. Vehicle drivers, signallers, tank and air crews, airfield ground personnel, mechanics, technicians and supply clerks all require some form of self-defence capability, and a small handgun strapped to the belt can be carried around without hindering a person's work. Such a weapon ought to be reasonably light, and be able to be carried, loaded with ammunition, for long periods in complete safety. Most people whose jobs require them to carry a small handgun rarely have time to practice, so great accuracy is unnecessary. In addition, their pistols are usually carried for weeks at a time and given little or no maintenance – thus simplicity and reliability are essential.

A handgun can also be regarded as a 'badge' of office and authority: the holster strapped to the belt of a senior officer is often regarded as a symbol of rank, even though the military usefulness of such a weapon is negligible. In combat an officer usually discards his handgun for a submachine gun or rifle.

Another important category of military user is the special forces soldier, whose duties may include anti-terrorist and hostage-rescue operations, bodyguard tasks or even assassination missions. These men either carry a handgun as a back-up weapon or as the main gun for close-quarter combat. They are comprehensively trained, and spend many hours honing their shooting skills on special training ranges. They require a weapon that is extremely accurate, has effective stopping power, and can be brought into action quickly and easily. Some tasks may demand a weapon that can be concealed, implying small overall size and a smooth outline to prevent snagging on clothing or equipment.

SILENCED WEAPONS

In certain situations, the special forces trooper may need a weapon that is silenced, or at the very least suppressed. Truly effective silencers are rare, although most handgun manufacturers make some form of suppressor that can be attached to their products. Suppressors are large diameter tubes filled with baffles, which are attached to the muzzle of a handgun. The baffles absorb much of the energy of the propellant gases as the bullet flies through, creating a much quieter report (handgun bullets are subsonic, so the bullet itself is relatively silent, though there will be some noise from the mechanism). Silencers wear out quickly, and only remain effective for a few shots before needing new baffles.

Major civilian handgun users are police and security agencies, and in some countries these also include anti-terrorist forces and bodyguard units. The ordinary

■ LEFT: A US Marine takes aim with a Beretta 92 handgun during a boarding team training exercise aboard fleet oiler USNS *Joshua Humphreys*.

Webley Mk VI

Calibre: .455in
Weight: 1.09kg (2½lb)
Length: 286mm (11¼in)
Effective range: 30m (32yd)
Rate of fire: single shot
Feed: six-round integral cylinder
Muzzle velocity: 200mps (656fps)

street policeman needs a weapon that can be carried in a holster for many years, and requires minimal care and maintenance. When called upon to use it, he could well be alone, so absolute reliability is paramount. He may also not need the stopping power that the military user needs, as incapacitation rather than death is often all that is necessary. There will often be innocent civilians present, so a less powerful weapon is more desirable to reduce the chances of dangerous ricochets and stray bullets punching through walls or doors.

For the first half of this century, there have been two main strands of handgun development, each with their supporters and detractors. The more traditional concept is that of the revolver, with the self-loader or 'automatic' being a more recent invention. The revolver holds a number of rounds (usually six) in a cylinder that rotates around its long axis. The cartridges are each held in their own firing chamber, which is aligned with the rear of the barrel by a pawl and ratchet mechanism. Behind this cylinder is a spring-loaded hammer which, when the trigger is pulled, drops onto a firing pin and detonates the cartridge igniter.

Originally, most revolvers were 'single action', ie the hammer is pulled backwards and cocked by hand (usually by the thumb). This motion also causes the cylinder to rotate to the next position. Pulling the trigger releases the hammer, causing it to slam into the firing pin. The disadvantage of such a system is that the rate of fire is quite slow, as the hammer must be recocked between each shot. It also means that in a quick-draw situation the first vital shot takes longer to fire. Advantages include greater safety, as two distinct operations are necessary before firing, and greater accuracy, as minimal pull is needed on the trigger.

Most weapons now use a 'double action' concept, where the initial pull of the trigger rotates the cylinder and causes the hammer to lift. Continuing the pull releases the

MR 73

Calibre: .38in
Weight: .88kg (2lb)
Length: 195mm (7¾in)
Effective range: 30m (32yd)
Rate of fire: single shot
Feed: six-round integral cylinder
Muzzle velocity: 225mps (738fps)

trigger and fires the round. A double-action weapon is faster to fire, although the force needed on the trigger often causes inadvertent hand movement and thus reduced accuracy. Where time permits, the hammer on a double-action revolver can be pulled back by hand and the weapon fired in single action mode.

Many revolvers are in use today, although they are normally in the hands of police rather than military users. Limited ammunition supply and slow reloading means that most military users have switched to magazine-fed semi-automatics. However, the revolver is valued by many policemen and women as a simple and extremely reliable firearm, and even if a round misfires, pulling the trigger causes the cylinder to revolve and the next round to rotate into position.

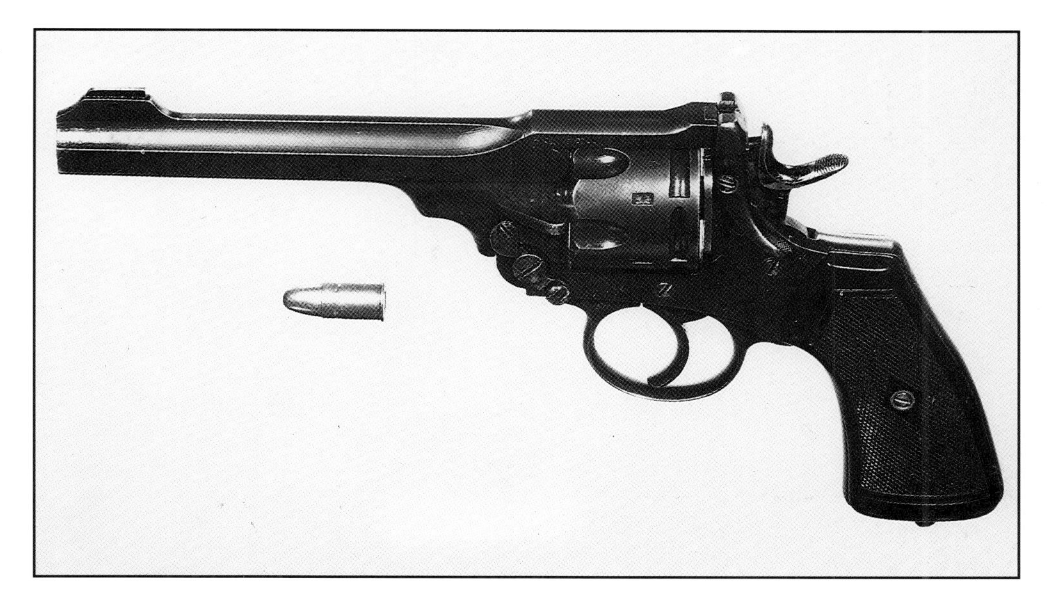

ABOVE: The Webley. This is the Mk VI version of the famous handgun. The Webley is one of the most accurate and strongest handguns ever built.

ENTER THE AUTOMATICS

Towards the end of the last century, the first self-loading handguns appeared, all using the recoil forces created when firing the round to eject the empty case and load the next. These pistols, usually referred to as 'automatics', now form the majority of military handguns. Most follow the same general principles and have similar shapes. They tend to have a rectangular outline, with the barrel covered by a top casing or 'slide'. Ammunition is held in a spring-loaded detachable box magazine which normally fits inside the butt. The weapon is cocked when the slide is pulled back, an action which pushes the hammer against a trigger sear and cocks it. When the slide is released it is pushed forward by a compressed return spring, taking the top round from the magazine and feeding it into the chamber and barrel. When the trigger is pulled, the hammer is released to fall on a firing pin protruding from the rear of the slide, driving it into the cartridge.

Most automatics use recoil principles to operate the mechanism, whereby the barrel and slide move to the rear, driven by the forces from the fired cartridge. After a short distance, the barrel is unlocked from the slide and held by some form of obstruction on the frame. The slide continues to move, pulling out the empty case and flipping it out through an ejection port. The hammer is recocked and the slide moves forward again, feeding the next round into the barrel. Once cocked, an automatic will fire every time the trigger is pulled until the ammunition runs out. The weapon has a high rate of fire, trigger forces are light, and the handgun is reasonably accurate. Once the magazine is empty, it is pulled out of the butt and a new one inserted. Some modern designs allow the hammer to be raised by the first pull of the trigger, which means that the gun can be carried with a round in the chamber and the hammer manually uncocked. Such a configuration is much safer to carry, as there is little risk of a cartridge being fired if a loaded handgun is dropped .

A sub-type of automatic is the machine pistol, which can fire bursts. These are comparatively rare, although designs of this nature pop up regularly through the years. Sometimes a modified conventional automatic, at other times a specially designed weapon, machine pistols tend to have an extremely high rate of fire, which causes a severe muzzle climb because of

Smith & Wesson Hush Puppy

Calibre: 9mm
Weight: .75kg (1 1/2lb)
Length: 188mm (7 1/2in)
Effective range: 25m (27yd)
Rate of fire: single shot
Feed: eight-round magazine
Muzzle velocity: 355mps (1165fps)

the strong recoil. To have any chance of hitting the target at all, the firer needs the support of a shoulder stock. Even so, the machine pistol still tends to be a way of spraying the contents of the magazine into the air. Most of the tasks originally earmarked for these hybrids are now undertaken by submachine guns or shotguns.

The formation that retained the revolver as the officer's sidearm for longer than most was the British Army. Heavy double-action revolvers were in British military service throughout both World Wars and well into the 1950s, long after most other nations had converted to self-loading automatics. This preference for a simple, reliable but powerful sidearm can be traced back to British nineteenth-century experience in the colonies and outposts of the Empire. Combat in these places often consisted of small detachments of troops facing large numbers of strong, fit and determined native warriors, and had shown the need for a handgun bullet with prodigious man-stopping capability. The British choice was a heavy lead projectile of .455in (11.5mm) calibre. The cartridge used by this round was comparatively short, so the muzzle velocity was low, usually around 198mps. The British .455in round depended upon the shock effect of the weight of the soft bullet and its deformation when it hit the target, rather than a high velocity.

Until the 1930s, British officers were expected to purchase their own revolvers, and any make was acceptable as long as it fired service ammunition. The best known and most popular of those in use during the early years of the century and throughout World War I was the Webley Mk VI. The successor to a long line of

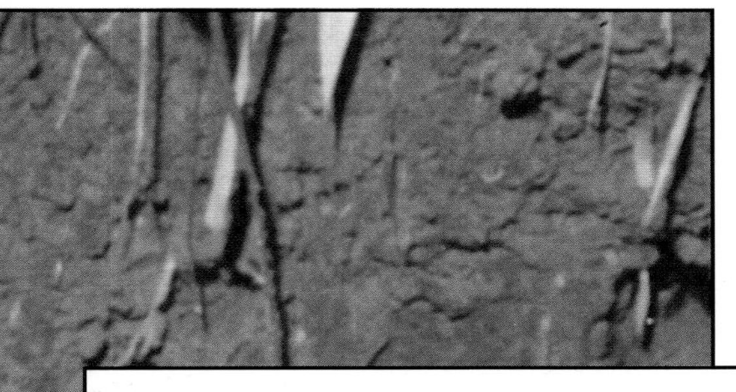

the rims of the empty cases and pulls them out from their chambers. Once six new rounds are fed in, the gun is snapped shut and automatically locked by the spring-loaded saddle catch.

The Webley has a distinctive outline: an octagonal barrel, a wide butt with a flat, squared-off top, and a lanyard ring below.

The Mk VI gave sterling service throughout World War I, being rugged and reliable enough to withstand the tough conditions of trench warfare. During World War I, an unusual short bayonet was produced for close-quarter combat, and some officers purchased this privately. Some also purchased a detachable wooden

Colt M1911A1

Calibre: .45in ACP
Weight: 1.13kg (2½lb)
Length: 216mm (8½in)
Effective range: 30m (32yd)
Rate of fire: single shot
Feed: seven-round detachable box
Muzzle velocity: 253mps (830fps)

■ LEFT: The Colt M1911, one of the most successful handguns in the world. The weapon is extremely robust, and its .45in bullet has enough stopping power to drop the most determined assailant.

butt which could be clipped on the hand-gun, allowing steadier aim from the shoulder. The Webley saw widespread British Army use until the 1930s, and was also issued to many British-influenced police and military forces into the 1950s.

After World War I, the British Army decided that the .455in cartridge was too powerful for general military use. It had a thumping recoil and gave out a large flash and loud report, characteristics which demanded a high level of training for accurate shooting. By 1923, Webley had developed a version of their earlier Mk IV revolver in .38in calibre and were selling this to foreign police and military users. The British Army came to the conclusion that the .38in bullet was perfectly adequate for service use, and decided to modify this handgun for their officers. The work was

Webley designs, the Mk VI is a very strong, well-made but heavy handgun which holds six .455in cartridges in its cylindrical magazine. The frame breaks open for cleaning and reloading by unlocking a saddle catch just above and behind the cylinder. The top frame, which holds both the octagonal barrel and the cylinder, pivots forward around an axis pin at the front of the revolver body, below the rear of the barrel. The hammer, trigger mechanism and butt are all part of the lower frame. As the weapon breaks open, a star-shaped extractor to the rear of the cylinder grips

A guide protrudes from the front of the frame to prevent the cylinder catching when the gun is being holstered. There is a straightforward screw-on blade foresight with a simple rectangular rear sight. The Mk VI is a double-action revolver, where the first pressure on the trigger advances the cylinder into place and raises the hammer to the cocked position, and further pressure releases the hammer and fires the round. Alternatively, a more accurate shot is achieveable by raising the hammer by hand, an action which also causes the cylinder to rotate into place.

carried out by the Royal Small Arms Factory at Enfield, London, so the new arm was called the Enfield No 2 Mk 1 Revolver. The design was similar to the Webley Mk VI, although at .82kg (1¾lb) it is much lighter. The No 2 is also 25.4mm (1in) shorter than the Mk VI, but in general appearance is almost identical. The same double-action mechanism is used, and the weapon has the Webley system of a break-open frame and saddle catch.

The original Enfield has a spur protruding behind the hammer for manual cocking, although complaints soon came from vehicle crews and others about this spur catching in clothing and equipment. The later No 2 Mk 1 deleted the hammer spur, although this meant that the revolver could only be fired as a double-action weapon. In an attempt to improve accuracy the trigger pull was reduced and thumb-grooves cut into the top of the grip. Most pistols were eventually modified to this configuration. Like its .455in predecessors, the Enfield No 2 is a tough and reliable weapon, and one which saw British service all throughout World War II and into the 1950s. Many are still in use in armies and police forces around the world.

Most other countries have long regarded the military revolver as obsolete, though as stated earlier, their simplicity and reliability have kept them popular with both police forces and sports shooters, especially in the United States. Smith & Wesson (S&W) has dominated this market with its series of simple but efficient designs in various calibres. Unlike the British pistols, S&W designs use a solid, one-piece frame, where the cylinder hinges out to the side for reloading. This is claimed to give a stronger and more reliable revolver than one which has a frame that breaks open.

One situation where the revolver has retained its dominance is when extremely powerful cartridges are used. Originally

■ RIGHT: A hand-held cannon: the Smith & Wesson .44in Magnum Model 29.

created by sports shooters hand-loading large cartridges to increase the power and velocity of the bullet, these 'Magnum' rounds have become popular with many law enforcement agencies. Probably the best known is the .44 Magnum, a cartridge with truly immense stopping power. A hit anywhere in the body from one of these is virtually guaranteed to incapacitate a human immediately, and the effect on large game is equally devastating. Some police shooters feel that such firepower is essential, especially when a single officer is facing multiple determined assailants. Disadvantages include the need for a large, heavy handgun, and the requirement for extensive training to overcome natural fear of its recoil, flash and bang.

SMITH & WESSON'S MODEL 29

The best known of these pocket artillery pieces is the S&W Model 29, the original 'Dirty Harry' gun. A massive revolver – over 356mm (14in) long and weighing 1.53kg (3¼lb) – it is chambered for the .44in Magnum cartridge. A solid, one-piece steel frame holds the cylinder and long barrel, while the shaped butt can be clad in wood or rubber. To reload, the cylinder hinges to the left of the frame and six rounds are inserted. The double-action mechanism can be fired by a straightforward pull on the trigger, though for accuracy the hammer can be manually cocked before firing. A monster such as this demands extensive training, as the firer must be in a stable, secure firing pose to absorb the massive recoil forces.

While the .44 Magnum is too much of a handful for most military users, some special forces soldiers may require its immediate man-stopping capability. The Model 39 has been seen in the hands of the French GIGN, and a number are in service with US Special Forces. Apart from these specialised uses, the revolver in general is no longer a standard military sidearm, having largely been overtaken by the automatic.

By the end of the nineteenth century, the self-loading automatic had matured to become reliable enough for the rough and tumble of military service. The first major force to adopt such a weapon was the army of Austria-Hungary with its 1908 model 8mm Roth-Steyr. Some of the best of the early designs came from Germany, and one of the most popular from Mauser. The Model 1896 (C/96) was designed to use the 7.63mm x 25mm Mauser handgun cartridge, and made use of a short-recoil system, whereby the barrel and breech

Walther PPK

Calibre: 7.65mm
Weight: 568g (1¼lb)
Length: 155mm (6in)
Range: 30m (32yd)
Feed: seven-round magazine
Muzzle velocity: 280mps (918fps)

block move together for a short distance before the barrel stops and the breech block continues to the rear. Ammunition is fed from a fixed magazine in front of the trigger, and models holding six or 10 rounds were available, all being reloaded by pushing a clip of rounds down through the open ejection port. The Mauser has a distinctive square body with an unsupported cylindrical barrel and a round 'broom-handle' grip. The handgun was often supplied with a wooden holster which could be clipped to the rear of the grip to form a shoulder stock.

The C/96 was not selected for German military service, although many were purchased privately, both in Germany and abroad. Later modifications created the Models 1898 and 1912, although it wasn't until World War I that the handgun achieved widespread success. The German Army had standardised on a 9mm x19mm cartridge and a pistol to suit, but production could not keep up with demand. In an effort to ease supply problems, Mauser rechambered the Model 1912 to take this round, and this version of the handgun rapidly gained popularity with German soldiers. Fitted with the wooden stock, it was a handy weapon for trench clearing and close-range combat, a predecessor of the submachine gun in these roles. To avoid confusion, the 9mm Mausers were identified by the number '9' engraved into their grips and painted red. Thousands of Mausers were sold around the world, and copies were produced in China and Spain.

In the 1930s, Spanish engineers developed a full-automatic version of the

Walther P38

Calibre: 9mm
Weight: .96kg (2lb)
Length: 213mm (8¼in)
Effective range: 30m (32yd)
Rate of fire: single shot
Feed: eight-round detachable box
Muzzle velocity: 350mps (1149fps)

Mauser which, when combined with a new detachable 20-round box magazine and the wooden stock, became a handy sub-machine gun substitute. These became especially popular in China, and Mauser eventually had to compete by developing its own machine pistol variant. The last Mausers, still closely resembling the original 1896 model, were produced in 1937, and the Chinese Type 80 machine pistol makes use of the Mauser action.

THE LUGER

The main German competitor to the Mauser was the Parabellum series, developed by Georg Luger from the earlier Borchardt handguns. The first of these designs fired a 7.65mm cartridge, but the army wanted a round with more stopping power. Luger quickly took the 7.65mm case, straightened out the bottle neck and fitted a heavier 9mm bullet. Experience with feed problems revealed that the bullet needed an ogival front section, and after a few years most were also made with a nickel jacket covering a lead core. Perhaps surprisingly, this stopgap 9mm x 19mm round was eventually to become the most widely used handgun and submachine gun bullet of the twentieth century. Parabellum was the name of the district in which Luger's pistols and cartridges were first produced, and the name has since become permanently associated with this round. The handgun designed to fire this cartridge was designated the Parabellum P08, and it quickly became the standard German Imperial Army sidearm.

The P08, better known as the Luger, uses a short-recoil system similar to Maxim's original machine gun concept, where the mechanism is locked by a long horizontal toggle behind the bolt. This toggle lock has a pivot halfway along its length, and when the barrel and bolt have recoiled a short distance, the pivot bends upwards like an elbow, unlocking the bolt and allowing it to continue to the rear. Two cylindrical grips protrude from the rear of the gun, and by pulling back on these a round is fed into the chamber and the gun cocked. Ammunition is fed from a detachable eight-round box which slots into the grip.

The P08 came in both standard form and with a longer barrel (the 'Artillery' model). A wooden stock could be clipped to the butt, and there was even a special 32-round drum magazine which fitted underneath, feeding through the normal magazine lips, and long-barrelled Lugers equipped with these extras were often used as carbines for trench warfare and local defence. Lugers saw service throughout both World Wars, although by the late 1930s the P08 had been largely superseded by later designs.

The United States Army was also quick to move to the new form of self-loading automatic. In 1907, a series of trials was carried out to find a handgun to replace the existing .38in calibre service revolvers. The requirement was for a weapon that would fire the large 11.5mm x 23mm round – a heavy, powerful and accurate man-stopper. The Army wanted to be sure of stopping a running target with one hit, and it felt that this bullet was the minimum size it could accept. The eventual winner of the 1907 trials was a square, solid-looking automatic developed by John Browning from his earlier work on self-loaders. Four years later this handgun entered service as the Colt M1911, and it was to become one of the most successful and popular military pistols of modern times. The ammunition became known as .45in ACP (Automatic Colt Handgun), and it has also gone on to widespread use in a variety of handguns and submachine guns.

A HANDGUN LEGEND

The Colt is large and heavy, and this, combined with the report and recoil from the .45in cartridge, demands high levels of skill from the firer. Despite this, the handgun has proved popular with its users, most of whom appreciate the feeling of security engendered by this intimidating beast. The M1911 uses Browning's system of locking the barrel to the breech and slide by a series of raised lugs on the barrel's upper surface, with corresponding recesses inside the slide. Attached under the rear of the barrel is a hinged link pin, which protrudes down into the frame. When a round is fired, the barrel and slide recoil together until the pressure in the chamber has dropped to a safe level. The link pin beneath the barrel is stopped by a slide lock on the frame, and acts as an axis for the rear of the barrel to rotate around. This motion causes the barrel to stop and tip down at the rear, unlocking it from the slide and freeing the slide. The spent cartridge case is extracted from the chamber, hits an ejection post, and is flipped out of the handgun through a port on the right

BELOW: The famous German Luger. This is the Model 1914 version, and is believed to have first entered service in 1917.

side of the slide. The return spring, lying under the barrel and pressing on the inside front face of the slide, is compressed, ready to propel the slide forward again. After the slide has stopped its rearward movement, it is pushed forward by this spring, stripping a fresh round from the top of the magazine as it goes. As the slide finishes its movement, the barrel is also pushed forward, tipping upwards until horizontal. At this point the locking lugs on top of the barrel slot into the recesses in the slide and the gun is now ready to fire again.

Eight rounds are held in a detachable box magazine inside the butt, forward of which is the trigger and guard. Sights are simple: a straightforward blade at the front and a corresponding slot aperture at the rear. There is a conventional safety lever at the rear left of the slide, and there is also a safety grip behind the butt. Only if the gun is gripped correctly will this be depressed and the hammer unlocked, free to fire.

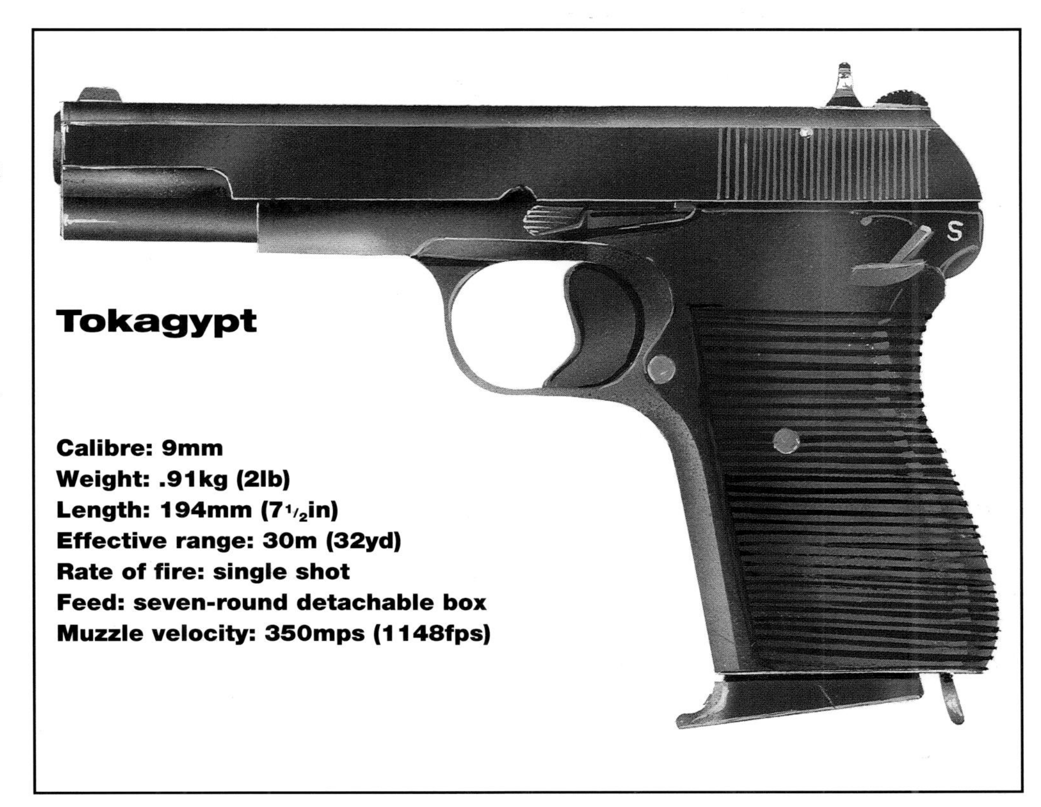

Tokagypt

Calibre: 9mm
Weight: .91kg (2lb)
Length: 194mm (7½in)
Effective range: 30m (32yd)
Rate of fire: single shot
Feed: seven-round detachable box
Muzzle velocity: 350mps (1148fps)

THE OLD WARRIOR

Following combat experience in World War I, the Colt was modified to become the M1911A1. This model has a more rounded shape at the rear of the butt, a lengthened butt safety, a shorter hammer spur, and shallow cut-outs in the frame, just behind the trigger. This weapon went on to see service throughout World War II and beyond, and it was not until 1985 that the US Army chose its replacement. M1911A1s were made by many other US companies, and were licence-built in Canada, Norway and Argentina. Some were even made in .455in calibre and were used by the Canadian and British forces in World War II.

Though it is 80 years since this handgun first entered service, millions are in use all over the world. Tough, reliable and packing a punch, they have endeared themselves to soldiers of all nations. The basic shape and concept has formed the basis for dozens of military automatics since, and the design has been copied in many countries. The Colt can be criticised for being too heavy and for firing an unnecessarily powerful round, but most American soldiers have a deep affection for this old warrior. By the mid-1990s it will no longer be in US service, although Browning's Colt will be in use elsewhere for many years to come.

John Browning continued to develop automatic pistols during the 1920s, although his final design was produced in Belgium rather than in the United States. Fabrique National (FN) had already worked alongside this prolific American designer, having manufactured a number of his early handgun designs. This latest handgun was designed in 1925, although it was to be 1935 before it entered production.

The Browning High Power GP35 is based upon similar principles as the Colt M1911, but is chambered to fire the 9mm Parabellum round. As this is a smaller and less powerful cartridge than the .45in ACP, the handgun is lighter and smaller than the Colt, and can carry more ammunition. Up to 13 rounds are held in a detachable box which fits into the butt. The GP35 is cocked by pulling back on the slide then letting it move forward under pressure from the return spring, this action causing the external hammer to be pushed back and a round fed into the chamber. There is no hammer decocking lever, only a simple safety catch which locks the slide and hammer. For safe carriage, the GP35 should only be holstered uncocked, which means that the firer first has to rack the slide to load a round after drawing the handgun. Short recoil is used, with the barrel locked into the slide by means of lugs on its upper surface. Instead of the M1911's link pin, the underneath of the barrel has a simple lug with a cammed slot cut in it. When the barrel and slide recoil, a pin on the lower frame enters this slot, forcing the rear of the barrel downwards and causing it to unlock from the slide.

The barrel is stopped by this pin, but the slide continues to the rear, extracting and ejecting the empty case as it moves. Once the hammer is recocked, the slide moves forward again, taking the next round into the chamber. When the last round is fired, a protrusion on the magazine platform causes the slide to lock to the rear, making the empty state obvious to the firer. Simple fixed sights are fitted, although some early models had an adjustable tangent rear sight and came with a wooden shoulder stock.

THE BROWNING HIGH POWER

Financial constraints prevented FN from producing the High Power until 1935, nine years after Browning's death. When Belgium was overrun by the Germans in 1940, the handgun was manufactured for their own army as the P640(b), though Belgian workmen managed to sabotage large numbers of these. Others managed to smuggle the manufacturing drawings out of Belgium, and the FN handgun soon entered production with John Inglis in Canada. Canadian and British forces employed the GP35 during the war, and in 1954 the British adopted it to replace their .38in revolver. It has since seen service with more than 50 countries, and has proved to be an excellent arm. The 9mm round creates less recoil and a quieter report than the .45in ACP, so it is easier to train recruits to use this gun effectively. Thousands of these handguns are still in use, although the lack of modern features such as an automatic hammer drop and double-action first shot means that this old soldier is coming to the end of its frontline life.

During 1929, the German firm of Carl Walther Waffenfabrik introduced a sleek, modern automatic designed for use with civilian police officers. The Walther PP (Polizei Pistole) fired a smaller round than the P08 service handgun: the 7.65mm x 17mm, also known as the .32in ACP. While this did not have the stopping power of the military 9mm Parabellum cartridge, it was felt to be adequate for police purposes. A later variant fired a short 9mm cartridge, also known as the .38in ACP. The PP has a modern appearance, with a clean outline and a minimum of protuberances. As the PP was designed for a reasonably low-powered cartridge, Walther's designers were able to use simple blowback to operate the mechanism. There is no locking system for the barrel. Once the round is fired, the time taken to overcome the inertia of the slide is enough to reduce the gas pressure to a safe level. The barrel is fixed in place, with only the slide moving backwards.

THE WALTHER PP

The PP was the first automatic to have a truly safe double-action mechanism. If the gun is cocked with a round in the chamber, the firing pin can be locked and the hammer dropped down, allowing the handgun to be safely carried with a round loaded. If quick-reaction fire is needed, simply pulling the trigger will raise the hammer and fire the round. An additional safety feature is a small pin that protrudes from the slide, just above the hammer, to show that there is a round loaded in the chamber. Walther also produced a shorter version of the PP for plain-clothes work, known as the PPK (K for *Kurz*, or 'short'). Both handguns proved to be reliable and popular with police and military forces, and are still in production today.

In the late 1930s, the German Army decided to replace the P08 Luger, and Walther put forward a version of the PP rechambered for the 9mm x 19mm Parabellum cartridge. The army rejected this on the grounds that the cartridge was too powerful for a simple blowback system, so Walther redesigned the weapon to use short recoil and a locked breech. After further design refinements, the new handgun entered military service as the P38. A neat, attractive design, the P38 is recognisable from its protruding barrel and large cutaway on top of the slide. When a round is chambered, the barrel is locked to the slide by a wedge plate beneath the chamber. When fired, the recoil causes the barrel and slide to move together a short distance, until the rear of the barrel is cammed down and unlocked from the slide.

The P38 uses the many safety features of the PP series. Once the weapon is loaded and cocked, the firing pin is locked and the hammer dropped by setting the safety catch. The gun can now be carried or even holstered in complete safety. To fire, the user simply pulls the trigger to raise then release the hammer. If time permits, the hammer can instead be raised by hand to allow a more accurate single action first shot. A small indicating pin to show a round is chambered is also present, and has since become almost a Walther trade mark. The P38 is well balanced and easy to shoot accurately, and, unusually for a German weapon, is extremely tolerant of dirt, dust and poor conditions. It quickly became popular in service, although it

■ RIGHT: The Tokarev TT33 handgun. The weapon is now obsolete and production ceased in 1954 in the Soviet Union.

never completely replaced the Luger in the wartime German Army.

When the *Bundeswehr* was being created in the 1950s, the P38 went back into production as the P1, again being issued as the standard military handgun. The only main change is the substitution of the steel slide for a lighter alloy item – in all other respects it is virtually identical to its wartime predecessor. The P1 is in service with over eight armies, including those of Germany, Norway, Portugal and Chile. It is safe, tough, extremely reliable and accurate, and it was not until the early 1990s that a replacement was required.

RUSSIAN AUTOMATICS

The Colt/ Browning mechanism had proved to be so effective that when, in the late 1920s, the Russians designed their own military automatic, it was an obvious basis from which to work. Feodor Tokarev's TT30 (Tula-Tokarev) uses the M1911 swinging-link, short-recoil system on a handgun chambered to fire the Russian 7.62mm x 25mm cartridge. The Tokarev has a similar appearance to the American weapon, although the rear edge of the slide has a distinctive rounded shape, and this is the main recognition feature of this handgun. Apart from using a different cartridge, the only other changes from Browning's design were those made in order to simplify manufacture, ease maintenance, and improve reliability. The hammer and lock can be removed as a single assembly for maintenance, and the ammunition feed lips are on the frame rather than the magazine, thus improving reliability and making the production of magazines easier and cheaper. After a few years a modified version was introduced, the changes being of a minor nature to further speed up manufacture. This revised weapon was known as the TT33, and it quickly superseded the earlier model in service.

The Tokarev is a typical Russian design, ie extremely tough and reliable, though perhaps not the last word in precision engineering and accuracy. It saw service with the Red Army throughout World War II and beyond, and Russian production only ended in the 1950s. The handgun has also been made under licence in a number of Warsaw Pact countries, and copies have been manufactured in China and elsewhere. A version chambered for 9mm Parabellum ammunition was produced by Hungary for export to Egypt, and this was known as the Tokagypt. Now regarded as obsolescent, the TT33 and variants can still be found with many armies, especially those who were at one time under the Soviet sphere of influence.

By the early 1950s, the Soviet Army decided to replace their Tokarevs with a newer design. Again, Russian engineers looked at the best pistols entering service elsewhere, and again they came up with a close copy of a Western design. The Pistolet Makarov (PM) is closely based on the Walther PP, having a similar double-action mechanism. Likewise, the PM can also be holstered or carried with a round in the chamber, as applying the safety catch locks the firing pin and drops the hammer. A new round was introduced for this handgun: a special low-powered 9mm x 18mm cartridge held in an eight-shot detachable box. This round is about as powerful as is safe for use in a simple blowback system, but the Makarov copes well and has proved to be tough and reliable in service. The only criticism from firers is that the butt is slightly bulky and at an awkward angle for accurate shooting. The Soviets obviously decided that the average military handgun shooter is not a particularly skilled shot anyway, and that reliability and ruggedness is more important than 'firing range' accuracy. Like its predecessor, the PM has seen use with the armed services of most of the former Warsaw Pact nations and Soviet allies. It has also been manufactured in East Germany and, as the Type 59, in the People's Republic of China.

The Soviets also produced another handgun which fired the 9mm x 18mm Makarov cartridge. The Stechkin is a large and relatively heavy weapon for such a low-powered round, the explanation being that it has a selective-fire capability. Normally equipped with a wooden dual-purpose holster and shoulder stock, the Stechkin is a well-finished weapon that can fire bursts from a 20-round box magazine. First issued in the late 1950s, it was soon withdrawn from widespread service. This is assumed to be because of the weight and complexity being more of a disadvantage than the dubious worth of burst fire from such a short weapon. Machine pistols require extremely well-aimed shots fired in controlled short bursts to get any benefit from the increased ammunition expenditure, and most Russian soldiers are not trained to such a standard. Where the Stechkin can still be found, however, is in the hands of special forces troops, who are trained to a high level of marksmanship. The Stechkin can be fitted with an effective silencer, and such weapons were carried by the *spetsnaz* troops who assaulted the Afghan presidential palace in 1979.

Pietro Beretta SpA has a long and honourable history of providing Italian soldiers with its firearms, and produced its first service automatic handgun in 1915. This fired a 7.65mm x 17mm (.32 ACP) cartridge, although some were made to shoot an Italian 9mm x 17mm round. The

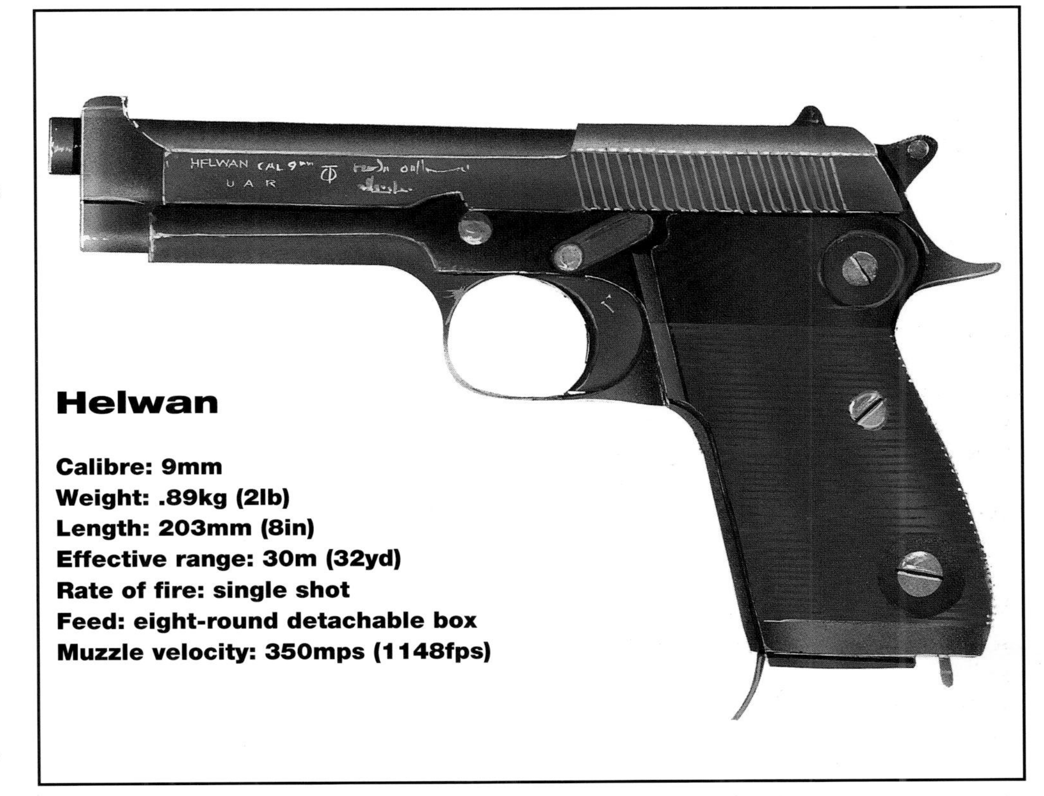

Helwan

Calibre: 9mm
Weight: .89kg (2lb)
Length: 203mm (8in)
Effective range: 30m (32yd)
Rate of fire: single shot
Feed: eight-round detachable box
Muzzle velocity: 350mps (1148fps)

handgun was developed throughout the 1920s and 1930s, and Italian troops fought World War II with the derived Beretta M1934, again firing the low-powered 9mm short round. After the war, the Italians followed most of Europe in selecting the 9mm x 19mm Parabellum round for their handgun ammunition, and Beretta designed the Model 1951 handgun to suit.

THE BERETTA M1951

The new round demanded a more sophisticated mechanism than the simple blowback of the earlier Berettas, so a form of short recoil similar to that used by the Walther P38 was chosen. The barrel has two lugs which lock into the slide which, after the initial recoil, is unlocked by the vertical movement of a locking wedge, with the slide continuing to the rear. The M1951 has the Beretta 'trade mark' of the barrel protruding a short distance in front of the slide, and the top of the slide being cut away from just behind the simple blade foresight to above the chamber. It has proved popular with Italian and some African armed forces, and has been manufactured in Egypt under licence as the Hellwan. A model of the M1951, known as the 951R, was produced, which could fire bursts from a 10-round magazine, but this did not see wide use.

By the mid-1950s, virtually all of the major nations had equipped their armed forces with reliable automatic handguns. A number of calibres and systems were in use, but the majority employed 9mm or .45in rounds. NATO had standardised on the 9mm x 19mm Parabellum round, and Georg Luger's hasty conversion was now in service with more handguns than any other cartridge. The main exceptions were in the United States and some of its close allies, whose servicemen stayed with the heavier .45in ACP. The forces of the Soviet Union and its clients also used a different round: either the Russian 7.62mm x 25mm or 9mm x 18mm low-powered cartridges.

The handguns in use were also a mixed bunch, although a large majority owed their inspiration to the work of John Browning. Millions of Colt M1911A1s and FN GP35s testified to the reliability of his designs, while many other pistols were simply national copies of his basic concepts. Other much-copied systems included the Walther wedge-locked, short-recoil method. Nations such as Austria, China, Hungary, Japan, Spain and the former Yugoslavia all produced their own pistols, although some of these were simply copies of existing designs. Most automatics in use were of single action design, and could not be carried safely with a round chambered. With the obvious exception of the Walther automatics and their clones, the firer first had to operate the slide of his automatic before being able to fire the first shot. Much of the development effort over the next 30 years would be spent in improving the quick response and safety of automatic pistols such as these. There would be few startling departures from accepted principles; rather, a gradual incremental refining of design.

THE NEW GERMANS

Heckler & Koch (H&K) has achieved great success with a roller-delayed blowback system in its range of assault rifles, machine guns and submachine guns, so it was an obvious development to incorporate this technique in a handgun. The P9 of the mid-1970s was designed to fire the now standard 9mm x 19mm Parabellum, and the P9S variant has proved popular with many military and police users. The mechanism is similar to that in the G3 rifle, where a two-part bolt is locked by two small rollers which it forced outwards into slots in the barrel extension. Once a round is fired, the recoil tries to push the bolt backwards, but first has to force the locking rollers inwards, guided by a cammed path on the barrel extension. Their resistance is enhanced by the mass of the rear part of the bolt, which has to be accelerated backwards before the rollers can move. By the time the whole bolt assembly and the slide are clear to move, the gas pressure has dropped to a safe level.

This is a simple, well-proved and reliable system, which has the added advantage of a fixed barrel. The P9 barrel also has unusual polygonal rifling, which supposedly offers less resistance to the bullet and creates less deformation. Other features include a concealed internal hammer. This provides an added safety because external hammers can catch on clothing, holsters or webbing equipment. Without an external hammer, there is no obvious indicator to the state of the handgun, so H&K incorporated a small signal pin which protrudes from the rear of the slide when the mechanism is cocked. When a round is in the chamber, the cartridge case ejector signals this by protruding slightly through the ejection port. A nine-shot magazine is inside the butt, and the front of the trigger guard has a reverse curve to aid a firer using a two-handed grip. The P9 has proved to be extremely popular with military and police users, and a number of variants exist, including a model chambered for the American .45in ACP round.

An H&K design which didn't achieve much success was the technically interesting VP70. At first sight a conventional blowback 9mm handgun, the VP70 makes extensive use of plastics in the receiver and frame. Blowback is normally too dangerous to be used with 9mm

Heckler & Koch P9S

Calibre: 9mm
Weight: .88kg (2lb)
Length: 192mm (7½in)
Effective range: 30m (32yd)
Rate of fire: single shot
Feed: nine-round detachable box
Muzzle velocity: 350mps (1148fps)

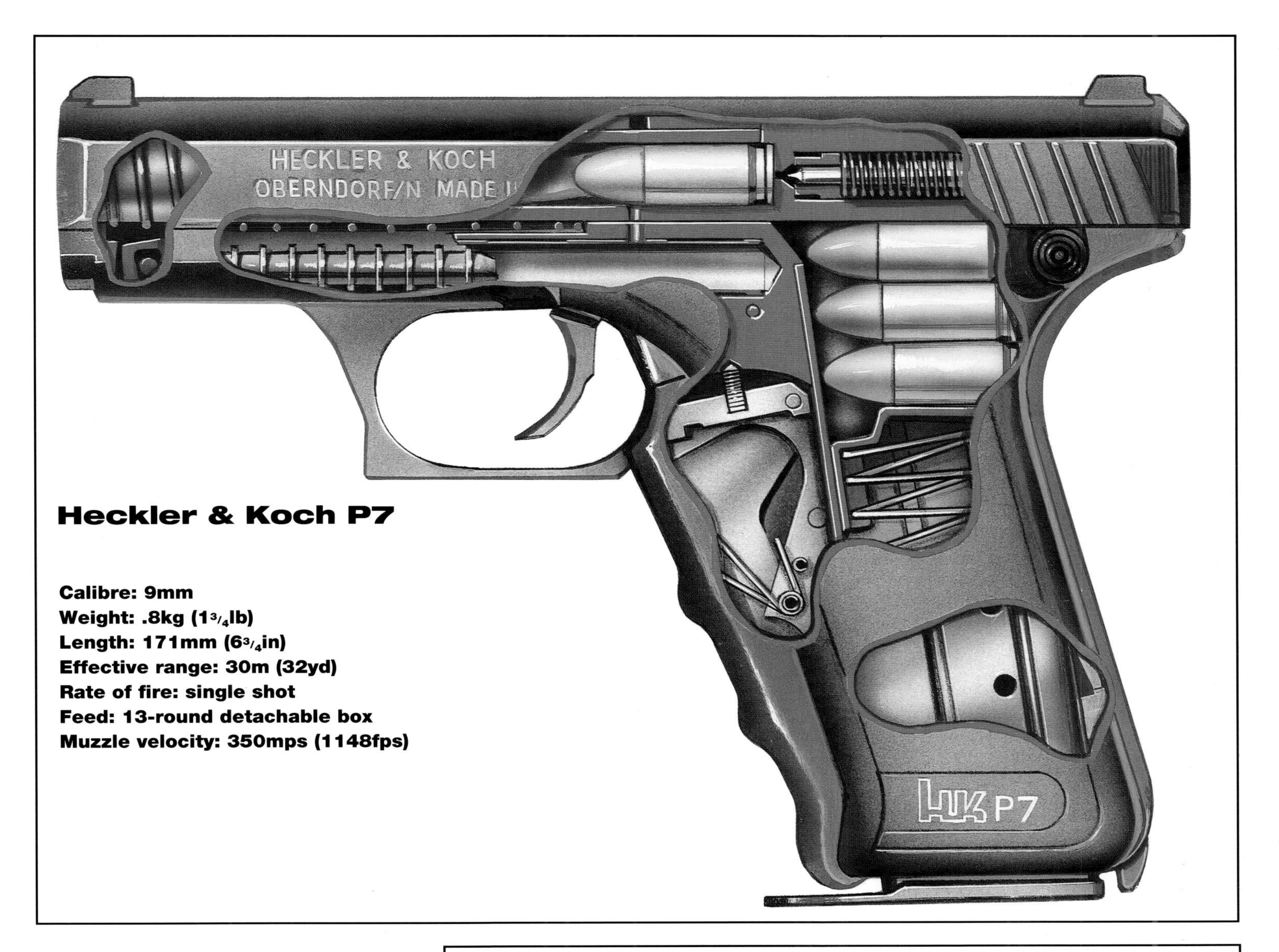

Heckler & Koch P7

Calibre: 9mm
Weight: .8kg ($1\frac{3}{4}$lb)
Length: 171mm ($6\frac{3}{4}$in)
Effective range: 30m (32yd)
Rate of fire: single shot
Feed: 13-round detachable box
Muzzle velocity: 350mps (1148fps)

Parabellum, but the VP70 has a strong return spring and heavy slide which absorb enough of the energy from the cartridge. Holding an impressive18 rounds in a box magazine, the handgun can only be fired as a double-action weapon, no manual cocking being available. The special feature of this weapon is that by attaching a special plastic holster/shoulder stock to the butt, the mechanism is altered to allow three-round bursts to be fired. By keeping the burst length down to three rounds only, it was felt that the normal disadvantages of a machine pistol, such as muzzle climb, would be overcome. However, apart from a few sales to overseas customers, the VP70 remains nothing more than a technological curiosity. In view of the wide selection of effective small submachine guns available to a prospective purchaser, one is tempted to ask, 'why bother?'

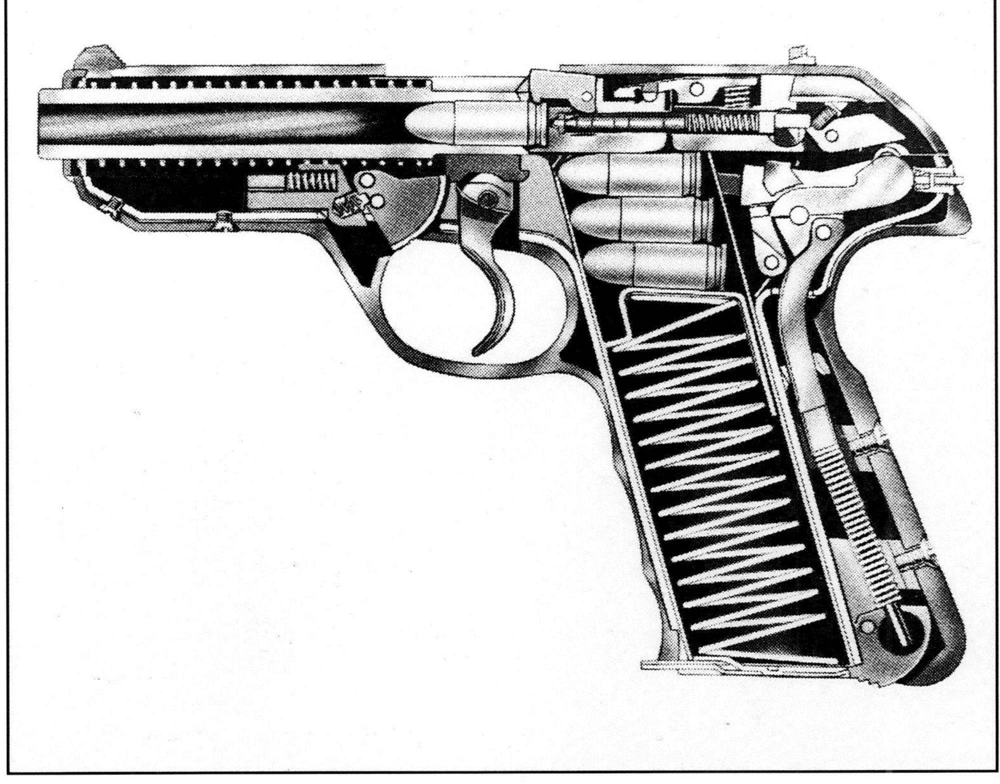

RIGHT: A cutaway view of Heckler & Koch's 9mm P9S handgun, a double-action gun with a polygonally rifled barrel.

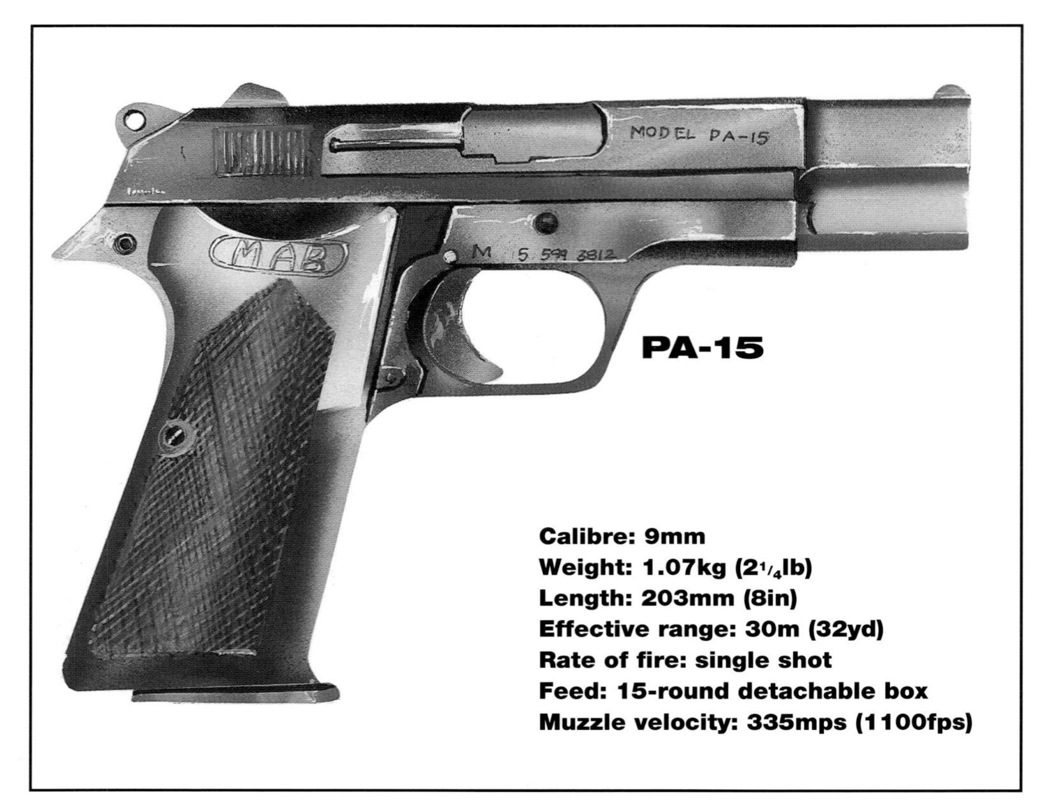

PA-15

Calibre: 9mm
Weight: 1.07kg ($2\frac{1}{4}$lb)
Length: 203mm (8in)
Effective range: 30m (32yd)
Rate of fire: single shot
Feed: 15-round detachable box
Muzzle velocity: 335mps (1100fps)

H&K's P9 was optimised for military users, so the next step was to produce a new handgun specifically for civilian police forces. The resulting P7 makes use of a number of unusual safety and operational features to create a superbly reliable weapon ideal for accurate, quick-reaction shooting. The two standard models, the P7M13 with a 13-round magazine, and the P7M8, which only holds eight rounds, are chambered for 9mm Parabellum ammunition. The P7 has a fixed barrel and uses a form of gas-delayed blowback originally incorporated in the last-ditch wartime 'Volkspistole'. As the bullet travels up the barrel, gas is tapped off from a small aperture just past the chamber. This high-pressure gas bleeds into a small cylinder underneath the barrel, which has a piston as its front face. The piston is directly connected to the slide, and the pressure in this cylinder opposes the movement of the slide until the gas pressure has dropped. The gas system also absorbs some of the recoil force normally transmitted to the firer, and is a remarkably simple and effective method of operation. There is no complicated locking system and few moving parts, and the only maintenance required is regular cleaning.

Once the slide is racked back by the firer, it moves forward under spring pressure, chambering a round in the process. So far, operation is like any other handgun, but from this point the P7 is handled differently from most others. The front edge of the butt is actually a cocking lever, and until this is depressed the gun is not cocked and is completely safe. Only when a proper grip is taken and the lever squeezed inwards is the spring-loaded firing pin cocked and the handgun ready to fire. There is no other safety catch, but by using this method the P7 can be carried for long periods with a round chambered. First-shot accuracy is also improved because, unlike most double action automatics, the trigger pull is light and smooth.

MINIATURE GERMANS

Angled for comfortable aiming, the butt is wide enough to allow the magazine to sit almost vertically, thus improving the feed geometry and increasing reliability. Sighting is by a simple fixed blade and aperture, although H&K has added white markers to aid rapid aiming. There is also a smaller variant, the P7K3, which does away with the delay system and is chambered for the low-powered 9mm Short (.38in ACP) or the 7.65mm (.32in ACP) cartridges. H&K has also modified the P7 for the .45in ACP round, using an oil and piston system to provide the delay and to absorb some of the recoil.

The P7 is a neat and popular weapon which has been procured by many military as well as police users. Ideal for accurate, quick-reaction shooting, it has found its way into the armouries of a number of special forces units and VIP protection detachments. It has also found favour with American police departments, a number of whom have ordered this fine handgun.

One of the most significant events in the history of modern small pistols has been the search by the United States government for a sidearm to replace the Colt M1911A1. What would seem to be a simple process has actually turned out to be a long, drawn-out tussle, where politics, emotion and lawsuits played as great a part as technology and engineering.

The decision to replace the Colt at all was a controversial one, as this handgun had come to be revered as the very symbol of American gunmaking. What made things worse was that long after all the NATO allies had done the same, the Army had finally decided to change to the 'European' 9mm Parabellum cartridge. This final abandonment of the .45in brought howls of protest from American traditionalists, who were wedded to the idea of firing the largest possible bullet from a sidearm. Things were to get worse.

ENTER THE EUROPEANS

In 1980, trials were held to find the handgun that best met the Army's stringent requirements. A huge amount was at stake, not only the hundreds of thousands of handguns that American forces would need, but the many more that would be sold to other countries who would follow the USA's lead. As the trials progressed, it rapidly became apparent that the products of American industry were lagging badly behind those from Europe. Complacency and traditionalism had left American gunmakers with designs that lacked most of the advanced safety features and modern operating systems of their European competitors. The 1980 trials quickly established the European ascendancy, even though they ended in acrimony and controversy, and with no weapon chosen.

Another series of trials took place in 1984, and again the Europeans dominated. Smith & Wesson had made a brave attempt with their Model 459, but this was eliminated for a number of reasons. The contest finally came down to a choice between two pistols, both of which fully met the technical requirements. The two finalists were the SIG-Sauer P266 (a Swiss design manufactured in Germany), and the Italian Beretta 92F.

The Swiss company SIG makes some of the most finely engineered firearms in the world, although legal restrictions make it difficult for them to sell abroad. In an effort to get around this problem, they have formed a long-term relationship with J P

Sauer & Sohn of Germany, which manufactures SIG handguns for export. It has a range of 9mm Parabellum modern automatics, all of which are superbly made and finished to a standard that is reflected in their price. When the US competition was announced, SIG put forward a handgun based on their existing P225, designated the P226.

The P226 uses short-recoil principles similar to the original Browning design, where a locking lug above the barrel fits into a recess in the slide. When recoiling, another lug under the barrel strikes a cross-piece on the frame, unlocking the barrel from the slide. Once a round has been loaded by racking the slide, the hammer can be dropped by operating a lever on either side of the frame. The firing pin is locked until the trigger is pulled, so the weapon can be safely carried with a round in the chamber. The handgun can be fired single action just by pulling the trigger, or, if time permits, the hammer can first be manually cocked. No other manual safety is fitted, and the SIG can be brought into action as fast as any revolver.

SIG VERSUS BERETTA

The gun is well balanced and has a comfortable grip, even though a 15-round magazine fits inside the butt. A double-handed grip is made easier by the reverse curve on the front edge of the trigger guard, and the gun has a light aluminium frame with a machined steel slide. Simple blade and aperture sights are standard, and the whole assembly makes for a superb 'shooter's handgun': accurate, reliable and pleasant to fire. The P226 passed the US technical evaluation with ease, although in the end its high price counted against it. SIG still benefited from its entry, however, as the glowing technical reports soon created new interest in its products, and increased sales of the earlier P225. A number of police and military agencies have procured SIG, among whom are reported to be the British Special Air Service, the US Secret Service and US Navy SEALs.

Beretta's design is based upon its earlier range of handguns, especially the Model 92 introduced in 1976. The Model 92SB was put forward for the US trials, and, after minor changes, emerged as the Model 92F. The Beretta makes use of the short-recoil system originally seen on the Walther P38. Modern features include a safety lever on both sides of the slide, which drops the hammer and locks the firing pin. Like the SIG, it can be fired as a double-action handgun by just pulling the trigger, or the hammer can be manually cocked for a single action shot. Up to15 rounds can be carried in the magazine, and simple blade and aperture sights are fitted above the slide. The trigger guard has a reverse curve on its front edge, and the butt front is curved to improve grip. A special hard-wearing plastic film covers the external components, which reduces wear in harsh service environments.

The Model 92F is a superb combat handgun, and also passed the evaluation process with flying colours. With two excellent designs to choose from, it appears that the final decision was made on the basis of cost, and thus the Beretta entered US service as the Handgun M9. The decision caused an immense amount of fuss, with many Americans disturbed that their next combat handgun was to be an Italian design. Smith & Wesson claimed unfair treatment, some elements in Congress tried to get the decision overturned, and the whole thing degenerated into a series of unseemly legal wrangles. Extra tests were carried out, with the same result. To add to the controversy, there were reports of technical problems with the early production pistols. Stories of cracks being found in some slides appeared in the press, and a number of servicemen were hurt when slides parted company with the rest of the handgun. The US Marine Corps soon restricted the number of rounds to be fired from each handgun, and the SEALs quickly discarded their Berettas in favour of SIGs, P9s and even veteran Colts.

The reason for these failures is hard to fathom, and no explanation has been made public. Thousands of Beretta 92s have been in use around the world with military and sporting users for over 15 years, and nothing like this has been reported before. Whether there have been problems in gearing the production lines to such large quantities, or whether faulty materials have been used, remains a matter for conjecture. Beretta insists that normal teething problems have been exaggerated in a further attempt to get the contracts rescinded. In a final ironic twist, Smith & Wesson has since passed into British ownership, so the only US serious contender at the time is now also owned by European interests. If the competition had been further delayed the story might have been different, as the US company Ruger has since brought out a superb 9mm automatic with all the safety and operational features expected from a modern handgun. This came onto the marketplace in 1985, a year after the M9 decision had been made.

THE MODEL 93R

A selective-fire model of the 92F has also been produced, known as the Beretta Model 93R, Recognisable by the addition of a muzzle brake, a longer 20-round magazine and an unusual fold-down front grip, the handgun has a selector mechanism to enable three-round bursts to be fired. The handgun is in most other respects identical to the 92F. A folding metal stock is usually fitted, and the gun is gripped with both hands, the thumb of the forehand fitting through the extra-wide trigger guard and the fingers holding the fold-down grip. The 93R is apparently used by Italian special forces and government bodyguards, although it is difficult to see what this weapon can do that a good submachine gun can't do better.

American companies are also manufacturing accessories for the 92F/M9, and one of these is the KAC lightweight suppressor which snaps on to the end of the barrel. An automatic handgun creates a fair amount of noise from the recoil action, so a locking bar can also be added to the frame of the handgun to prevent operation

■ RIGHT: The Makarov self-loading handgun. The weapon is generally well made, but the handling is awkward because of the bulky grip.

of the slide. The firer has to absorb a greater recoil impulse, and he will have to reload each new round manually, but it does allow for a remarkably silent shot. This is supposed to replace the existing silenced handgun used by US Special Forces and SEALs, which is a modified 9mm S&W Model 39 with an add-on suppressor. One of the roles of this combination is the silent killing of enemy guard dogs, hence its unofficial designation of 'Hush Puppy'.

Most other manufacturers have continued to build upon existing concepts to create the current generation of automatic pistols. FN has its Mk 3 High Power, Walther its P88 and the Czechs their Vz 75 (licence-built by SIG), while others have stuck to modified Browning designs. A weapon that stands out from the others is the Russian PSM, a handgun first spotted by the West during the 1980 invasion of Afghanistan. This automatic bears a close resemblance to the Walther PP, although it fires a barely effective 5.45mm round. Used by police and internal security forces, it has some utility for close-range work.

At the opposite end of the scale is a tendency to move to larger calibres and more powerful rounds than 9mm. Magnum rounds such as the .357in and .44in are already popular with sports and police shooters, although they have failed to attract military interest. Virtually all the weapons used to fire such cartridges have been solid-framed revolvers, but in the 1970s a team of US designers came up with an automatic handgun firing the .357in Magnum round. Development of the gun was then taken over by Israeli Military Industries, which named it the Desert Eagle and rechambered it for the more powerful .44in Magnum cartridge.

The Desert Eagle is a massive cannon, a heavy and intimidating piece of iron-mongery. Looking rather like an oversized Colt, it actually uses gas operation in a

■ **ABOVE: The Beretta Model 1934 handgun. The gun was well made, though a little underpowered for military use.**

Smith & Wesson 1006

Calibre: 10mm
Weight: 1.19kg ($2\frac{1}{2}$lb)
Length: 216mm ($8\frac{1}{2}$in)
Effective range: 30m (32yd)
Rate of fire: single shot
Feed: nine-round detachable box
Muzzle velocity: 375mps (1230yd)

similar way to an assault rifle. Gas is bled off from the barrel into a cylinder, the pressure of which drives a piston to the rear. The bolt is a two-piece item: the front locks on to the barrel by way of a number of locking lugs, while the rear part is attached to the slide. When the Eagle is fired, the piston forces the slide backwards, and this initial movement causes the front of the bolt to rotate and unlock, rather like that in an AK or M16 rifle. Only seven rounds are carried, although even a glancing hit from one of these should guarantee incapacitation of a human target.

The weight, report and recoil from this beast demand exhaustive training for a firer to use with any degree of effectiveness, so military sales are limited to special forces and other marksmen. Some police users may also find the Desert Eagle attractive, although most law enforcement agencies are not able to train ordinary street officers to a sufficiently high standard. There is a longer-barrelled sports version available and one chambered for the .41in Action Express round.

MORE LETHAL BULLETS

There is a faction in both police and military circles that insists on heavy bullets fired from powerful cartridges, and a number of rounds have been developed to replace the venerable .45in ACP. The .41in Action Express has already been mentioned, but there is also a lot of interest being shown in 10mm cartridges. The first major customer for 10mm ammunition is the FBI, which has picked a Smith & Wesson automatic as its next-generation firearm. The FBI felt that 9mm did not have sufficient stopping power to guarantee the safety of a lone agent, and plumped for a modern high-powered alternative. FBI agents spend many hours training on the range, so handling such a powerful cartridge is less of a problem than it would be for an ordinary policeman.

The handgun chosen is based on the Smith & Wesson 1006, a stainless steel handgun with a close physical resemblance to the M1911A1. It has a double-action trigger mechanism and uses the well-proved Browning tipping barrel, short-recoil system. Nine rounds are held in the butt magazine, and the gun is slightly heavier than the the Colt. Conservatism has won over innovation, although the

■ LEFT: The SIG P226, a handgun that is superbly engineered and incredibly reliable. It is reportedly used by Britain's Special Air Service.

handgun does make use of some of the internal safety features of the latest European designs. The FBI version is known as the 1076, and has a shorter barrel and the decocking lever moved from the slide to the frame. The fact that 10mm has been chosen by the FBI should ensure that other law enforcement agencies will give serious consideration to this calibre, and Smith & Wesson should be able to export further variants of the 1000 series of handguns.

THE FUTURE FOR THE HANDGUN

The pace of handgun development at times seems rather snail-like, with the same systems and concepts in use for decades. Progress is normally incremental, with designers building on what has gone before. Looking at the current state of handgun technology, it seems that future developments will be concentrated in the areas of new materials, improved safety and quick-reaction capabilities.

Perhaps a pointer to the handgun of the future is provided by a series of automatics from Austria, produced by Glock GmbH. Awarded an Austrian Army contract in 1983, its Glock 17 model has achieved spectacular export success in both police and military roles since. Plastic materials form a large part of the structure, the frame being a one-piece polymer item. This initially gave rise to press headlines about the 'hijackers delight': a plastic handgun which could pass undetected through airport security systems. A few minutes of thought would have indicated that a handgun with a steel barrel, slide and internal components contains more than enough metal to trigger any security system, and would still show up on all x-ray machines. What these new materials do allow, however, is a reduction in the number of individual parts (only 33) and the manufacture of a lightweight, strong handgun.

The Glock operates only in double-action mode, and there is no external hammer assembly. First trigger pressure pulls back a striker pin, releases the trigger safety and disengages two other safety devices. Further movement releases the striker and fires the round. Unlike most other double-action pistols, trigger pressure is light and smooth, making accurate shooting much easier. The firer can also adjust the trigger pressure to his or her own preference. After each shot, the striker is left uncocked and the safety mechanisms are back in place. The internal safeties are so effective that no other safety or decocking lever is fitted, making for an extremely smooth and uncluttered exterior.

Glock 17

Calibre: 9mm
Weight: .65kg (1½lb)
Length: 188mm (7½in)
Effective range: 30m (32yd)
Rate of fire: single shot
Feed: 17-round detachable box
Muzzel velocity: 350mps (1148fps)

Glock 20

Calibre: 10mm
Weight: .75kg (1½lb)
Length: 210mm (8¼in)
Effective range: 30m (32yd)
Rate of fire: single shot
Feed: 15-round detachable box
Muzzle velocity: 375mps (1230fps)

The basic Glock holds a useful 17 rounds of 9mm Parabellum ammunition in the butt. It is a superb weapon, one which has been referred to by some authorities as the best handgun currently available.

Despite the historical evidence as to its effectiveness, the machine handgun lingers on. The Glock 18, for example, is such a variant. No shoulder stock is used, and larger magazines of 19 or 33 rounds can be attached to the butt. Many components are different from the standard handgun, and a Glock 17 cannot be converted to this capability. Even with the use of modern materials and systems, it is hard to see a market for this weapon. Other models include the compact Glock 19, the Glock 20 – chambered for 10mm Auto – and the 21, firing the venerable .45in ACP round.

The Glock 17 has proved to be very successful in a short period, being bought by law enforcement and special forces users from over 42 countries. Many US government and law enforcement agencies use this Austrian design, valuing the combination of light weight, reliability, safety and ease of use. Some US soldiers also prefer the Austrian to their Italian-designed M9s, and a few Glock 17s have found their way into special forces use. The Glock represents the current pinnacle of handgun design, and is a pointer to the future.

CHAPTER 4
SUBMACHINE GUNS

'Cheap and nasty', 'not a proper soldier's weapon', 'a tin toy' – these are just some of the comments that were made about submachine guns in the 1920s and 1930s, and many soldiers held such opinions throughout World War II and after. The object of such derision is a weapon that is generally simple, cheap and crudely made. However, it is also remarkably effective, and has been carried by millions of soldiers throughout the twentieth century.

The submachine gun (SMG) is normally defined as a hand-held automatic weapon firing pistol-style ammunition. Intrinsically inaccurate and only effective at short ranges, such burst-fire weapons fall between the handgun and the assault rifle in the array of tools available to the modern infantryman. Most SMGs are comparatively small and light, have detachable box magazines holding large (around 30 rounds) quantities of ammunition, and can deliver devastating fire at close ranges. Their maximum effective range is usually around 100m (110yd), though the chances of hitting a man-sized target with most SMGs at this distance are not good.

SUBMACHINE GUN USERS

By far the most common SMG operating mechanism is simple blowback. Most SMGs have a large, heavy bolt, which has sufficient inertia to absorb much of the recoil force as the bullet is fired. By the time the bolt has moved backwards and extracted the spent case, the gas pressure in the chamber has dropped to a safe level.

These light weapons are normally carried by various user groups. The first soldiers to carry submachine guns, for example, were specialised assault troops, who had to attack enemy positions from close ranges. Because of their compact dimensions, submachine guns have also been popular with troops fighting in built-up areas. Soldiers in such environments need a weapon that is light, easy to carry, simple to handle and one that will deliver large amounts of fire at the pull of the trigger. Such users also want to be able to carry large quantities of ammunition and have the ability to reload quickly, even when under fire themselves. Stormtroopers, paratroopers and assault pioneers have all been traditional users of the SMG, although by the 1960s many had changed to assault rifles. Nevertheless, simplicity and cheapness has kept the SMG popular with many elite units.

LEFT: The Sterling submachine gun. It was adopted by the British Army in 1956 and is still in service. It is one of the most reliable submachine guns in service.

SPECIAL FORCES SMGS

In the second category of user are those men whose main function would be hindered if they carried a rifle. Signallers, drivers, ammunition carriers, missile crews and rear area headquarter and supply staff all tend to carry SMGs, usually of a type that can be slung over the shoulder, and often with the stock folded. Officers and senior NCOs are still often expected to carry handguns, but when they are faced with actual combat they usually try to find a rifle or SMG to fight with.

A third, more specialised category of user is the special forces soldier. Such men expect to take part in close-range combat, often at night, and sometimes after an ambush. Lots of noisy firepower can give the edge in a firefight, or at least will keep the heads of enemy troops down long enough to effect an escape. Because of their high rates of fire, SMGs are generally not carried by elite troops on operations behind enemy lines – the expenditure of ammunition would be too great. For more specialised tasks such as disposing of sentries or springing night ambushes, a modified submachine gun can make a good silenced weapon. Subsonic bullets mean that there is no sharp crack from the projectile, while a reasonably sized weapon allows for an effective suppressor to be designed as part of the structure, rather than as an add-on afterthought. Special forces often have a counter-terrorist role, where they may be called upon to carry out ambushes or even rescue hostages held by terrorists. In these situations they need the firepower of an

Bergmann MP18

Calibre: 9mm
Weight: 4.19kg (9¼lb)
Length: 812mm (32in)
Effective range: 100m (110yd)
Rate of fire: 400rpm (cyclic)
Feed: 32-round drum
Muzzle velocity: 380mps (1247fps)

ABOVE: The Bergmann MP28/II, a direct descendant of the MP18.

SMG, but they must also be able to aim accurately and control burst fire to avoid civilian casualties. Most hostage-rescue teams are, therefore, equipped with submachine guns that are more accurate and better made than those used in conventional combat.

EARLY SUBMACHINE GUNS

During World War I, emplaced machine guns, extensive trench works, artillery and barbed wire had created formidable defensive systems on the Western Front. The terrain between and around the trenches was blasted by shell- and machine-gun fire, in many cases the only cover being provided by small depressions and shell-holes. Most infantrymen were equipped with superbly accurate rifles: long, cumbersome, heavy weapons tipped with a sword bayonet. However, in the conditions of trench warfare the range and accuracy of these rifles were largely irrelevant. Enemy troops were well protected in their defensive earthworks and usually kept out of sight. If an enemy attack came, friendly machine guns and artillery provided most of the defensive firepower. If friendly forces were on the offensive, riflemen would normally be unable to see any targets until they were almost on top of enemy trenches, where confused, close-range combat would often take place. Some soldiers found that their rifles were so awkward that they preferred to carry spades, pickaxe handles and clubs. Handguns and grenades were also useful for this kind of conflict, and many German soldiers made use of Mauser and Luger handguns, which had high-capacity magazines and shoulder stocks.

SCHMEISSER'S BERGMANN

Close-range combat, therefore, demanded a short, handy weapon that could provide lots of firepower at short ranges, and would survive the rigours of trench warfare. A number of designers were working on various concepts, and the first nation to deploy an automatic weapon of such a description was Italy, with its unusual twin-barrelled Vilar-Perosa. The Germans were soon to follow, and in 1916 were developing a short automatic weapon which was the first true submachine gun. Designed by Hugo Schmeisser and built at the Bergmann factory, the weapon entered initial production in early 1918 as the Bergmann MP18/I.

Firing the 9mm Parabellum pistol round, the Bergmann is an extremely simple design which uses blowback as the operating principle. It has a tubular metal receiver held in a wooden rifle stock, and a cylindrical jacket around the barrel, drilled to allow cooling air to pass through. Ammunition is fed from the right from a detachable 32-round clockwork drum (known as a 'snail drum'), originally developed for the Luger. The mechanism is simplicity itself: a large, heavy cylindrical bolt takes up virtually the whole diameter of the receiver, and attached to it is a cocking handle that protrudes from the right side. The firer pulls this back, compressing a large return spring behind the bolt, until the bolt is locked in place by the trigger sear. When the trigger is pulled, the bolt is pushed forward, stripping the next round from the magazine and pushing it into the chamber. The firing pin is fixed and forms part of the bolt, and it slams into the rear of the cartridge as the bolt is pushed home. The cartridge fires even as the bolt is still moving forward, and it is this momentum that helps absorb the initial recoil forces from the shot. After the round has left the barrel, the recoil forces the bolt backwards,

Thompson M1

Calibre: .45in
Weight: 4.74kg (10½lb)
Length: 813mm (32in)
Effective range: 50m (55yd)
Rate of fire: 700rpm (cyclic)
Feed: 20- or 30-round box magazine
Muzzle velocity: 280mps (919fps)

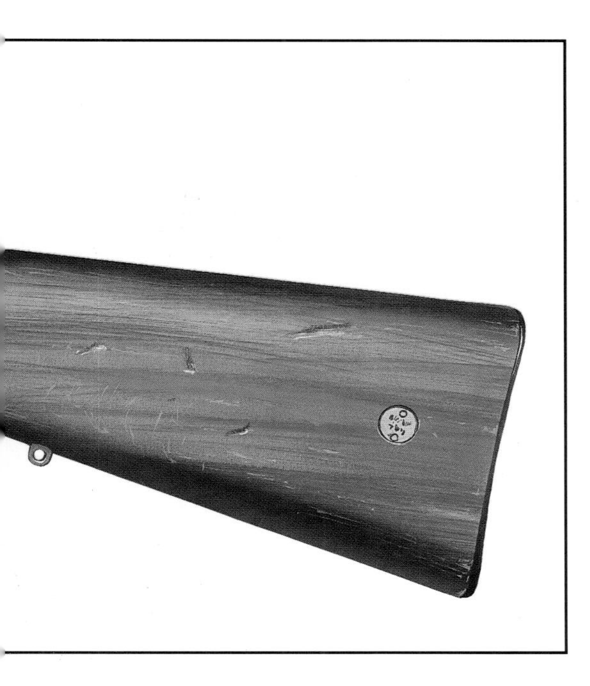

extracting and ejecting the empty case and compressing the return spring. If the trigger has been released, the bolt will be locked again by the sear to await the next round. If the trigger is being held down, the bolt immediately flies forward again to fire the next round.

The MP18/I was manufactured using the limited mass-production techniques of the time, and it was solid and well made compared to some later SMGs. An effective weapon, it was initially plagued by feed problems because of the shape of the early 9mm Parabellum ammunition. However, once the bullet had been redesigned with a more pointed ogive front section, most of these difficulties disappeared. The spring-driven 'snail drum' magazine was also a source of stoppages, and was never really rugged enough to withstand the harsh conditions of the battlefield. In theory, MP18s were allocated at a rate of six per infantry company. Unfortunately for the Germans, mass production came too late for widespread use, although 30,000 had been made by the end of the war.

During the 1920s, some were retained by German police units, and many more were exported to other police and military forces. Later models were modified to use straightforward box magazines holding 20, 32 or 50 rounds. Later improvements created the MP28/II, which incorporated a separate firing pin and the ability to fire single shots as well as bursts. Bergmanns were also made under licence in Spain and Belgium, and were exported to many nations. While the small submachine gun had little effect on the course of the war, this class of weapon was quickly proving popular with many soldiers and para-military policemen. Schmeisser's design concepts had, despite some initial problems, proved to be successful, and the basic principles of the MP18/I were to be used in virtually every successful SMG for the next 30 years.

THE AMERICAN 'TOMMY'

Another early experimenter with sub-machine guns was to be found in the United States Army. Colonel J T Thompson had experience in the Ordnance Department, and had worked for the Remington Arms Corporation. He had also seen the need for a new type of weapon to break the deadlock of trench warfare, and had started development of his own design of submachine gun. The war ended before development was complete, and in fact the Thompson gun did not appear until 1921. Post-war budget restrictions meant that the new weapon was not procured by the US Military, and initial sales were low. A number of Thompsons were used during the Irish Civil War in the 1920s, and the weapon also became notorious as the 'Chicago Piano' in the hands of gangsters. Various law enforcement agencies also procured this SMG in response to attacks by armed criminal gangs.

THE THOMPSON AT WAR

Various models of Thompson were made, and the most popular between the wars was the M1928. The Thompson is a heavy and sturdy weapon which was built to peacetime standards of quality and finish. The M1928 has a wooden stock and pistol grip, together with a wooden, pistol-style foregrip under the barrel. A safety lever sits above the grip, and in front of that is a selector for single shots or bursts. The receiver is a strong, square-sectioned piece which holds the trigger, magazine feed and relatively long barrel. On the 1928 model the rear of the barrel is shrouded with distinctive cooling fins, and the muzzle has a compensator attached. This is a device which has slots cut into the top edge, through which gases are vented as the bullet passes the muzzle. The reaction force caused by these gases pushes down on the barrel and helps control muzzle climb when firing bursts.

The Thompson was chambered for the then US standard handgun round: the .45in ACP. A large, powerful bullet, it gives the Thompson more stopping power

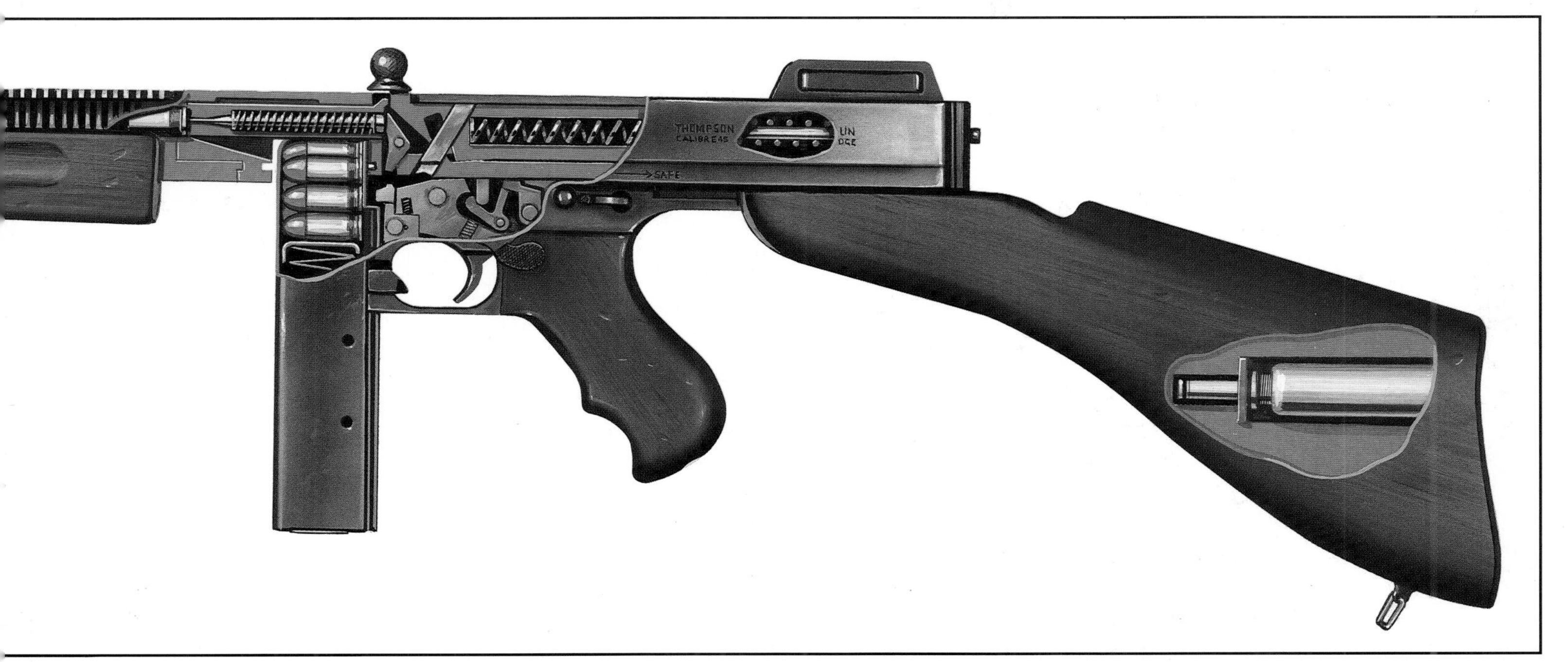

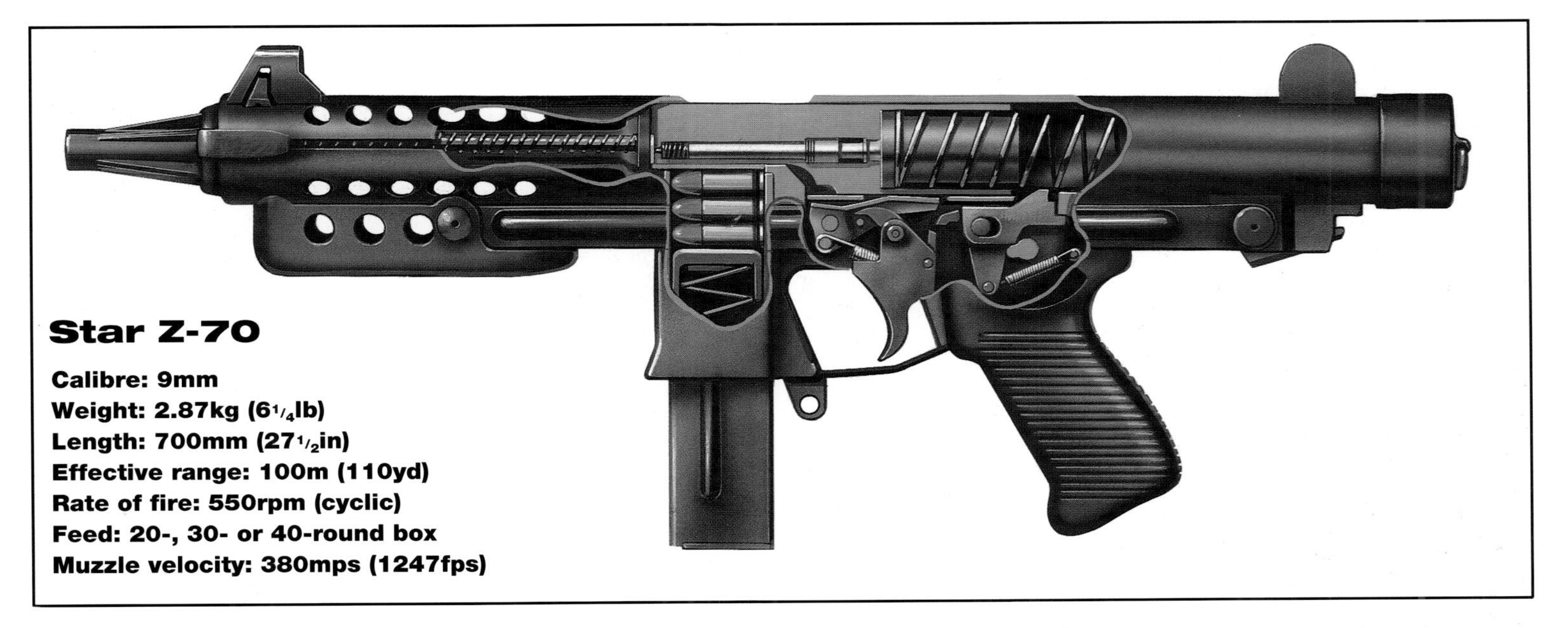

Star Z-70

Calibre: 9mm
Weight: 2.87kg (6¼lb)
Length: 700mm (27½in)
Effective range: 100m (110yd)
Rate of fire: 550rpm (cyclic)
Feed: 20-, 30- or 40-round box
Muzzle velocity: 380mps (1247fps)

and range than most other comparable SMGs, although at a cost of increased weight. The M1928 is a blowback weapon which, unusually for an SMG, makes use of a method of delay known as the Blish system. The weapon is cocked by pulling back on a cocking knob protruding above the receiver (the knob being slotted so as not to obscure the sights). The bolt has another saddle-shaped piece sitting across it, with the vertical edges set into grooves cut in the side of the bolt in such a way that the whole saddle leans backwards at 45 degrees from vertical. When the bolt is pushed closed, the bottom ends of this saddle lock into recesses in the receiver. As the round is fired, the pressure first has to push the saddle upwards within its grooves until the bolt is free to move. As the bolt is quite heavy, and only handgun ammunition is used, this is actually an unnecessary complication, but it does give the weapon a slow, controllable rate of fire. Ammunition feed is from either a simple 20-round box magazine, or a large spring-driven drum holding 50 rounds.

When the US Army rearmed in the late 1930s, the Thompson was eventually accepted, entering service in 1938. Another customer was Britain, who purchased as many 'Tommy' guns as could be spared to alleviate her desperate shortage of weapons in 1940. By this time it was apparent that the Thompson was too complex for rapid mass-production, and attempts were therefore made to simplify the design by deleting the front pistol grip and replacing it with a horizontal block under the barrel. Further simplification involved redesign of the mechanism by the Savage Arms Company, which eventually created a new variant of the basic SMG.

■ LEFT: The famous Thompson sub-machine gun, seen here being carried by an American paratrooper in World War II. This is the M1 version of the weapon.

THE THOMPSON M1

The new model entered service in 1942 as the .45in Thompson M1, and made greater use of manufacturing techniques such as stamping and spot welding. The biggest change was to the mechanical operation. Gone was the Blish delay system; instead, a heavier bolt was substituted which used mass and forward momentum to prevent the chamber being opened too soon. The cocking handle was also moved to the right side of the receiver, and the cooling fins and compensator were no longer fitted to the barrel. The distinctive pistol-style foregrip was also removed, substituted with a simple horizontal wooden block. The drum magazine could no longer be used (it was too fragile and unreliable for combat). Therefore, a new 30-round box was devised. A further simplification incorporated a fixed firing pin into the bolt, creating the M1A1. In this guise, the 25-year-old Thompson served throughout World War II, proving popular with American and British troops alike. While a touch heavy, it was robust and well made, and was very reliable.

The 1930s saw SMGs being developed in many countries, including Italy, Switzerland, Spain (with its popular Star SI35), the Soviet Union and elsewhere, though it was Germany who was giving most thought to tactical usage. By the late 1930s, her newly enlarged army was looking for replacements for the World War I Bergmanns, and a number of designers put forward their ideas. The Erfurter Maschinenfabrik Geipel GmbH (abbreviated to Erma) company and its designer, Vollmer, had already manufactured a reasonably successful SMG in 1930, and some of the principles used in this weapon were applied to a new design. The new gun, a compact, light and portable weapon, was first accepted into service by the Panzer Corps for its mechanised infantry and vehicle crews. Quickly issued to other troops, the new 9mm Parabellum weapon was to become one of the most famous and instantly recognisable SMGs ever, even if most people referred to it by a wrong designation.

THE LEGENDARY MP38

The MP38 was the first 'modern' SMG, and like the Bergmann it set standards that most other designs have since tried to follow. There was no wood used – everything was made from either metal or high-impact plastic. A tubular receiver sits on a flat body, with an unshrouded barrel protruding forward. The rear of the body has a pistol grip beneath it, with the actual grips sheathed in plastic. The stock is the first successful folding one used on a military weapon, and is made from tubular steel, being hinged at the body of the gun. The chamber is near the front of the body, and a long, 32-round box magazine protrudes below, with the housing used as a forward grip. The gun operates using simple blowback principles, although it was the first to have a safety device to catch the bolt if it moved inadvertently. Earlier SMGs could sometimes be fired accidentally if dropped on a hard surface, the impact moving the bolt enough to fire a round. As in virtually all SMGs, a large

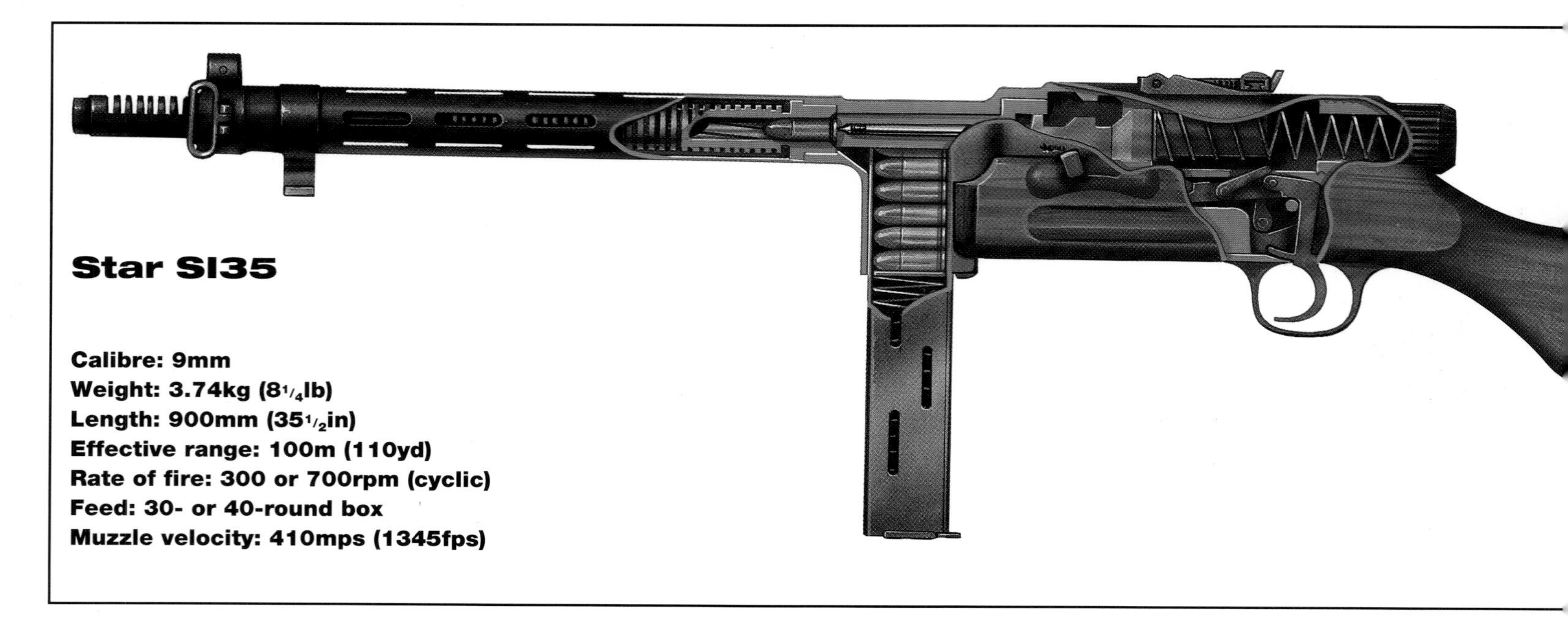

Star SI35

Calibre: 9mm
Weight: 3.74kg ($8\frac{1}{4}$lb)
Length: 900mm ($35\frac{1}{2}$in)
Effective range: 100m (110yd)
Rate of fire: 300 or 700rpm (cyclic)
Feed: 30- or 40-round box
Muzzle velocity: 410mps (1345fps)

return spring sat behind the bolt, although on the MP38 it is protected from dust and snow by a telescopic metal housing.

THE GERMAN MP40

Portable and effective, the MP38 quickly found favour with German mechanised troops, and was also widely issued to other troops for assault and security duties. Minor problems were suffered because of the magazine feed, but on the whole the MP38 was extremely reliable and effective. However, as the war progressed, production could not keep up with demand, because the MP38 had been designed to peacetime standards, with many components machined from solid metal. A redesign was quickly put in motion, substituting sheet pressings, spot welding and other techniques to create a simpler weapon that could be produced much faster than before, and by less-specialised manufacturers. The new variant was the MP40, and over one million were produced before the end of the war. Other versions included one with a twin magazine system and another with a wooden stock, but neither of these proved popular. The MP38 and MP40 were superbly effective weapons, and in many ways became the symbol of the German stormtrooper. Allied soldiers were equally impressed with them, and some employed captured weapons in preference to their own SMGs. In an ironic twist, these weapons became widely known as the Schmeisser, although Hugo Schmeisser had nothing to do with the design. The name has stuck, as has the incorrect Allied name for the MG42 machine gun, and for many British and US soldiers, 'Schmeisser' and 'Spandau' became words that instilled fear and respect on the battlefield.

The other wartime combatant that made great use of SMGs was the Soviet Union. The PPD34 had entered service in 1934, designed by Degtyaryov and based loosely on the Bergmann MP28/II. It was a simple blowback weapon with a wooden stock, and normally fed from a 71-round clock-work drum. It was well made, with a chrome-plated barrel lining to increase longevity. It fired a 7.62mm x 25mm cartridge, at the time the standard Soviet handgun bullet. It was a reasonably effective weapon, although the magazine feed gave some trouble. A later version, known as the PPD40, was issued in 1940. Simplified to ease manufacture, the PPD40 dispensed with the existing drum magazine, and used instead another 71-round design copied from that on the Finnish Suomi.

Operation 'Barbarossa' (22 June 1941) quickly plunged the Red Army into crisis, as vast numbers of men and their equipment were overrun and captured in the first weeks of the German advance. Hastily raised formations needed weapons, and Soviet industry was desperately trying to manufacture small arms as quickly as possible. Georgii Shpagin led a team that designed a cheap, simple but effective submachine gun, one which the factories could turn out by the million. The PPSh41, as it was known, was crudely made and finished, and used the minimum amount of high-quality materials in its manufacture. In a typically Russian improvisation, early models made use of aged M1891 rifles: each barrel was cut in half to provide barrels for two SMGs.

The PPSh41 is a simple blowback weapon which fires the Russian 7.62mm x 25mm handgun cartridge. Made largely from sheet metal stampings riveted and welded together, the Shpagin nevertheless retains chrome plating as a barrel lining. A traditional wooden stock is fitted, in front of which is the magazine feed. A curved 35-round box can be used, but the more common item is a 71-round drum, similar to that on the PPD40. The barrel has a slotted jacket around it, and the end of this slopes backwards and has a slot in the top edge to act as a crude form of compensator. A cocking handle sits on the right-hand side of the receiver and is used to pull the bolt back against the trigger sear. The first production weapons had an optimistic leaf sight ranged to 200m (220yd) and a small lever in front of the trigger, within the large guard, for selecting bursts or single shots. Later models just had a crude aperture flip sight and could fire full-automatic only.

SOVIET SIMPLICITY

A typical Russian design, the PPSh41 was crudely finished, but nevertheless was a simple, tough and reliable weapon. It would continue to function in the worst environmental conditions, withstanding dust, mud, snow and ice without serious problems. Conscript soldiers with little technical or formal education could still operate it, even when frightened, cold, hungry and exhausted. By the end of the war, over five million of these cheap, handy SMGs had been made, and whole assault battalions had been equipped with them to give devastating close-range firepower. Thousands were dropped

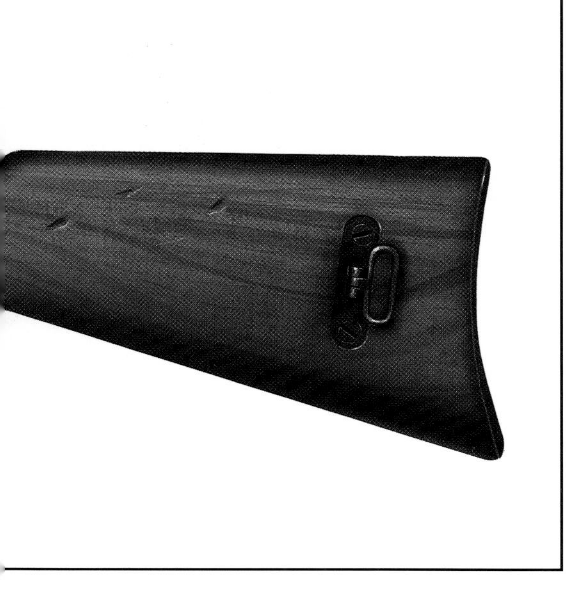

behind enemy lines to equip the large partisan formations that were causing dismay and disruption to German supply lines and communications. After the war, the PPSh was supplied in generous quantities to Soviet client states and communist guerrilla forces, who also valued its ruggedness and simplicity. Copies were made in a number of countries, the most widespread of these being the Chinese Type 50. The Chinese weapon also formed the basis of some other designs, most noticeably the Vietnamese K-50, although this SMG has a very different outline from its parent weapon. The PPSh41 and its copies became for many the symbol of guerrilla forces around the world, a symbol that was only changed by the widespread use of the next Russian world-beating weapon, the AK-47 assault rifle.

Another wartime Soviet SMG was the PPS42, again a blowback weapon, but of even more crude design than Shpagin's. When the city of Leningrad (now St Petersburg) was under siege, it became impossible for the Russians to bring additional weapons in from outside the city. A Leningrad engineer named Sudarev devised a 7.62mm blowback SMG which could make use of low-grade metal stampings, and which was crudely spot-welded and riveted together. The PPS42 looks rough, but it turned out to be a remarkably effective weapon. A simple square-sectioned metal body holds a barrel shrouded in a drilled casing, and a metal pistol grip protrudes from the rear of this body. The skeleton stock is a simple steel folding item, and the 7.62mm handgun ammunition is supplied from a 35-round box. A later model was designated the PPS43, and by the time the war had ended over one million had been made. Again widely exported after the war, it was copied by the Chinese as the Type 54 and many were used against American soldiers in Southeast Asia.

Britain had resisted for longer than most the incorporation of submachine guns in the national armoury. Many Army officers thought them to be cheap, gimmicky weapons only suitable for paramilitary police forces and security units. Real soldiers were trained to high standards of marksmanship, and deserved 'real' weapons: long rifles made from high-quality machined steel and complete with polished walnut furniture. The shock caused by the German *Blitzkrieg* jolted the British out of this complacency, and they set about raising new formations and re-equipping the remnants of the old. New weapons of all types were desperately needed, and orders were placed in the United States even as British industry tooled up to meet new demands. The military authorities had been impressed by the performance of the German MP38s, and had finally realised the utility of submachine guns, so some of the first requests to the Americans were for Thompsons. Thousands of M1928s crossed the Atlantic and soon became a favourite with those troops lucky enough to be issued with them.

BRITISH SUBMACHINE GUNS

Attempts were also made to produce an indigenous SMG, although with the pressure of the times it was decided to copy an existing model. George Lanchester of the Sterling Armaments Company took the well-proven German 9mm Parabellum M28 as a basis for the first British SMG, and Sterling quickly tooled up for production. The resulting Lanchester was still made to peacetime standards, using finely machined components and a well-finished wooden stock. As production was just about to start, however, another design appeared and was immediately accepted for Army service. Rather than waste the tooling, Sterling produced the Lanchester for the Royal Navy, and these finely made weapons saw service with Naval landing parties and security detachments for many years after the war.

The SMG that was chosen in preference to the Lanchester was very definitely a wartime expediency, designed in a matter of months during 1940. The designers were a Major Shepherd and a Mr Turpin, both of whom worked at the Royal Small Arms Factory, Enfield. Their initials were combined with the first two letters of the factory's location to give the name of the new weapon – the Sten.

THE STEN GUN

Designed to be simple and cheap to make, the Sten is a straight blowback weapon firing from an open bolt and with a fixed firing pin. A tubular receiver holds the large cylindrical bolt, behind which is a strong return spring. A large slot is cut along the right side of the receiver, through which protrudes a cocking handle, which is fixed to the bolt. 9mm Parabellum ammunition is fed from a straight 32-round box magazine, which pushes into a feed slot on the left of the gun. The first model, the Mark 1, was reasonably well finished, although it made use of welded stampings rather than traditional machined and forged components. There was some wood used around the fore-end, in a folding foregrip and in the stock, although the latter was actually a steel-framed skeleton item. The barrel was shrouded by a perforated cooling jacket and ended in a cone-shaped compensator, designed to help control muzzle climb. Simple and effective, the Sten was soon put into production, although it did not receive a unanimous welcome from the troops. Compared to their Brens, Lee-Enfields and Thompsons, the Sten appeared to be a cheap, crude, little toy. Cheap and crude, yes, but the Sten was certainly no toy – it worked and it worked well, though it had to be reasonably well looked after if it was to function reliably. The magazine held the ammunition in a single column, which sometimes meant the spring would not push strongly enough to place the top round in position for loading. The magazine lips were also rather fragile and easily deformed, and were a continual source of stoppages. There was also no bolt safety fitted. If a Sten was dropped on a hard surface, the bolt could be jolted enough to fire a round. Nevertheless, if care was taken with the magazines the Sten would give good and reliable service.

As production of the Mark 1 got under way, the designers were simplifying their creation even further to make it even cheaper and quicker to make. The Mark 2 Sten has been described by one expert as 'the ugliest, nastiest weapon ever used by the British Army', and close inspection of one reveals a weapon that looks as if it has been made in a backyard garage. Many

MP40

Calibre: 9mm
Weight: 3.97kg (8¾lb)
Length: 832mm (32¾in) – stock extended; 629mm (24¾in) – stock folded
Effective range: 100m (110yd)
Rate of fire: 500rpm (cyclic)
Feed: 32-round magazine
Muzzle velocity: 380mps (1247fps)

■ LEFT: Two French members of the Waffen-SS. The submachine gun is the MP40, which has erroneously gone down in history as the Schmeisser.

actually were, as the Mark 2 was designed to be made using the most simple manufacturing techniques possible. All the wood was removed, the weapon being made solely from roughly finished metal riveted and welded together. The barrel is unprotected, with no jacket apart from a short, perforated collar which also doubles as the foregrip. The stock is a straight steel tube with a steel shoulder plate at the end. There is no pistol grip either, because a vertical triangular web at the front of the stock has a hole for the thumb, and the fingers are bent around the front edge of this web. A stud above the trigger guard is pressed from either side to select single shots or bursts. An unusual innovation is the ability to rotate the feed collar, complete with magazine, through 90 degrees to the vertical to cover the ejection and feed ports and prevent dust clogging the weapon. The Mark 2 was also made in Canada, and the Canadian models had a slightly better finish, a different pattern of stock, and were equipped with a detachable short bayonet. Stens were also manufactured in Australia (as the Austen), although the Australians quickly replaced it with an indigenous submachine gun design – the Owen.

Over two million Sten Mark 2s were made in three years, and six could be made for the same price as one Thompson. Many soldiers regarded it with suspicion, but the weapon was remarkably effective and fulfilled its role in exactly the way intended by its designers. Development continued, with a Mark 3, a compact Mark 4 (never produced) and the Mark 5, a later peacetime model with a wooden stock, pistol grip and a better finish. There was also a silenced version of the Mark 2, with an integral silencer and barrel assembly fitted in place of the standard barrel. The silencer contained a system of baffles which absorbed energy from the muzzle gases and reduced the report from the weapon to a remarkable degree; the main sound from the Mark 2(S) was made by the bolt as it slid forward. The temperature quickly built up in the silencer, however, and only single shots were recommended. A later silenced model was known as the Sten Mark 6.

Thousands of Stens were dropped to resistance fighters all over occupied Europe during the war. It was ideal for this role, as it could use 9mm handgun and SMG ammunition captured from the Germans. Stens were also easily broken down into component assemblies and hidden, allowing them to be smuggled past German checkpoints. Some were even made by resistance groups with access to light engineering facilities, although these were sometimes of dubious effectiveness. Shepherd and Turpin's cheap and nasty stopgap may have won no prizes for quality and finish, but it was there when it was needed and worked well enough in action. Many British soldiers who fought with Stens would have preferred Thompsons or even German MP40s, but neither of these fine weapons could be made as quickly as a Sten, and in action the Sten did the job as well as any other. It was, perhaps, the Germans who paid the greatest compliment to the Sten, as the basic principles of the British weapon were copied in a cheap, emergency SMG used to equip the Home Defence (*Volksturm*) in the closing days of the war.

THE GREASE GUN

The United States also had problems in producing enough Thompsons to meet the demands of an expanding army, and by 1941 was examining a number of existing weapons to see if they were suitable for service. None fully met the US Army's requirements, although weapons such as the Reising 50, the UD M42 and the Hyde M2 saw military service in limited numbers. What the Army really wanted was a cheap, effective weapon that could be manufactured quickly and used with the minimum of specialised training. George Hyde and Frederick Sampson studied the production methods of the British Sten, and eventually came up with their own design – the M3 – which was approved for service in December 1942.

Another workmanlike SMG, the M3 was manufactured largely from steel sheets, stamped, pressed and riveted or welded together. It has a simple cylindrical receiver, with an unprotected barrel protruding from the front. A pistol grip and trigger assembly sit below the rear of the receiver, and the retractable stock is a simple steel wire bent to shape. A straight 30-round box magazine sits just behind the barrel, and the ejection port is on the top surface of the receiver, directly above the magazine and protected by a hinged dust cover. Firing from an open bolt, the M3 is another simple blowback design which relies on the forward momentum of the bolt to hold the breech closed until the gas pressure drops to a safe level. This bolt is cocked using a handle on the right side of the body. The bolt, unusually, slides back and forward on two guide rods, thereby removing the need for precision shaping inside the receiver. There is no fire selector, but the rate of fire is slow enough for single shots to be picked off using the trigger only. The M3 is chambered for the standard .45in ACP round, although it was designed to be easily converted to 9mm by replacing the barrel and bolt and putting an adaptor into the magazine feed.

THE M1 IN USE

The M3 quickly entered service and proved to be an effective close-quarters weapon. Like their British counterparts with their Stens, American troops were at first scornful of this simple gun with its cheap look and light, 'tinny' feel. The overall shape also looked ugly compared to the finely finished Thompsons, and gave rise to the M3's nickname of 'Grease Gun'. There were similar magazine and feed problems to those encountered with the Sten, and again this was a weakness that lasted throughout the American weapon's service life. Initial use had also thrown up some other minor difficulties, so by 1944 a revised version, the M3A1, was in full production. Some parts were redesigned to ease maintenance and stripping, but the one significant change was to the bolt. No cocking handle is fitted on the A1; instead, the user just sticks his finger into a recess in the bolt, using this to pull it backwards and cock the weapon. The ejection port and its hinged cover are larger than on the earlier model, and this cover has a protrusion that fits into the recess in the bolt to act as a positive safety lock. Throwaway plastic caps are also

Heckler & Koch MP5

Foresight Assembly

Cocking Lever

Barrel

Hand Guard

Chambered Round

Below: Compact and deadly: the shortened version of the MP5, the MP5K.

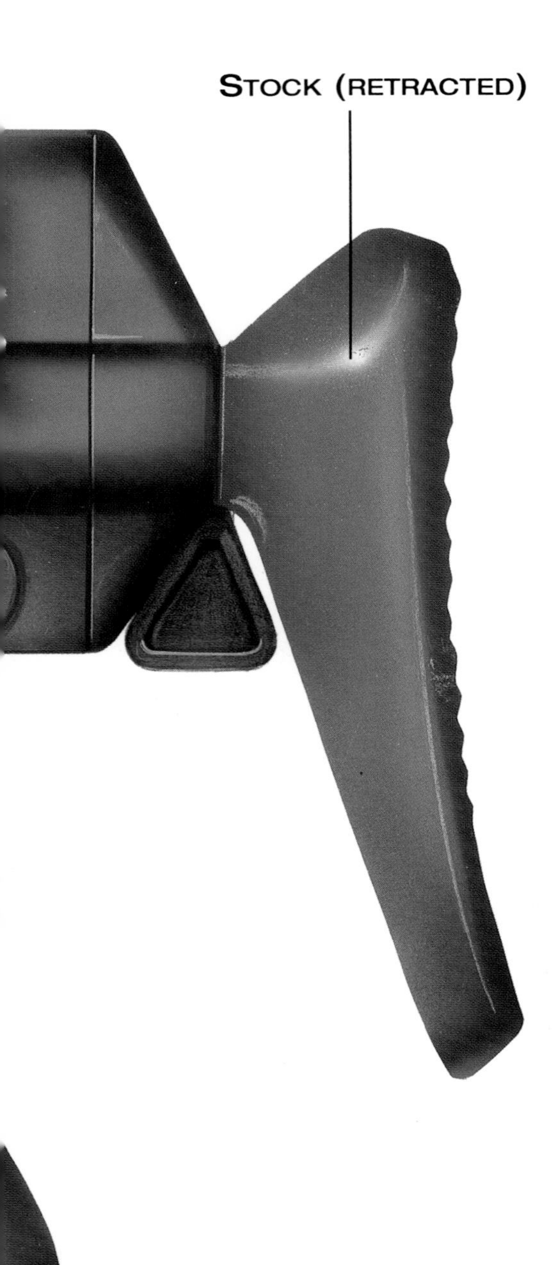

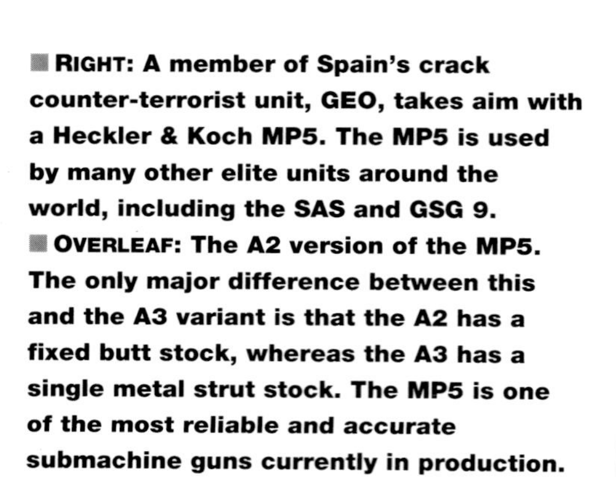

■ RIGHT: A member of Spain's crack counter-terrorist unit, GEO, takes aim with a Heckler & Koch MP5. The MP5 is used by many other elite units around the world, including the SAS and GSG 9.
■ OVERLEAF: The A2 version of the MP5. The only major difference between this and the A3 variant is that the A2 has a fixed butt stock, whereas the A3 has a single metal strut stock. The MP5 is one of the most reliable and accurate submachine guns currently in production.

Calibre	9mm
Weight	2.55kg ($5\frac{1}{2}$lb)
Length	490mm ($19\frac{1}{4}$in)
Effective range	200m (220yd)
Rate of fire	800rpm (cyclic)
Feed	15- or 30-round magazine
Muzzle velocity	400mps (1313fps)

PPSh41 SMG

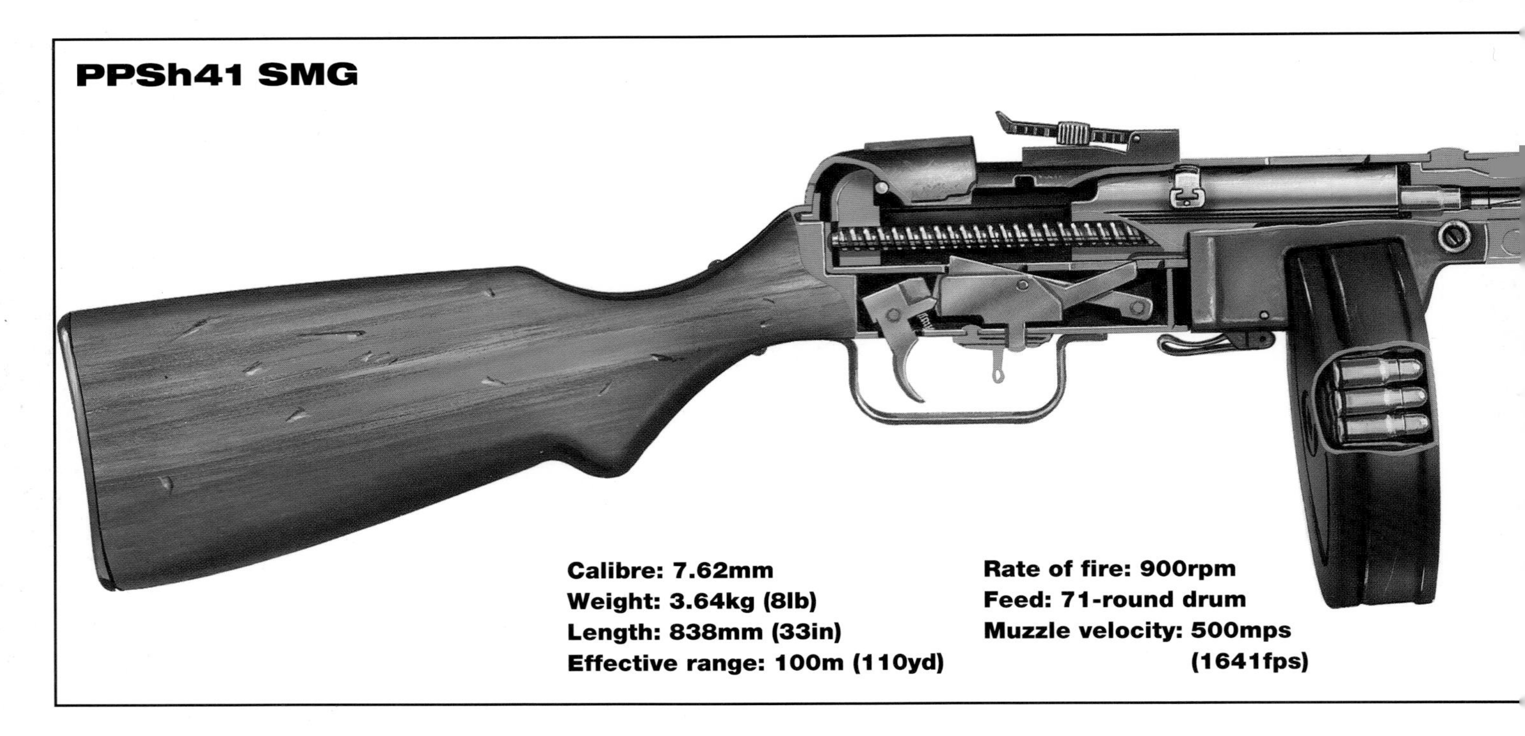

Calibre: 7.62mm
Weight: 3.64kg (8lb)
Length: 838mm (33in)
Effective range: 100m (110yd)
Rate of fire: 900rpm
Feed: 71-round drum
Muzzle velocity: 500mps (1641fps)

provided to protect the magazines, although fragile feed lips still demand care in handling. The M3 proved to be every bit as successful as the Sten and the Soviet wartime SMGs, and thousands remained in service until the 1960s.

EARLY POST-WAR SMGS

Many other nations procured SMGs just before and during World War II, also appreciating the simplicity and cheapness of these effective short-range weapons. Italy had a number of 9mm Beretta designs, Finland the heavy but accurate Suomi, and Japan made do with an MP28-derived SMG firing the barely adequate 8mm Nambu cartridge. The heyday of the SMG as a frontline weapon was soon to pass, however, and most of the next generation of designs would only be improvements on those designs already in use. Once the assault rifle became the standard military small arm, many of the roles previously taken by SMGs became the province of the new class of weapon. Many armies relegated their SMGs to secondary tasks, such as security and police duties, or for the personal protection of troops without rifles. New designs continued to appear, however, and three distinct lines of development were followed. The first was the 'traditional' SMG: a cheap, simple weapon that can be used offensively in combat operations. The second was the creation of a class of 'personal defence' weapons. Usually much smaller than a traditional SMG, these bridged the gap between the machine pistol and the full-blown weapon. The third class of SMG was the converted assault rifle, firing rifle bullets or rechambered for handgun rounds.

The first post-World War II SMGs had similar configurations to those that were used during that war, and showed no great advance in design or technology. The Swedish M45 Carl Gustav is typical of these weapons, having a simple Sten-type tubular receiver and using a straightforward blowback method of operation. It was a much better made weapon than most wartime models, however, and was also manufactured under licence in Egypt as the Port Said. The only new design element in the M45 was the use of a 36-round magazine, wh the 9mm ammunition was stored in two interleaved columns, which made for a shorter magazine with a more reliable fe than the earlier single-column ones.

As the French Army was being rebuil there was a need for a cheap French-designed weapon to complement its self-loading rifles, and one which could be manufactured quickly. France still had large colonial commitments, where a submachine gun would be applied to

Sten Gun

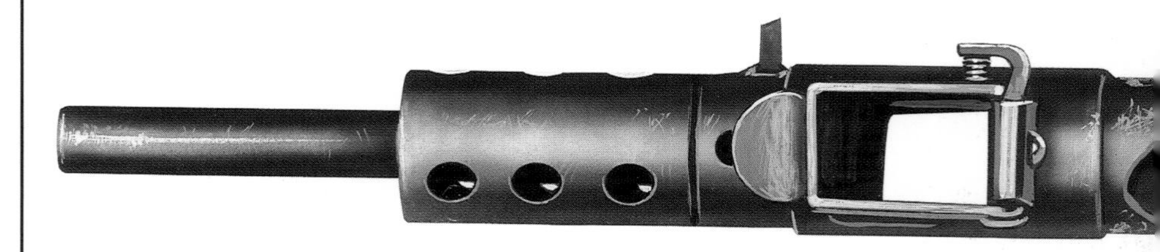

Calibre: 9mm
Weight: 2.95kg (6½lb)
Length: 762mm (30in)
Effective range: 40m (43yd)
Rate of fire: 550rpm (cyclic)
Feed: 32-round magazine
Muzzle velocity: 380mps (1247fps)

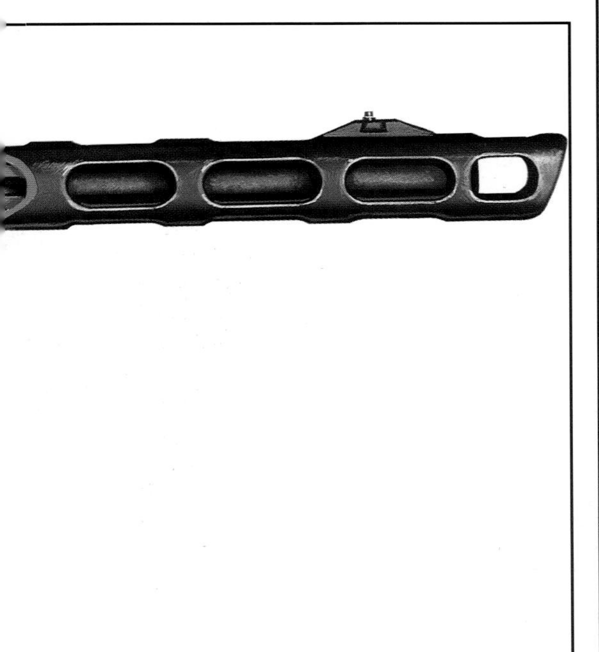

paramilitary policing duties, so the MAT 49 was brought into service in the late 1940s. Made from steel pressings and stampings, the MAT is nevertheless a solid and rugged weapon, having a receiver with a distinctive square outline. The barrel protrudes from this receiver and is protected by a perforated guard for much of its length. Under the front of the

RIGHT: It looked crude and cheap – and so it was, but the Sten gun was produced in huge numbers in World War II. What's more, it worked surprisingly well.

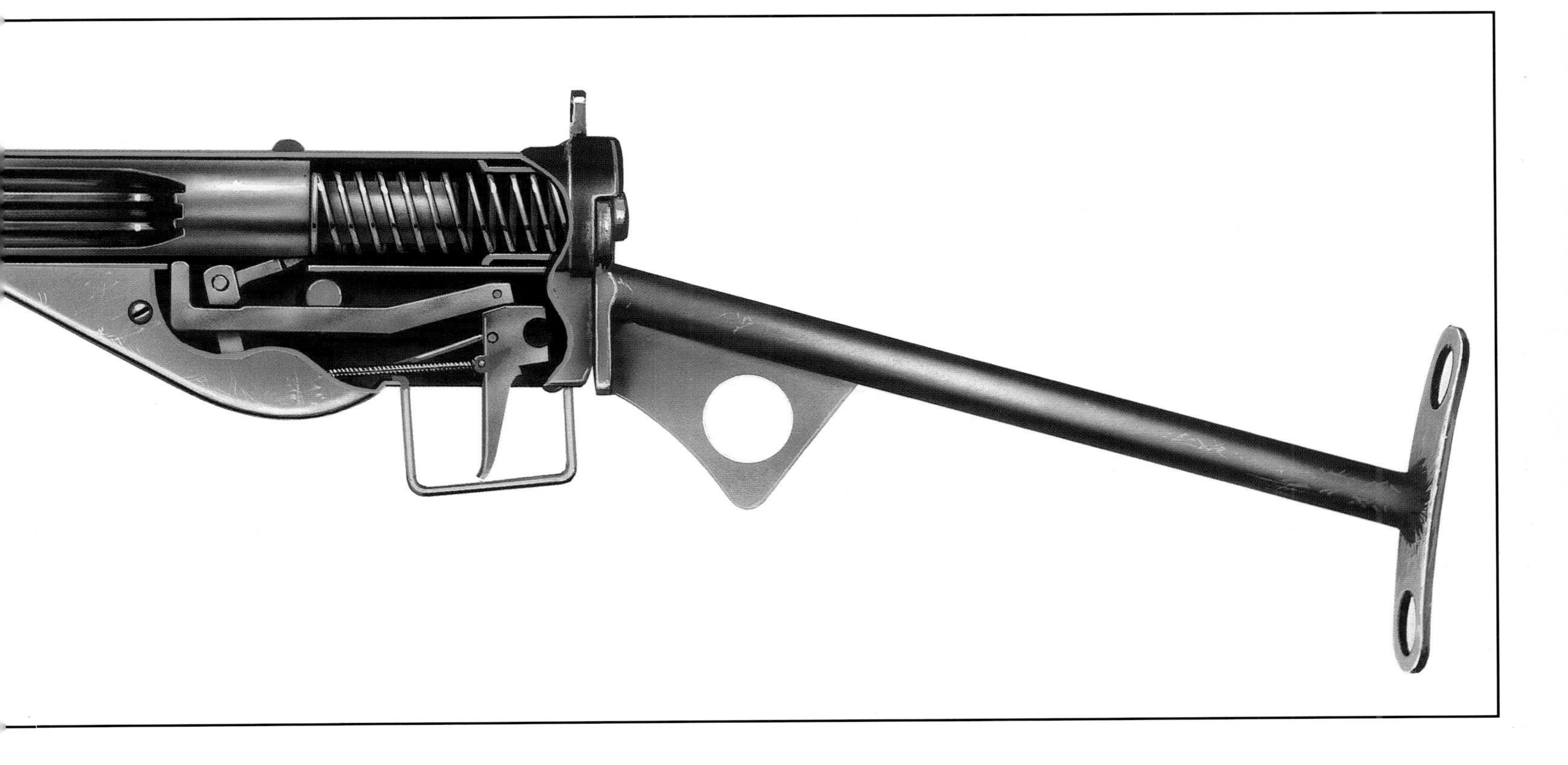

receiver is a combined magazine housing and foregrip, which holds a 20- or 32-round magazine. Behind this is the trigger assembly and pistol grip and, further to the rear, the extendable wire stock.

The MAT fires from an open bolt, which is pulled back using the large cocking handle on the left of the receiver. The bolt is a large machined item with a protruding front face, and as the bolt closes, this face fits into the hollow caused by the barrel extension. Such a configuration creates an extra seal to prevent gas leakage from the chamber, and provides extra protection to the firer if a round misfires or a cartridge case bursts. Reliability is enhanced in dusty conditions by use of a hinged cover over the ejection port, which flips open as the gun is fired.

The MAT has a number of other safety features, unusual in this type of weapon. The magazine housing can be unlocked and, complete with magazine, folded forward to lie underneath the barrel. When the magazine is folded like this, no ammunition can be fed into the gun and it cannot be fired accidentally. The magazine housing also seals the feed port, further protecting the mechanism from dirt, and being folded like this makes the weapon easier to carry by paratroopers and vehicle crews. To prepare the MAT for firing, the user simply swings down the magazine housing and slots it into place. Another safety feature is a lever on the rear of the pistol grip, which has to be depressed before either the bolt can be pulled back or the trigger pulled. This means that the weapon will not fire if dropped. The MAT 49 quickly proved popular with French troops, and saw extensive service in the colonial campaigns of the 1950s and 1960s. Tough and reliable, it could easily withstand the dusty conditions of North Africa. Its only weak point was the use of a single column magazine, a type of design prone to stoppages. Many were issued to colonial police forces, and the MAT can still be seen in use today in areas where the French once had influence.

THE STERLING

Britain also faced a number of low-intensity colonial conflicts after the war, and the Army quickly realised that something better than the wartime Sten was required. George Patchett already had an improved SMG design in service in 1944, and it was a weapon derived from this gun that would eventually enter service in 1953 as the L2A1 Sterling. The Sterling can almost be thought of as a properly made Sten, and both have many design and concept similarities. The big difference is in the build standard. Sterlings are made to last, using high-grade materials and more machining than is common in an SMG.

The L2 has a simple tubular receiver that merges into a perforated cooling jacket, which extends for the full length of the barrel. Below this is a plastic-covered pistol grip and trigger, with a combined safety and selector lever directly above. The bolt is a large, carefully machined item with an integral firing pin, and has a

M3A1

M2

Calibre: 9mm
Weight: 3.29kg (7¼lb)
Length: 890mm (35in) – stock extended; 705mm (27¼in) – stock retracted
Effective range: 100m (110yd)
Rate of fire: 625rpm (cyclic)
Feed: 32-round magazine
Muzzle velocity: 365mps (1198fps)

number of external ribs which sweep dirt and fouling out of the receiver. A curved cocking handle protrudes from the right of the bolt, which is used to pull it back against the trigger sear. The Sterling is another open-bolt blowback weapon, again relying on the mass of the bolt to hold the chamber closed until gas pressure drops. As in the Sten, 9mm Parabellum ammunition is fed from the left of the weapon, although the curved 34-round magazine is a much more solid and reliable design than its predecessor. Empty cases are ejected through the large port on the right. Recoil is absorbed by a strong two-stage return spring, which sits inside the section of the receiver that extends behind the grip. A metal skeleton stock is fitted behind the grip, and this item can be folded forward to clip underneath the barrel if required.

Later models of the Sterling were the L2A2 and A3, although the modifications were minor. It is a popular and reliable SMG, having been used by the armed forces of over 90 countries and manufactured under licence in both Canada (as the C-1) and India. Unlike the Sten, it easily withstands rough handling and the rigours of military service, and will keep operating in almost any type of terrain and climate. Other versions of the Sterling include single-shot police carbines, shortened personal defence weapons and standard SMGs with fixed plastic stocks. As the British issued the FN FAL-derived Self-Loading Rifle to their infantry, the Sterling became more and more a self-defence weapon for non-infantry troops, and served in this role into the 1990s, where it is finally being replaced by the SA-80.

A silenced version of the Sterling was also developed, designated the L34. Such weapons only have a limited usefulness, as on the battlefield there is usually so much other noise that a silenced SMG is irrelevant. Their main employment is with special forces, where they are used for disposing of sentries, assassinating key officers and in ambushes at night. As with

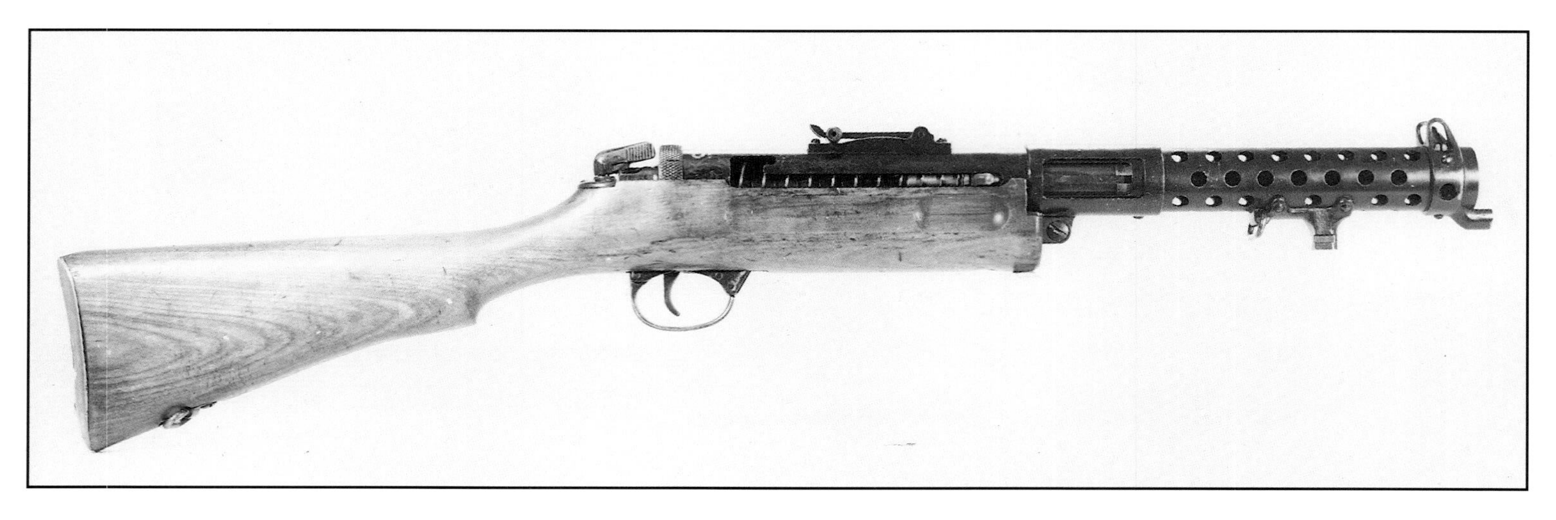

■ ABOVE: The British Lanchester was a direct copy of the German MP28 submachine gun. However, it copied a design that worked, and the Lanchester continued in service until the 1960s.

the Sten Mark 2S and Mark 6, the L34's silencer is no add-on afterthought; rather, it is integrated with the barrel in a specially manufactured version of the weapon. Over 70 tiny holes are drilled along the length of the barrel. As the bullet passes, the gas seeps through these holes into a metal casing surrounding the barrel. The end of this casing extends beyond the muzzle, and has a spiral diffuser which swirls the gases coming from the barrel and reduces their energy. A wooden block is fitted under the silencer as a foregrip to protect the hand from the high temperatures reached. Other modifications to the gun are a lighter bolt and return spring, as the blowback energy from this weapon is not as great as on the normal L2.

The L34 is a rugged weapon which, unlike some others, can withstand bursts being fired through the silencer. The silencer is also so efficient at reducing the energy of the bullet that ordinary 9mm Parabellum ammunition is used rather than the special low-powered subsonic rounds needed by some other silenced SMGs. In British service it is carried largely by special forces and paratroopers, and it has been exported to similar units elsewhere. The L34 is not completely silent, however. Like any other open-bolt weapon there is a fair amount of sound from the bolt slamming forward, but this is small compared to the report of an unsuppressed round. The British design is a good compromise between silence, ruggedness, reliability and general utility.

One nation that still equipped its frontline infantry with SMGs in the 1950s was Israel, whose hard-pressed army needed an effective weapon that could be produced quickly using national resources. Major Uziel Gal took elements of the Czech CZ23 and 25 to design an effective SMG which packed a surprisingly long barrel into a remarkably short overall package. The new weapon was issued to the Israeli Defence Forces in the early 1950s, and designated the Uzi.

THE ISRAELI UZI

The Uzi is a compact weapon, and makes use of a number of features which have since found their way into other SMG designs. It has a square outline and is made from steel pressings riveted and spot-welded together. It uses a blowback mechanism, but has a bolt that actually wraps around the end of the barrel. The bolt face and firing pin are some 95mm (3¾in) back from the front edge of the bolt, the rest of which surrounds the chamber and rear of the barrel. Slots are cut in the bolt to allow empty cases to pass through when being ejected, and by using this wraparound method a sufficiently massive

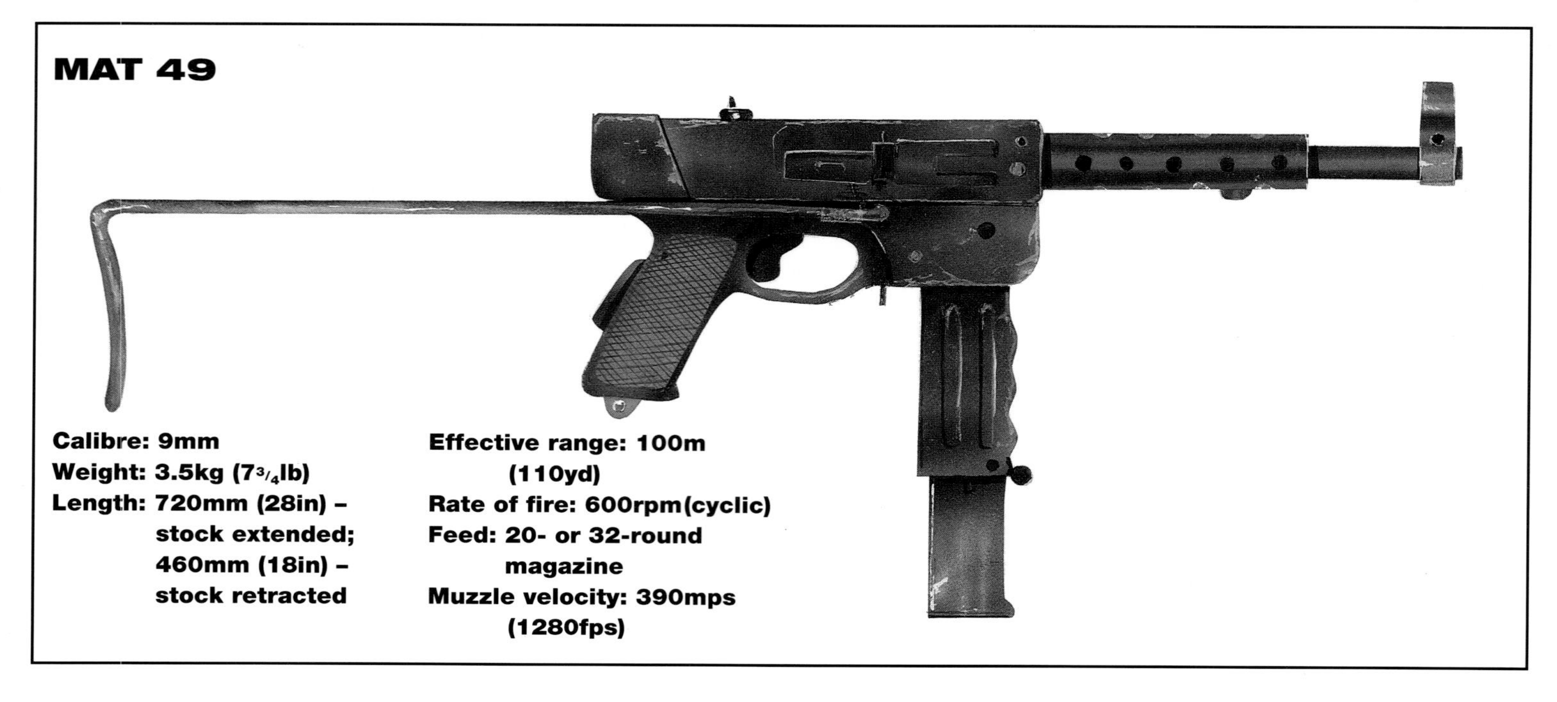

MAT 49

Calibre: 9mm
Weight: 3.5kg (7¾lb)
Length: 720mm (28in) – stock extended; 460mm (18in) – stock retracted
Effective range: 100m (110yd)
Rate of fire: 600rpm(cyclic)
Feed: 20- or 32-round magazine
Muzzle velocity: 390mps (1280fps)

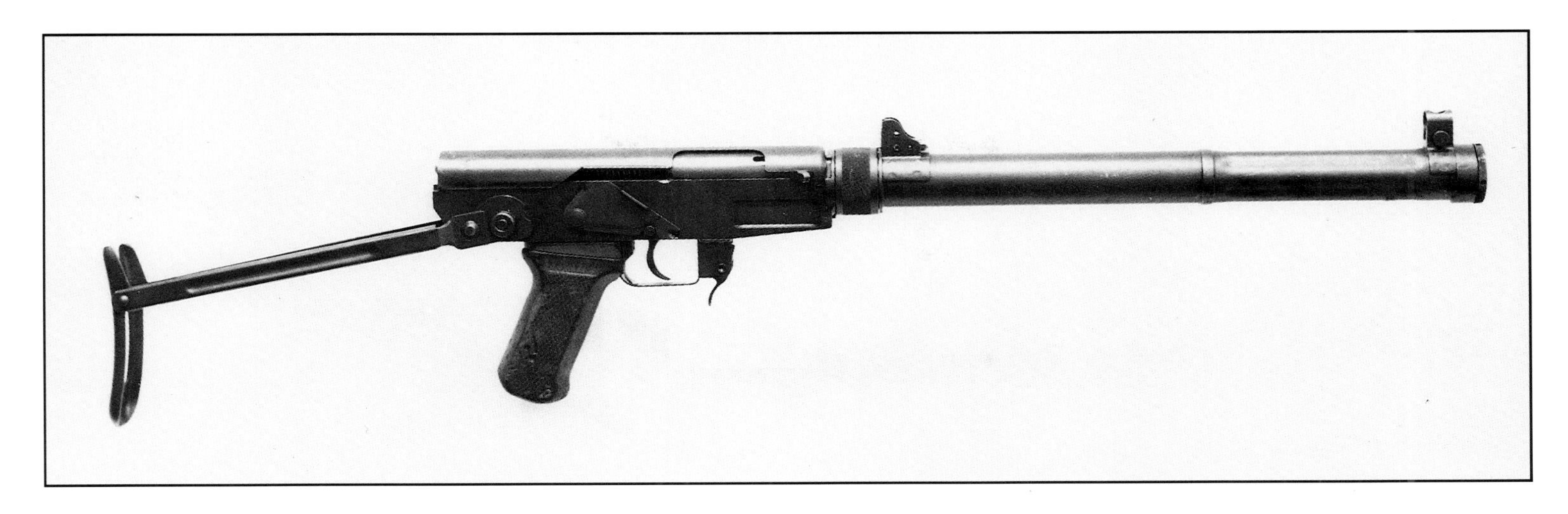

■ ABOVE: The Chinese Type 64 submachine gun. It was designed from the outset as a silenced weapon, and the silencer is an integral part of the gun. It is capable of firing single shots and full-automatic.

bolt can be made that takes up little space, The return spring sits round a guide rod above the level of the barrel, which extends forward of the chamber.

LETHALITY IN A TINY PACKAGE

A large pistol grip extends beneath the centre of the body, with the trigger assembly in front of this. The ammunition feed is actually through the butt, and 25- or 32-round magazines are inserted from below the grip, a system that helps the firer replace magazines quickly, especially in darkness. A plastic shroud below the front of the receiver provides a foregrip. Early models had a fixed wooden stock, though most Uzis have since been fitted with a folding metal item. The grip is positioned roughly at the point of balance, which makes the weapon much easier to control when firing bursts. Safety features include a combined safety/selector lever above the left side of the grip, and a button on the rear of the grip, which must be squeezed before the bolt or trigger are free to move. There is also a catch on the cocking handle slide that prevents the bolt moving forward and firing a round if it is released accidentally before reaching the trigger sear.

The Uzi is reliable and surprisingly accurate; it has been used by the armed forces of over 20 nations and has also been licence-built by FN in Belgium. Israeli troops have fought numerous battles with this tough little gun, and even though it has been replaced in many formations by the Galil assault rifle, it will remain in service for years to come. Israeli Military Industries has not rested on its laurels, however, and a number of variants have been developed. The mini-Uzi is some 95mm (3¾in) shorter than the standard model, has a much simpler wire folding stock, and has compensating slots cut into the top of the muzzle. In virtually all other respects it is identical to the basic model. An even smaller version is the micro-Uzi, which at 250mm (10in) in length is almost the same size as a large handgun. It retains a wire folding stock and the bolt has a heavy tungsten insert to slow the rate of fire to a reasonable level. The micro-Uzi is too small and short-ranged for the battlefield, but it makes for an effective, easily concealed bodyguard and personal defence weapon.

THE BERETTA 12

Wraparound or telescopic bolts have become popular with many SMG designers, and a well-known gun using this principle is the Beretta 12, a 1959 design used in Italy and at least seven other countries. The Beretta has a tubular body which houses both the receiver and the barrel, with only a small length of barrel protruding from its housing. As in the Uzi, it is a simple blowback weapon where the bolt extends forward of the chamber, with slots cut in it to allow spent cartridges to be ejected. The receiver also has grooves cut into the inside to allow normal operation to clear any dust, sand or snow from the mechanism. The 12 is a sturdy design made from steel stampings welded together, and the receiver, magazine housing and pistol grips are formed as one unit. There are two pistol grips, one at each end of the body, and further stability is given by a folding wire stock. A push-through selector lever sits just in front of and above the rear grip, and behind this is a push-button safety catch. This actually unlocks the main safety system, which is a lever built into the front of the grip. Unless the grip safety is squeezed, the bolt will not move, whether it is in the cocked or uncocked state.

ITALIAN INGENUITY

The Beretta fires 9mm Parabellum ammunition from a 32-round box magazine located between the two pistol grips, although 20- or 40-round options are also available. The cocking handle is a curved triangular item rather like a shark's fin, which protrudes from the front left of the body. A later model, the 12S, has a combined safety/selector lever but retains the grip safety, has improved sights and has its external surfaces coated in a protective epoxy resin finish. There are no other modifications available apart from a detachable fixed wooden stock which can be used with both weapons. The Beretta is a compact and efficient SMG which is extensively used by Italian paratroopers and special forces, and is popular with many other soldiers.

In the 1990s, conventional military SMGs are still being brought into service around the world, virtually all firing Georg Luger's 'stopgap' 9mm Parabellum round. Examples include the Spanish Star Z-70, which incorporates a hammer system in the bolt that can only be operated by the trigger, thus preventing accidental discharge if the weapon is dropped. Other 9mm SMGs are made by Austria, Brazil, China (including the silenced Type 64), Chile, Mexico, the former Czechoslovakia, Peru, Portugal, Vietnam and, until it erupted into civil war, former Yugoslavia.

THE BOER BXP

A nation relatively new to weapons design is South Africa, and one of its first products is a capable and efficient submachine gun. First seen in the early 1980s, the BXP is very similar to the Uzi in that it has a square body made from steel

ABOVE: The Sterling submachine gun is a no-nonsense submachine gun that works in all types of environmental conditions. The silenced version is used by the SAS.

stampings. The BXP again makes use of a telescoped wraparound bolt and has the magazine feed through the grip, so like the Uzi it is well balanced and easy to control, even when firing with one hand. There is a metal stock which folds under the weapon and provides a foregrip when stowed. The cocking handle is on the top of the casing, but is slotted to prevent obstruction when sighting. A simple safety catch is fitted above the grip, and there is also an extra bolt safety to prevent firing if the weapon is dropped. Fire selection is easy: when the trigger is pulled to the first pressure one round is fired; pull it to the second pressure and the gun will fire a burst (22- or 32-round magazines are available, and the muzzle will accept a range of compensators and add-on suppressors). The iron sights can also be supplemented by a 'singlepoint' device (where the other eye is kept open and an aiming mark superimposed on the firer's binocular vision) for quick-reaction snap shooting. In addition, stripping and assembly of the weapon is very easy. The BXP has proved effective with the South African military and police forces, although it is unlikely that many will be exported.

GERMAN PRECISION

One of the most significant modern SMGs comes from Germany, although this weapon approaches SMG design from a different angle. The Heckler & Koch MP5 series first entered service in the early 1970s, and has gone on to establish itself as the 'Rolls Royce' of SMG design. Superbly made precision weapons, they fire from a closed bolt and employ the roller-delayed blowback system used in virtually all H&K rifles, handguns and machine guns. Virtually every other SMG ever made relies on the forward momentum of the bolt to hold the breech shut while the gas pressure drops to a safe level, but the MP5 fires from a closed bolt.

The Heckler has a two-part bolt; the rear part forces two small rollers on the front part outwards, where they lock into recesses in the barrel extension. When the round is fired by the spring-loaded firing pin, the recoil forces first have to overcome the resistance of these rollers and the leverage needed for them to force the rear part of the bolt backwards. Once this happens, the bolt is free to open and extract the empty case (this mechanism is more fully described in the rifles chapter). While this is a rather complex system for an SMG, it means that the first shot is fired from a closed bolt, and is therefore significantly more accurate than one from an open-bolt SMG.

THE HECKLER & KOCH MP5

The MP5 is made from steel stampings, although materials and assembly are to extremely high standards. Underneath the body is a pistol grip and trigger mechanism, and a plastic shroud underneath the barrel acts as a foregrip. A narrow tube runs along the top of the receiver, and this contains the return spring and a cylindrical extension to the bolt carrier. The cocking handle protrudes from the left of this tube and is situated right up at the front of the weapon. An adjustable drum rear sight is fitted, similar to that on the G3, and the foresight can also be set in windage and elevation. Various telescopic, laser or night sights can also be fitted. The MP5A2 has a fixed plastic stock, but the A3 is equipped with a high-quality extendable stock. 9mm Parabellum ammunition is held in a curved 15- or 30-round magazine, which feeds just in front of the trigger group. There is a safety/selector lever above the trigger, and on most weapons a three-round burst is selectable.

Such build quality and precision operation is not normally required in a submachine gun, but the Heckler has carved itself a niche as the preferred weapon of many of the world's special forces units. Its combination of firepower and accuracy makes the MP5 ideal for hostage-rescue teams, and it has virtually become the badge of such units. First used in action in 1977 by the German GSG 9 when it stormed a terrorist-held airliner in Mogadishu, it was also seen by millions of television viewers in the hands of British Special Air Service troops as they stormed the Iranian Embassy in London in May 1980. The Heckler & Koch has since been procured by the majority of Western hostage-rescue teams.

Such usage has caused a rash of new sub-variants to be produced, many with subtle variations in sights, stocks and other features. New models include a weapon chambered for 10mm, and another which uses the new generation .40in Smith & Wesson cartridge. The best known MP5 variants, however, are the silenced MP5SD series and the compact MP5K. The SD has an integral silencer built around the barrel, which taps off gas through tiny holes drilled in the barrel and absorbs the residual muzzle energy in a diffuser chamber. The SD can safely handle bursts of ordinary 9mm Parabellum ammunition, and as the weapon fires from a closed bolt, is probably one of the most accurate and silent mass-produced suppressed weapons around. Six versions are available, with various minor differences between them.

The MP5K series (K for *Kurz* or short) is a compact weapon only 325mm ($12\frac{3}{4}$in)

ABOVE: French soldiers in Indochina during the early 1950s. They are armed with MAT 49 submachine guns. The magazine housing could be folded forward (as shown above) if required.
RIGHT: The compact Czech Skorpion machine pistol: tiny but deadly.

long. Instead of a stock it has a forward grip handle. Apart from a shorter barrel and smaller 15-round magazine, it is mechanically identical to the full-sized SMG. The MP5KA1 has smooth surfaces and minimal sights, and is ideal for use as a concealed bodyguard or personal defence weapon, and all the MP5K guns are handy but effective weapons for police and security units. Sadly, such characteristics also make them desirable to terrorists and criminals, but as yet there is little evidence to suggest widespread use by such people.

The MP5 series has not made quite the same impact with conventional forces, and it is easy to see why. First, precision engineering comes at a cost, and the MP5 rather belies the traditional 'cheap and cheerful' image of the SMG. Second, while it is a superb and reliable weapon, it does demand care and attention, and is perhaps too well made to tolerate extended combat in dust, sand, mud or snow. Nevertheless, the Heckler & Koch design has made its mark on the modern weapons scene.

PERSONAL DEFENCE WEAPONS

A category of submachine gun that continues to see development is the personal defence weapon. This is usually small and easily carried, sometimes concealable and often capable of being fired instantly, without having to cock the weapon first. The actual borderlines between definitions are hazy, and some personal defence weapons are virtually full-blown submachine guns, while others verge on the machine pistol.

One of the earliest of such weapons was the Czech vz62 Skorpion, a tiny machine

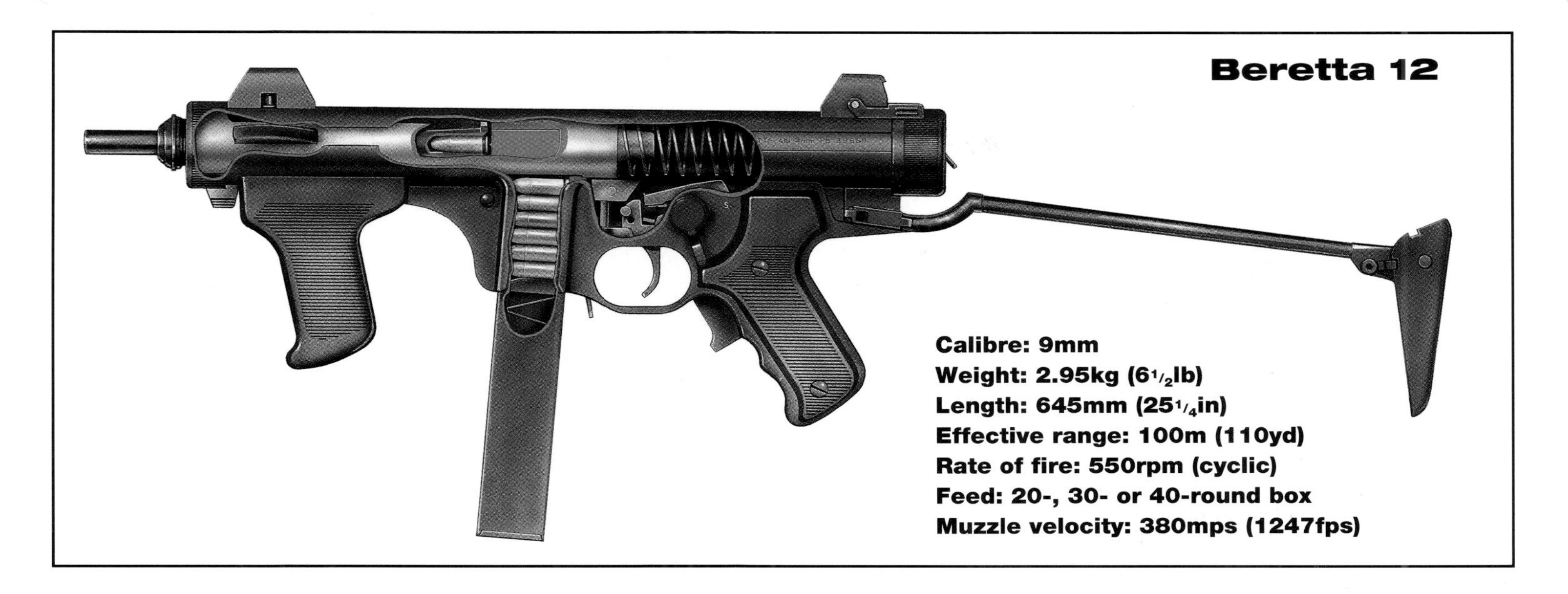

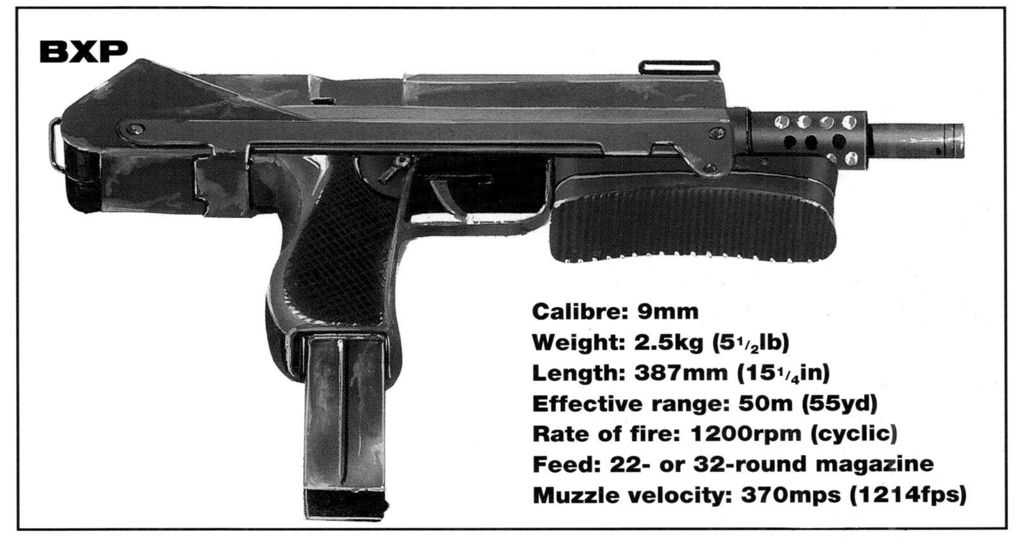

handgun/SMG which fires from a 10- or 20-round box magazine. It has a folding wire stock and a wooden grip, and is chambered for the marginally useful 7.65mm x 17mm cartridge. There are also versions chambered for 9mm Short and 9mm Makarov, and all use simple blowback, with the empty cases ejecting through the top of the casing. A selector switch is above the grip, and the weapon can be controlled reasonably easily, even one-handed. Such a short gun would normally have a ferociously high rate of fire, so a spring-loaded delay device is fitted which brings this down to manageable proportions. The Skorpion is a compact weapon that is effective for the personal defence of signallers, vehicle crews and the like, although its limitations prevent other uses.

POLISH MINIATURE

Poland produced a similar overgrown machine pistol in the PM63, which even has a slide and barrel assembly like an automatic handgun. The slide is locked back when the weapon is cocked, and moves back and forward as it is fired, to the detriment of steady aim and accuracy. The PM63 is slightly larger than the Skorpion, and is chambered for the more capable 9mm Makarov round. A 25- or 40-round box magazine fits into the butt, and there is a metal extending stock and fold-down foregrip. Fire selection is by trigger pressure, and the rate of fire is controlled by a similar delay device to that used on the Skorpion. The PM63 is used for personal defence, but it also has some utility as a compact assault weapon.

One personal weapon that is sold as a submachine gun is the Ingram MAC 10, a tiny, square-sectioned gun that looks like a mini-Uzi. The Ingram first entered service in 1970, and for a time was used by military security detachments and anti-terrorist units. A simple and reliable blowback weapon, it makes use of a telescopic bolt and magazine feed through the butt. It is chambered for 9mm Parabellum and holds the ammunition in a 32-round box. A wire stock extends to the rear for firing from the shoulder. The weapon is cocked by pulling the slotted handle on top of the casing, and the bolt can be locked by turning this through 90 degrees. There is also an additional safety catch forward of the trigger guard. The MAC 10 is a solid and rugged design, and variants exist chambered for .45in ACP and 9mm Short calibres. The barrel will take a specially designed suppressor, although the bullet is still supersonic and will give off a sharp crack typical of such rounds. The only disadvantage of the MAC10 is its short length, which makes for an intrinsically inaccurate weapon. Once the MP5 series had proved itself, the Ingram was quickly discarded by anti-terrorist groups and most other military users, although some remain as personal defence weapons. Unfortunately, the compact size and firepower has made the MAC 10 popular with criminals, who care less about inaccuracy and the possibility of hitting bystanders than do the military.

Another modern personal defence weapon is the Italian 9mm Spectre M4, which, like the MP5, fires from a closed bolt. Once a round is chambered, the firing hammer can be manually decocked in a similar way to that on a modern double-action automatic handgun. The Spectre can then be carried in complete safety with no chance of accidental firing, even if dropped on a hard surface. When the weapon is needed in action, the firer simply pulls the trigger to fire the first round, after which the SMG operates like a normal blowback weapon. The Spectre is small (350mm/13¾in), has a metal folding stock, and carries a useful 50 rounds in a unique four-column magazine. It is an

UZI SMG

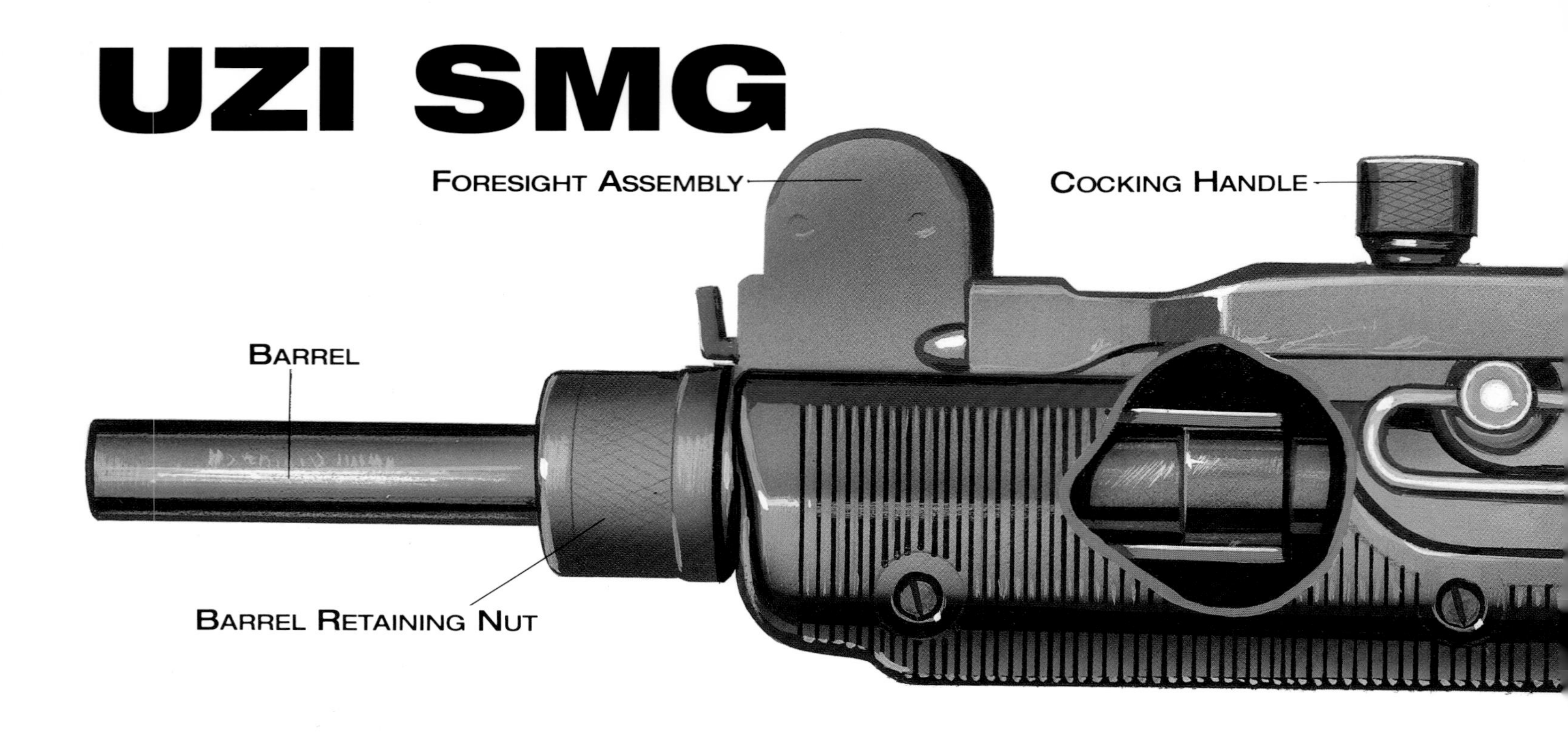

Below: The Uzi was first designed in the early 1950s, and though rather long in the tooth, is still a fine weapon.

ideal weapon for security forces and bodyguards: easily concealable but able to be brought into action quicker than many other SMGs.

ASSAULT RIFLE SMGS

The final category of SMG is that comprised of converted and shortened assault rifles, either firing full-powered rifle ammunition or handgun rounds. While a 9mm conversion on an assault rifle may seem a retrograde step, such a beast could be popular for a number of reasons. Police and security forces, for example, may occasionally need the firepower of an automatic weapon, but in such situations a full-blown assault rifle would have too much power, resulting in a high risk of ricochets and stray shots hitting innocent bystanders. In addition, the converted assault rifle will often be more accurate and built to a higher standard than most SMGs, and if it is based on the same weapon used by that nation's infantry, then logistic and training considerations will be greatly simplified.

The Americans have the Colt SMG, which is a shortened M16 chambered for 9mm Parabellum ammunition. It has the extendable butt of the Colt Commando and, apart from the modified magazine housing and barrel, is almost identical to the assault rifle. It fires from a closed bolt and will feed from either a 20- or 32-round magazine. The Colt 9mm is in service with the US Drug Enforcement Agency, the armed forces, and military and security agencies of a number of other countries. Its nearest competitor is probably the

■ **LEFT: The Uzi was a design that worked from the beginning. It has the main mass of the bolt forward of the breech, thus making for a compact weapon. The weapon balances so well that single-handed fire is relatively easy.**

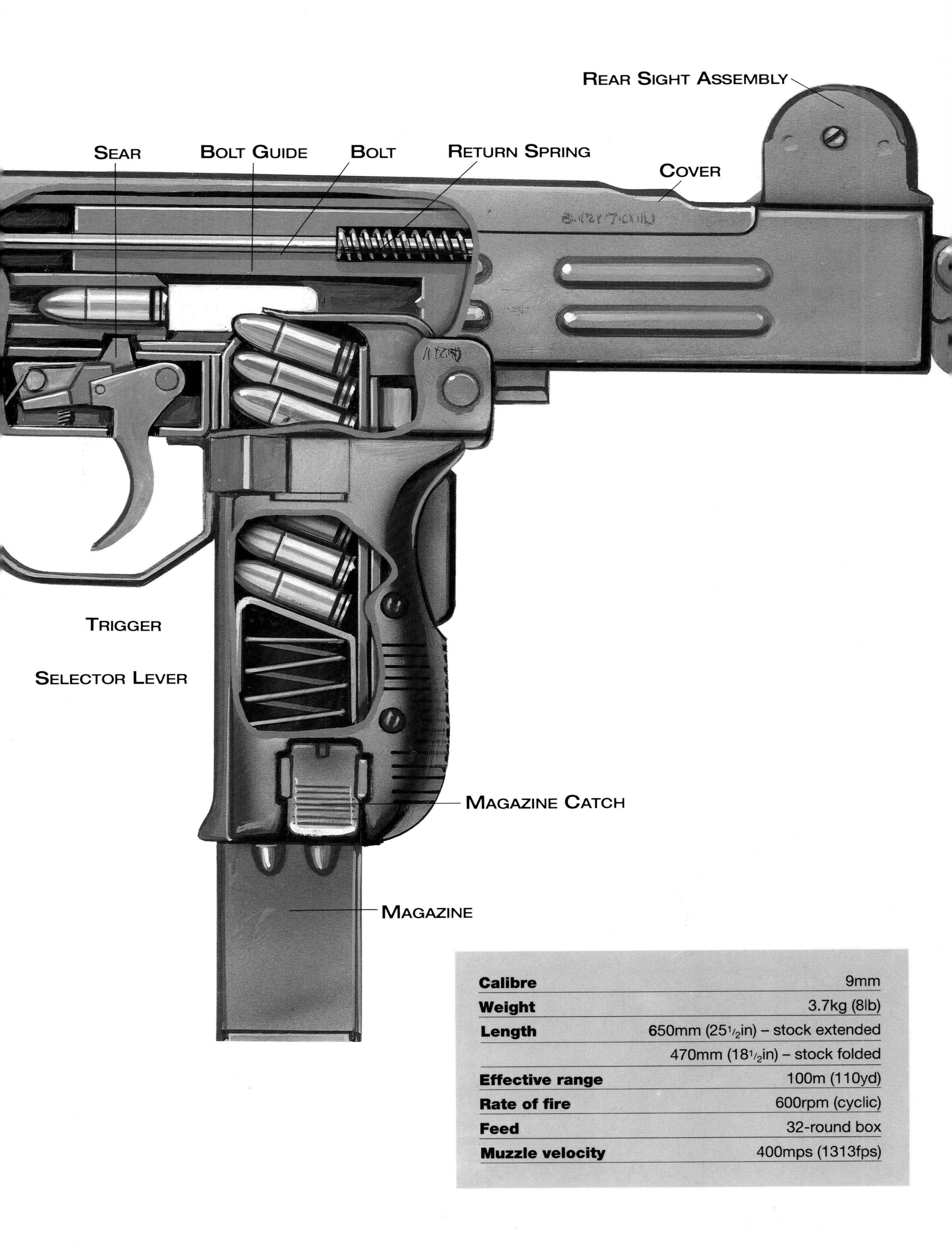

Calibre	9mm
Weight	3.7kg (8lb)
Length	650mm ($25\frac{1}{2}$in) – stock extended
	470mm ($18\frac{1}{2}$in) – stock folded
Effective range	100m (110yd)
Rate of fire	600rpm (cyclic)
Feed	32-round box
Muzzle velocity	400mps (1313fps)

Austrian Steyr Para, a 9mm SMG conversion of the AUG rifle. Steyr's modular design allows any AUG assault rifle to be converted by simply changing the barrel, bolt and magazine feed, though most Para versions are supplied factory-built.

AUTOMATIC CARBINES

Shortened weapons firing full-powered 5.56mm rifle ammunition are on the borderline between the SMG and the carbine, and their employment will depend upon the tactical philosophy of the user. Good examples of such weapons are the 5.56mm Colt Commando and the Heckler & Koch MP5 clone chambered for 5.56mm, known as the HK53. One of the most widely distributed of such weapons is the Soviet AKSU, which is chambered for the 5.45mm AK-74 round and uses the standard AK-74 plastic-coated magazine. This short, stubby gas-operated weapon has a folding metal stock, and, while it operates in exactly the same way as a conventional AK, tends to be regarded by Russian/CIS armies as a submachine gun. As the barrel and gas tube are significantly shorter than on the rifle, a gas expansion chamber is fitted to the muzzle to reduce the recoil energy and muzzle flash.

Possibly originally designed as a firing-port weapon for the BMP infantry combat vehicle, the compact AKSU has been widely issued as a close-quarter and personal defence weapon in the Russian and CIS armed forces.

THE FUTURE OF THE SMG

It seems that future development of the SMG will be largely in the field of personal defence weapons, rather than in traditional battlefield models. The assault rifle has assumed many of the roles initially carried out by SMGs, although the latter still remain as a cheap, quick alternative. If a nation needs to arm large numbers of its men in a hurry, it is likely that the SMG will still be chosen as a quick and effective method. It may be that concepts like the American Calico will become more popular, where up to 100 rounds of 9mm ammunition are carried in a spiral configuration inside a cylindrical magazine above the gun, although this negates the concept of a cheap, simple weapon. For short-range infantry firepower, attention seems to be turning to combat shotguns because of their wide range of extremely destructive ammunition, or hand-held grenade launchers firing high-explosive projectiles.

Personal defence weapons, however, seem a fruitful field for further development. The Spectre M4 may give some pointers to the direction this is taking, and rapid-response, short-range weapons with plentiful ammunition could become more common. One of the most distinctive new designs is the P90 Personal Weapon from the Belgium firm FN. Designed around a new 5.7mm x 28mm cartridge with improved ballistic characteristics over the venerable 9mm Parabellum, the P90 is

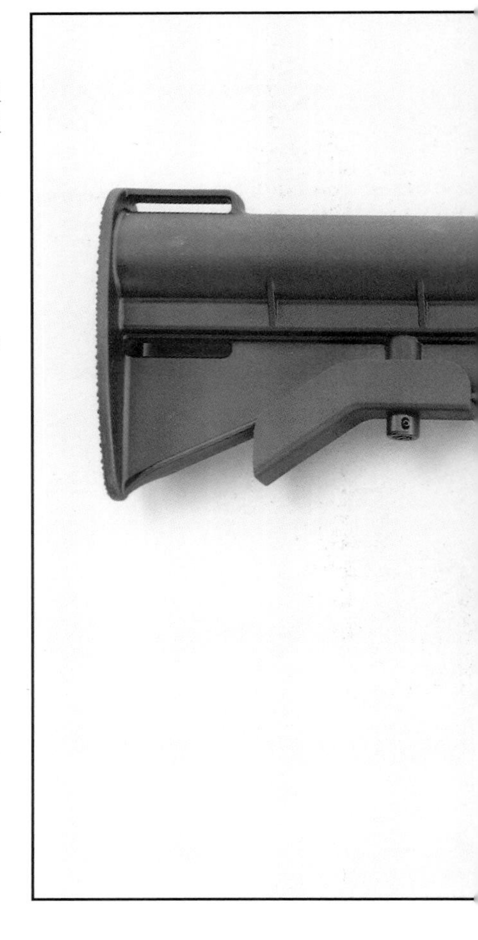

purposely designed for use by all the signallers, drivers, clerks and support personnel who don't carry a rifle, but sti need to be able to defend themselves.

The P90 is a selective-fire, blowback weapon that fires from a closed bolt. It h

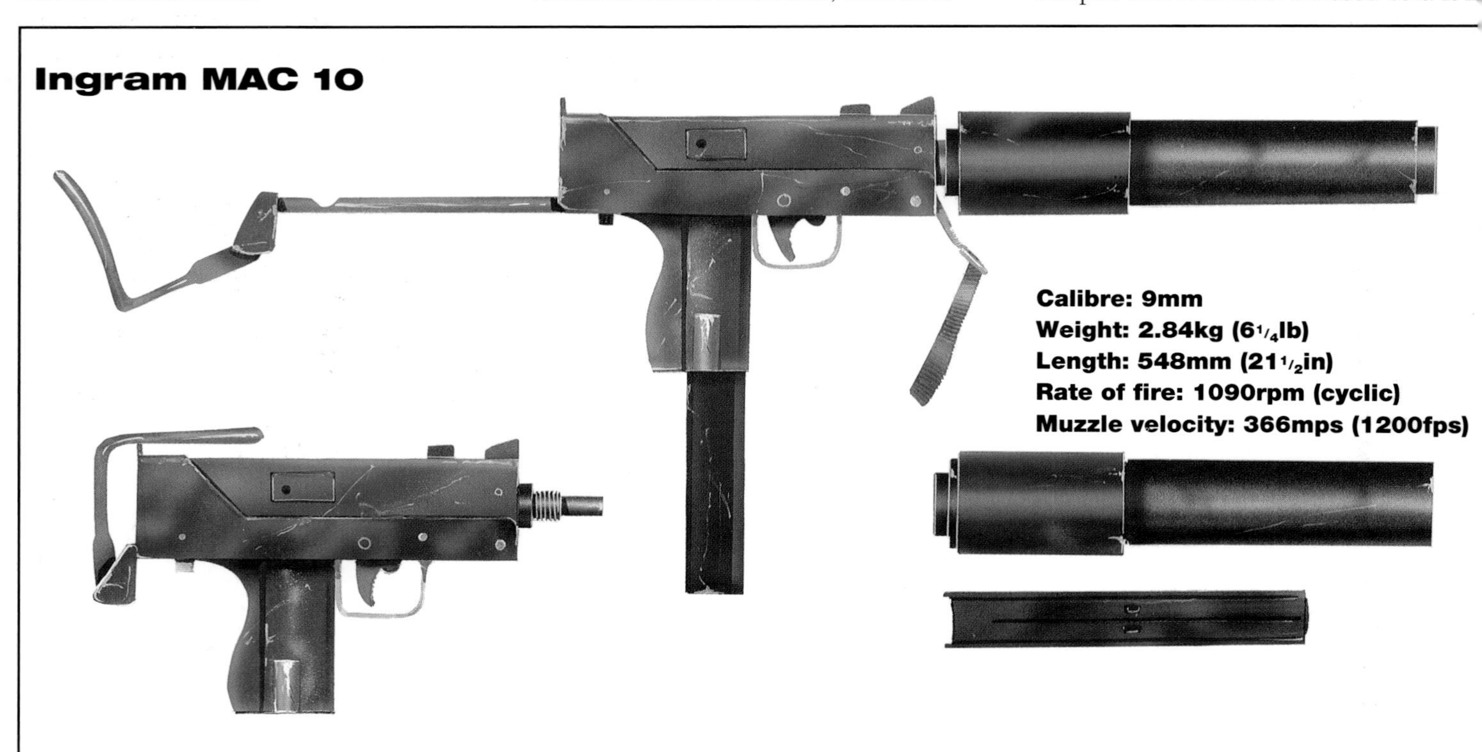

Ingram MAC 10

Calibre: 9mm
Weight: 2.84kg (6¼lb)
Length: 548mm (21½in)
Rate of fire: 1090rpm (cyclic)
Muzzle velocity: 366mps (1200fps)

a receiver made largely from moulded plastic, formed into a basically rectangular shape. The front of this casing is moulded into two grips, with the trigger as part of the rear grip. A short muzzle protrudes from the front of the weapon, and just behind this is a permanently attached optical collimating 'singlepoint' sight. A semi-transparent plastic magazine lies horizontally along the top edge of the receiver, and it holds up to 50 rounds. It has an integral turntable mechanism to rotate the cartridges to the correct orientation before they feed into the weapon. The bullets lie in a double-row configuration, and they are sorted into a single row at the mouth of the magazine by a clamp (empty cartridge cases are ejected downwards). The P90 is designed to be fired from either shoulder. The selector switch is on both sides of the body, the safety is a rotary switch under the trigger, and the empty cases are ejected downwards through the hollow grip. Emergency iron sights are fitted for use if the optical sight is damaged, and there are two sets, one on each side of the sight mount, so that the weapon can again be aimed from either shoulder. The whole weapon is one of the strangest looking devices ever seen, and it will be fascinating to see how such a design develops, and if it ever enters service.

■ ABOVE: The Colt 9mm submachine gun. This is a delayed blowback weapon that has a straightline construction. This, combined with the lower recoil of the Parabellum cartridge, makes for an accurate gun with little muzzle climb. Note the spent case deflector behind ejection port.

■ RIGHT: The Spectre submachine gun, a weapon that has a unique four-column magazine. This means that up to 50 rounds can be held in the weapon – handy to have in a firefight!

CHAPTER 5
SHOTGUNS

When most people talk of infantry weapons they usually mean rifles, handguns, machine guns and grenades, but few realise just how often the shotgun has been employed as a weapon of war. Throughout the twentieth century, long-barrelled, smooth-bore guns have proved invaluable additions to the infantry's armoury, especially for those facing combat at very close ranges and in jungle or urban terrain. The majority of these weapons were originally derived from sporting and hunting guns, and in many cases shoot exactly the same types of ammunition. Surprisingly, it is only in the last 20 years or so that special purpose weapons designed from the start to meet military and police requirements have been manufactured.

SHOTGUN MECHANISMS

Traditional sports guns have one or two barrels, and have to be broken open to feed individual cartridges (sometimes known as 'shells') into the breech. Their mechanism is normally single action, where one or two hammers usually have to be cocked by hand before the trigger can be pulled. To help the dispersion of the pellets, a sports weapon may have a slightly oval-shaped barrel, although this prevents the use of more specialised ammunition. Shotguns used for hunting larger game or for combat often have cylindrical barrels instead, which allow the use of solid projectiles such as large-diameter lead slugs.

An ammunition supply of only two cartridges is a totally inadequate load for many sports and all combat roles, so from the early decades of this century the magazine-fed weapon has been developed, the most common type holding the shells in a long tube which lies horizontally under the barrel. This tube is not detachable, and the rounds are loaded into the weapon one at a time. To chamber a round from the magazine, the firer has to operate a feed mechanism. On most guns this is done by sliding a moving foregrip back and forth. A system of rods and levers connects the grip to a feed ramp, which lifts the cartridge from the magazine up to the barrel and rams it home. Once the round is chambered, the bolt is locked shut, either by rotating a number of lugs into recesses on the barrel extension (rather like a typical assault rifle) or by tipping up or down behind a locking lug. After the cartridge is fired, the firer has to open this bolt, extract the spent case and load the next, again by racking the foregrip. This back-and-forth hand movement has given rise to the name 'slide-' or 'pump-action' for this style of shotgun, and a skilled gunner with a well-designed weapon can fire more than one aimed shot every second. Slide-action is a simple and rugged method of operation which is unlikely to be affected by dirt, grit or mud, and if a round misfires the user simply pumps the action once more to eject it and load the next.

■ LEFT: A US Marine team conducts ship boarding training armed with Beretta handguns and Remington M870 Mark 1 pump-action shotguns.

SEMI-AUTOMATIC SHOTGUNS

The slide-action shotgun still needs time for each new shot to be loaded, and demands a fairly high level of manual dexterity from the firer. In an effort to improve rapid-response firepower even further, shotgun designers have also produced a number of semi-automatic weapons. These are normally gas operated: energy from the high-pressure gas caused by firing the cartridge is used to unlock the bolt, extract the spent case and load the next round. Most of the operating principles of such weapons are familiar concepts already seen in assault rifles, but with modifications to account for the very different style, size and weight of typical shotgun ammunition. Most semi-automatic shotguns still make use of fixed tubular magazines, but some recent designs incorporate detachable boxes. There have even been attempts to produce combat shotguns capable of firing bursts, but such fearsome devices have yet to be made reliable enough for service use.

A major advantage the combat shotgun has over other military weapons is the ability to use a wide range of ammunition, which can be selected according to the operational mission. The standard shotgun

cartridge usually consists of a brass base which holds the primer and provides a gas seal, in front of which is a plastic casing containing the propellant and a number of lead pellets. Shells are available holding different sizes and quantities of pellets, and each type is designed to fulfil a different purpose. 'Birdshot', as its name suggests, contains a few dozen tiny pellets normally used against birds, small game and vermin. Military uses for such a round are almost non-existent, although police units may consider a form of birdshot if a non-lethal shot is required. 'Buckshot' covers a class of cartridge that holds between nine and 12 lead balls, each about 7.62mm (1/3in) in diameter. At close range (below 40m/44yd) buckshot has roughly the same effect as a long burst from a submachine gun, but with all the rounds fired at once. Cartridges of this nature are usually employed on combat operations, and have given rise to the colourful nickname of 'reloadable claymore'. The rate at which the buckshot spreads depends largely on the length of the barrel, although the pattern can be further controlled by 'choking' the muzzle. This is where the barrel is designed to be slightly narrower just before the muzzle (the choke can be part of the initial design or added as a separate device, precisely measured to suit the gun and the ammunition).

For longer range or more penetrative power, a single solid lead slug can be fired, and these can remain effective up to a range of 50m (55yd). Many of these slugs are rifled to improve accuracy, and some specialised designs can be effective up to 200m (220yd). While such a slug needs to be aimed at a point target, the effect on a person of being hit by a heavy projectile nearly 20mm (3/4in) in diameter is devastating, even if body armour is being worn. Some specially shaped slugs are made from tungsten and will penetrate hard cover, doors and armour.

A more sophisticated type of round is the high-explosive slug, a shotgun grenade that can be fired into a room or vehicle at over 100m (110yd). Ammunition of a less lethal nature includes CS gas grenades, incendiary compositions and flares. For non-lethal riot control there are cartridges firing rubber or plastic projectiles, or even plastic 'birdshot'. For hostage-rescue missions there is the 'Hatton' round, which is specially designed to blow the hinges off a locked door without harming the occupants of a room. The only major disadvantage of many of these rounds is

ABOVE: The USAS-12 automatic shotgun.

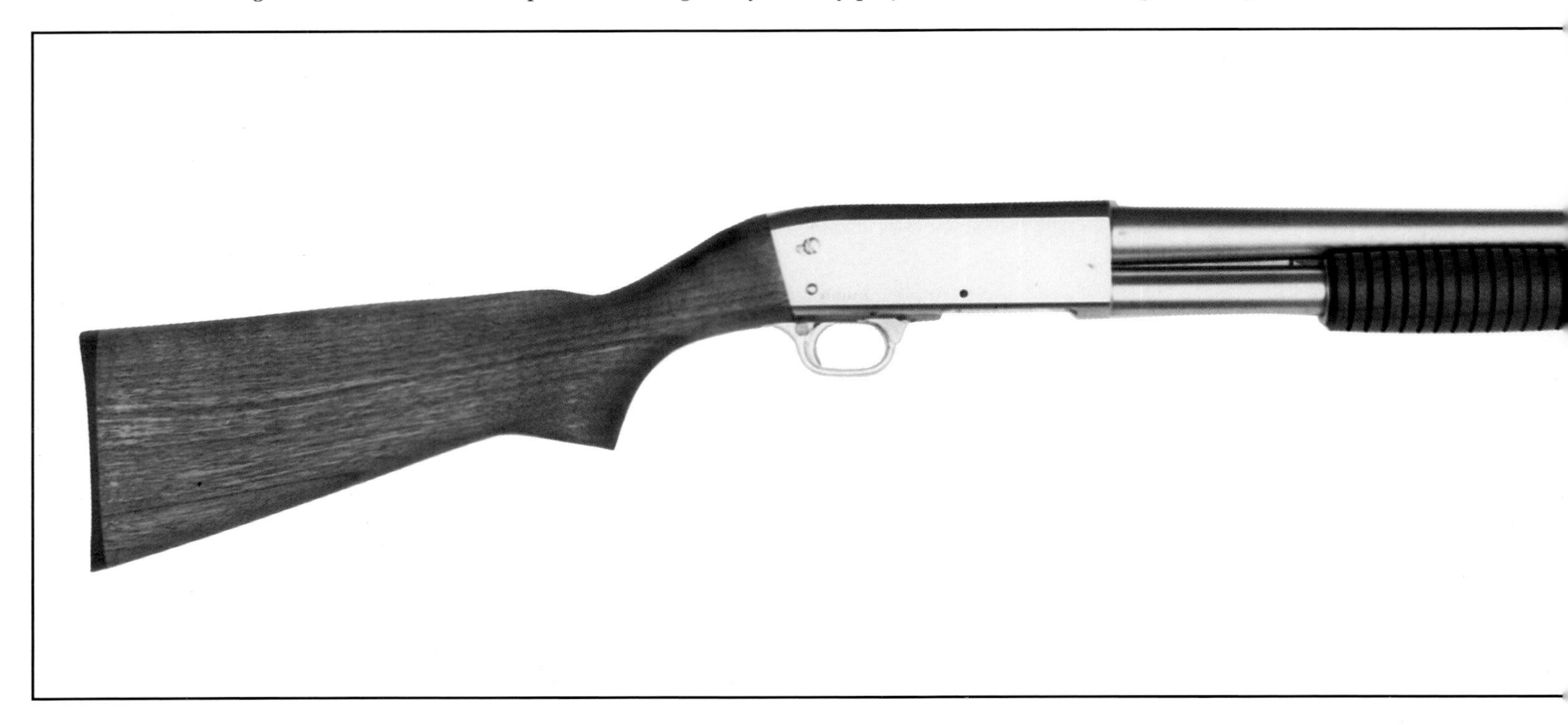

Ithaca Model 37

Calibre: 12-gauge
Weight: 3.06kg (6¾lb)
Length: 508mm (20in)
Effective range: 40m (44yd)
Rate of fire: single shot
Feed: five-round tubular magazine
Muzzle velocity: 400mps (1313fps)

the varying recoil forces and gas pressures they create. Many are too 'soft' to operate the firing mechanism of a semi-automatic shotgun, and normally have to be fired from a pump-action weapon instead.

Unlike other weapons, the size or calibre of a shotgun is not given in inches or millimetres, but uses an archaic system of measurement given in 'bores'. The number of 'bores' quoted is the number of lead balls, of the same diameter as the barrel, that are needed to make 1lb (.45kg) in weight. A 12-bore (often called '12-gauge') shotgun, therefore, means that a lead ball the diameter of the barrel weighs one twelfth of a pound (38g), which equates to a diameter of about .73in (18.5mm). A number of calibres are used by sporting users, but virtually all military and police weapons are 12-bore, firing cartridges 70mm (2¾in) long.

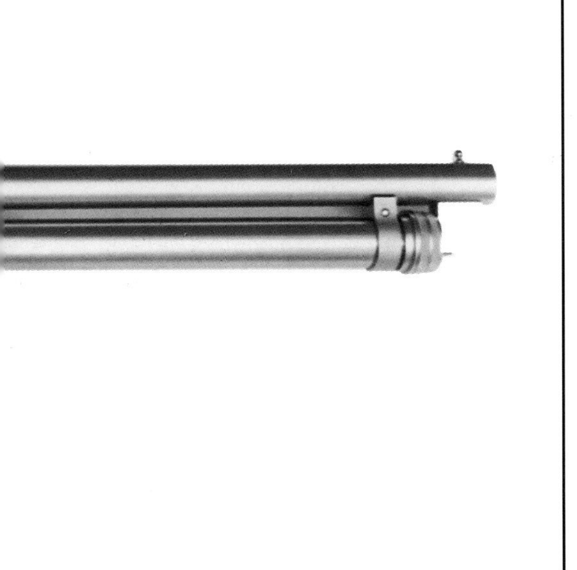

THE SHOTGUN IN COMBAT

During the twentieth century, the first widespread use of the shotgun by the military was during World War I. The traditional rifles carried by most infantrymen proved to be too long, cumbersome and awkward to handle in the type of close-range brawl that ensued when trench fighting took place. Some officers and wealthier soldiers, especially those from 'country' backgrounds, took to carrying their sporting shotguns in place of their revolvers and rifles. As most of these single-action weapons were simple double-barrelled sports guns, it meant that only two shots could be fired before reloading. Nevertheless, the effect of multiple lead pellets blasted into a trench or dugout at close range was surprisingly effective in both attack or defence. Towards the end of the war, specially modified military shotguns were being issued, especially to American troops, although the results achieved were largely overshadowed by the advent of the submachine gun.

The shotgun again became popular during World War II, especially with the United States Marine Corps (USMC). US Marines often had to fight through thick jungle terrain during the campaign in the Far East, and found the slide-action shotgun a valuable tool for ambushes and for killing enemy troops in cover. After the war, British troops operating in similar terrain in Malaya would often carry semi-automatic shotguns, especially the lead or 'point' man of a patrol, who could quickly return a devastating amount of short-range fire if the patrol was ambushed. Both types of weapon are still used today, carried by all sorts of infantry or special forces units, even if they are never likely to fight in jungle. Any terrain where sudden close-range combat is likely is a good place to have a shotgun to hand.

Paramilitary, security or police units sometimes also have a requirement for a short-range, powerful anti-riot and combat weapon. A shotgun can be useful in this scenario because most of the rounds it fires lose their energy very quickly, thus creating less of a hazard for innocent bystanders. The corollary to this is that the spread of fire from a typical shotgun cartridge is such that precision aiming, even at close ranges, is really impossible. Police users, however, can make use of a wide range of special ammunition types, such as low-powered, non-lethal rounds (for example, rubber birdshot), baton rounds and CS gas dispensers.

Finally, special forces soldiers will often have a use for a shotgun. While these men may not always operate in rough, closed-in terrain, they are still more likely than other troops to encounter close-range combat with the minimum of warning. Special forces may also have a hostage-rescue role, although here a shotgun must be used sparingly. While ideal for blowing open locked and barricaded doors or firing CS gas into a room, the shotgun is really too much of an area weapon to be able to pick out the terrorists in an enclosed space, while at the same time leaving the hostages unharmed. Britain's Special Air Service has employed shotguns for years, but it is interesting that when its hostage-rescue team stormed the Iranian Embassy in May 1980, the men were armed with Heckler & Koch MP5 submachine guns rather than shotguns.

LEFT: The Ithaca Model 37 Military and Police pump-action shotgun, a weapon designed to stand up to strenuous use. This particular model has a chrome finish.

Remington 870

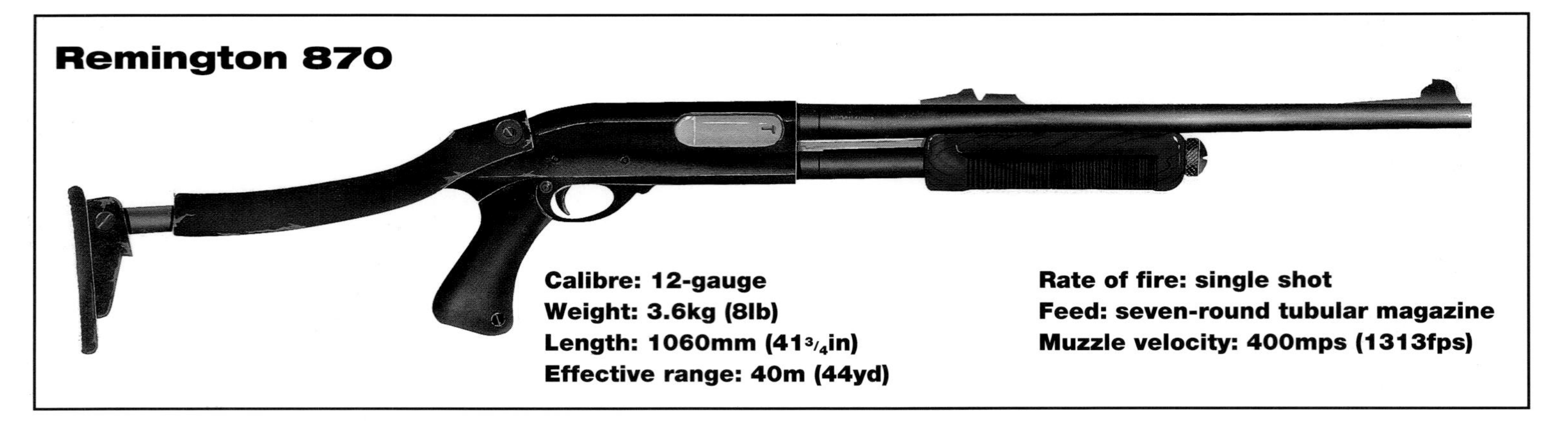

Calibre: 12-gauge
Weight: 3.6kg (8lb)
Length: 1060mm (41¾in)
Effective range: 40m (44yd)
Rate of fire: single shot
Feed: seven-round tubular magazine
Muzzle velocity: 400mps (1313fps)

The United States was one of the first nations to issue the shotgun as a military weapon, and the Winchester Model 1917 entered service just in time to see combat in World War I. Used during assaults on enemy positions, the weapon was actually referred to as a 'Trench Gun', and quickly proved to be popular with the troops. A pump-action derivative of a 12-gauge commercial hunting weapon, it carries seven brass cartridges in a tubular magazine under the barrel. Ammunition is loaded one shell at a time into a large port beneath the receiver, and the cases are ejected through a port in the right side. The barrel itself is rather long and heavy, with a perforated heat guard above and wooden foregrip below, and has fitments to take a sword bayonet. The hammer is an external one, and the trigger sits rather far back against the wooden stock. An extremely solid, well-made weapon, overall the M1917 is perhaps too heavy to be rapidly brought to bear on the target.

By the beginning of World War II, the Model 1917 had been replaced by another Winchester: the Model 12 trench gun. Again a 12-gauge weapon, it bears a strong similarity to its predecessor. Finely polished wood makes up the stock and slide-action foregrip, while the receiver is machined from solid steel. The tubular magazine sits under the barrel and holds seven shells, and the barrel is again protected by a perforated heat guard. Underneath the muzzle is a metal piece with a U-shaped underside, which can be used to hook onto a trench lip or sandbag when in a defensive position, and for more aggressive operations a bayonet can be fitted. The Model 12 has an internal hammer, so the receiver is relatively smooth and free from any protrusions which could catch on clothing or equipment. As with many pump-action weapons, the shells are loaded into the magazine one at a time from underneath the receiver, and the spent cases ejected through the port on the right-hand side. The Model 12 was used extensively by US troops in the Pacific theatre, where close-range combat in thick jungle was common. The USMC was especially keen on having this rapid-response firepower, and the weapon stayed in service with the Marines until the mid-1960s.

THE FEATHERLIGHT

The year 1937 witnessed the commercial debut of a superbly engineered slide-action gun from the Ithaca Gun Corporation of New York State. Known as the 'Featherlight', it was a good .45kg (1lb) lighter than its contemporaries, even though it still used solid-steel machinings for the receiver. The Featherlight, or Ithaca Model 37, quickly became popular with sports users, and while military use has remained limited, the Ithaca has become one of the most widely used police shotguns of modern times.

The Featherlight looks pretty much like any other pump-action gun, with a smoothly finished wooden stock and foregrip and a tubular magazine under the barrel. Closer inspection, however, reveals a shorter receiver than most comparable weapons, and no obvious ejection port. Instead, the shell feed is designed so that ammunition is fed into the magazine and empty cases are ejected through the same port, which is underneath the receiver. As well as resulting in reduced length and weight, this system gives greater protection to the mechanism from rain, snow and dust. It also provides greater protection to the user should a cartridge case split, and makes the gun safe to be used by left- or right-handed firers.

The Ithaca is available in a number of bores, but virtually all military and police users fire 12-bore guns. There are many options available, with various magazines, barrels and stocks, all offering slightly different capabilities. The standard magazine holds five rounds, but most combat users have the special eight-shot extended version. To allow use of solid slugs and special munitions, many also have the fully cylindrical barrel (known commercially as the 'Deerslayer') rather than the standard oval-shaped item. A variant specifically devised for the police and special forces user is the Ithaca Stakeout, a shortened weapon ideal for concealing under a coat or in a vehicle. The Stakeout has no stock; instead, there is a hefty pistol grip at the rear of the receiver and a supporting leather handstrap attached to the foregrip. At 336mm (13in) the barrel is also some 280mm (11in) shorter than the standard model, and the magazine only holds four rounds (although one can be carried in the chamber). The Stakeout demands a well-trained operator to withstand the recoil without the use of a shoulder stock, but it is an effective, lethal, concealable short-range weapon.

THE REMINGTON

In 1966, when the USMC selected a replacement for its Model 12 trench gun, it chose a weapon that would become the most popular pump-action shotgun ever, reaching sales of over four million. Most of these are for civilian sports use, but hundreds of thousands have also been procured for military service, and the weapon is especially popular with elite and special forces units. The Remington 870 first saw daylight in 1950, and since then a bewildering variety of options and configurations have become available. The USMC weapon is known as the M870 Mk 1, and uses a 12-gauge barrel some 533mm (21in) long with an extended seven-round tubular magazine. The M870 has a machined steel receiver with an internal hammer, and with the usual feed port and

■ RIGHT: A US Marine boarding team. The soldier at the front is carrying a Remington M870 Mark 1 shotgun, the standard US Marine Corps shotgun.

Mossberg 500 ATP8

ejection port underneath and on the right respectively. There is a traditional wooden stock, and a long wooden foregrip with finger slot is used to operate the action. To please military traditionalists, the front of the tubular magazine is shaped to allow attachment of a standard M7 bayonet, although the combat utility of such a configuration is very doubtful. Normal rifle sights are used by the Marines: there is an adjustable ramp rear sight midway along the barrel and an adjustable blade above the muzzle.

Other forces use Remingtons in different configurations, sometimes with longer barrels proofed for Magnum cartridges, sometimes with different magazines and sights, and even with metal folding stocks. The folding stock combines the concealability of a police stakeout model with the controllability and accuracy of a shoulder-aimed weapon. The 'Remmy' is regularly used by Britain's Special Air Service when patrolling in thick jungle-type terrain, or for anti-terrorist operations, loaded with special ammunition for blowing in locked and barricaded doors. Used around the world, the strength and reliability of this old trooper will keep it popular with soldiers even with the appearance of more 'advanced' automatic weapons which employ new materials and technology.

Cut-down versions with no stock and a shorter barrel have been designed so they can be slung under the barrel of an assault rifle, and a good example is the Ciener Ultimate combination, with the shotgun clipping under an M16A1. Both weapons are independent and retain their own magazines and trigger mechanisms, although to fire the shotgun the user has to grip the magazine housing of his rifle, tuck the stock and pistol grip under his arm, and hold the foregrip of the Remington. This combination could be useful in urban combat, where the shotgun would be able to deliver special rounds such as armour-piercing slugs through doors and walls, or even CS and high-explosive grenades, before the firer switches to rifle shots.

■ ABOVE: The Mossberg 500 series of shotguns. All have been carefully designed to ensure absolute reliability.

THE MILITARY MOSSBERG

A close American competitor of the Remington is the Mossberg 500 series, referred to as ATP8. Designed for military and police use, the Mossberg is another straightforward pump-action gun, again with an ejection port on the right of the receiver. The weapon is immensely strong and reliable, and all barrels have been proofed for high-powered Magnum loads. Twin guide rods reduce the risk of the bolt jamming, and there are also two ejectors as a further insurance. A bewildering variety of configurations are available, including different lengths and shape of barrel and stock, some with wooden stocks (sometimes with rubber recoil pads), some with no stocks and just a pistol grip, and others with simple folding metal stocks. Most military/police users prefer the flexibility of a cylindrical barrel, which allows the use of more specialised ammunition. Later improvements include slots cut into the top surface of the muzzle to act as a compensator and to help control

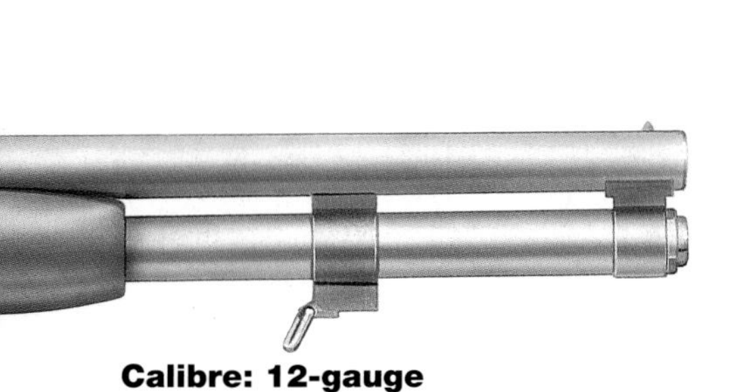

Calibre: 12-gauge
Weight: 3.06kg (6¾lb)
Length: 1009mm (39¾in)
Effective range: 40m (44yd)
Rate of fire: single shot
Feed: eight-round tubular magazine
Muzzle velocity: 400mps (1313fps)

muzzle jump. A more radical development is the fitting of the Mossberg 500 mechanism into a plastic bullpup body, perhaps a forerunner of the next generation of combat shotguns. While the Mossberg series has not been as widely used as the Remington, it has still racked up a respectable level of sales to military users worldwide.

THE SEMI-AUTO

While a pump-action mechanism is extremely rugged and reliable, it still requires an appreciable amount of time to cycle the action and load the next round, and the firer's aim is often disturbed by this necessary hand movement. It would appear obvious that a semi-automatic weapon would overcome these problems, but such designs have been surprisingly slow in gaining military acceptance. The first semi-automatic shotgun was actually patented in 1900, and was a product of that most prolific of small arms designers, John Moses Browning. After being unable to reach agreement with Winchester, Browning had offered his new design to FN, and it was the Belgian company that first put this weapon into production.

The Browning A5 uses a long recoil system, where the bolt and barrel recoil together over the full length of the receiver

■ BELOW: The ferocious Franchi SPAS 12 12-gauge semi-automatic shotgun. The version shown here has a special device to enable the firer to carry and fire the gun with one hand.

■ BOTTOM: The SPAS 12 can fire a range of ammunition, from pellets to solid slugs.

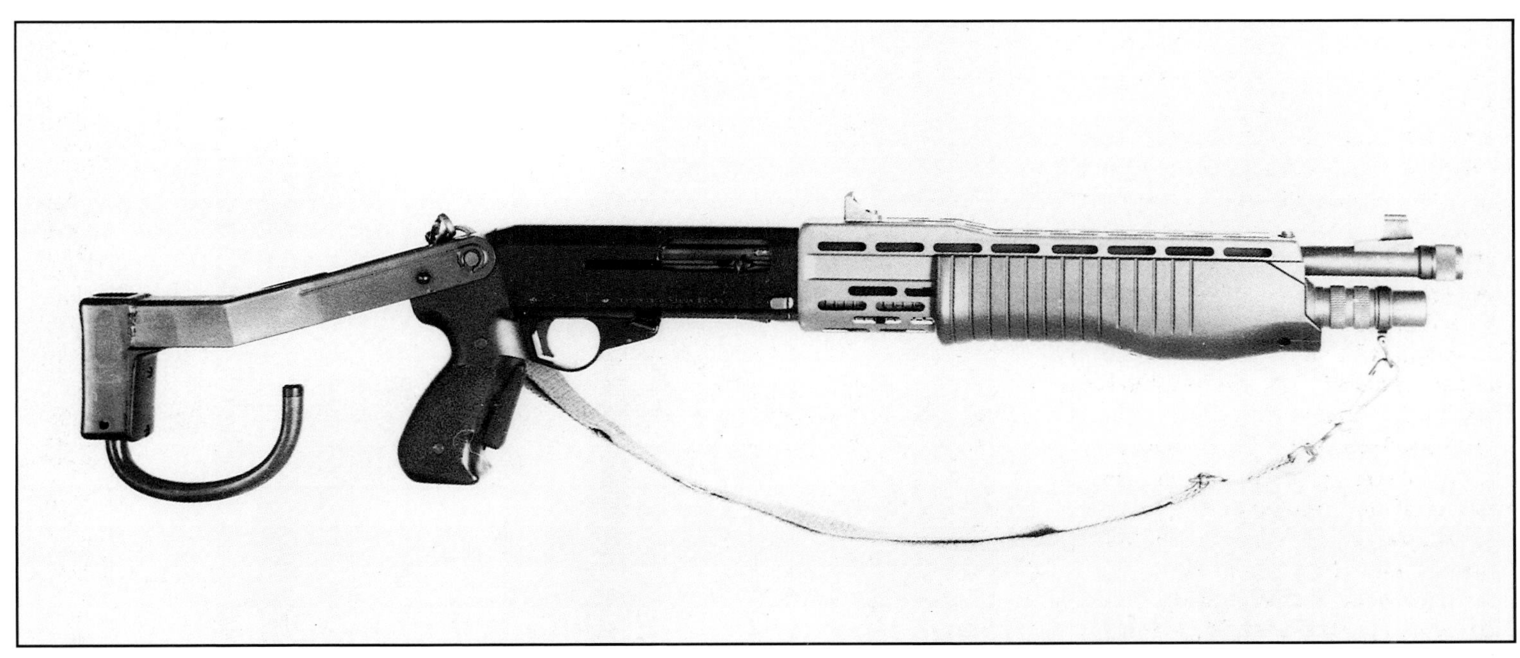

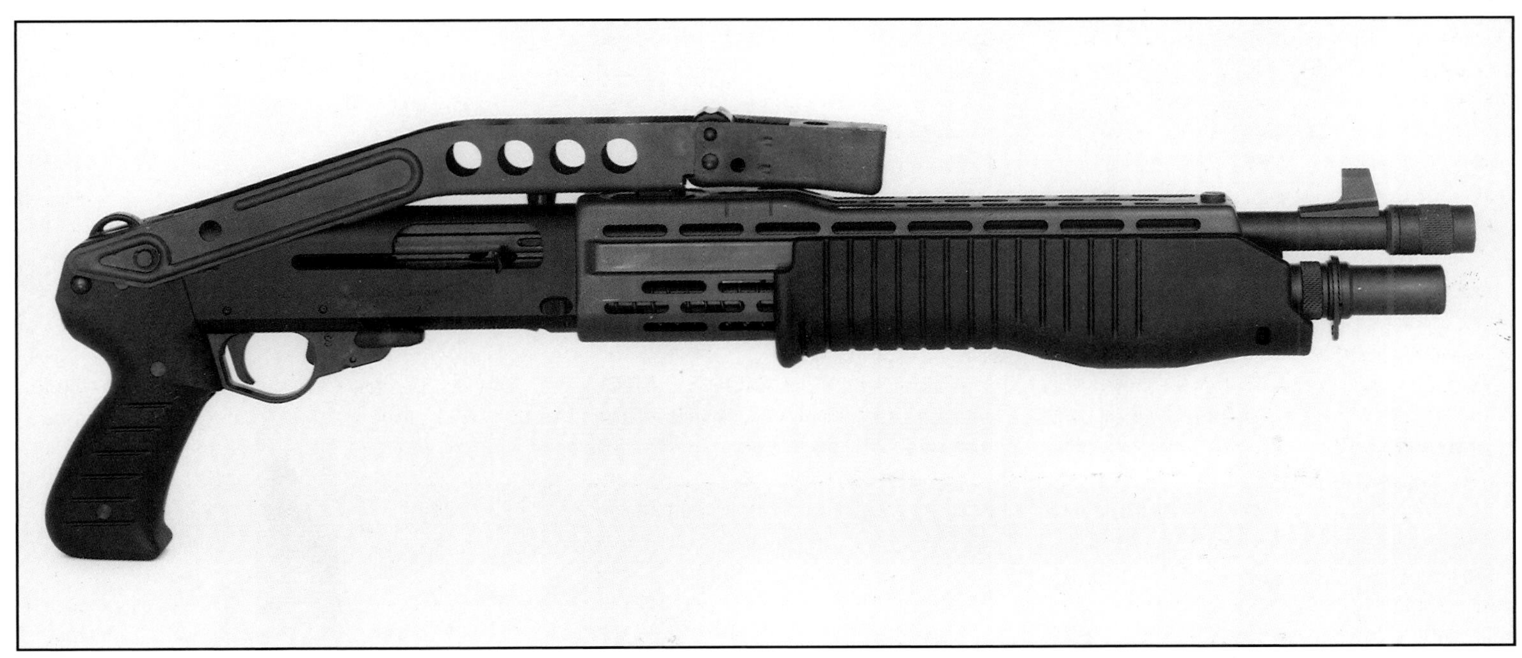

before the bolt unlocks and the barrel returns forward. Five shells are held in the tubular magazine, and there is a perforated muzzle brake and compensator at the end of the barrel. The stock is wooden and the receiver has a distinctive square-backed outline, with an ejection port revealing the bolt and cocking handle on the right. A tough, rugged design, the A5 became immensely popular with sports shooters and hunters, although it never achieved the massive military success it perhaps deserved. Its best known military employment is when the British Special Air Service took Brownings on jungle patrols in Malaya during the early 1950s.

PARAMILITARY SEMI-AUTOS

Most other semi-automatic shotguns designed and built up to the late 1970s were sporting weapons, although some were in the hands of police and military forces. Weapons such as Remington's Model 1100 and Beretta's M303 are popular around the world; both use gas operation with a bolt which tips to lock against lugs on the receiver (rather like the FN FAL assault rifle). Service users were still suspicious, however; many felt that a good slide-action was still more reliable in a tight spot and could more easily adapt to the wide range of military ammunition. By 1979, however, a weapon appeared that was specifically designed for the military, with no concessions to sports users whatsoever.

THE SPAS 12

Luigi Franchi is a long-established Italian company that designs and builds military small arms. During the 1970s, it analysed the requirements for a military and police shotgun, and came up with a completely new design which, unlike most others, was not a conversion from a sports or hunting model. Its 12-bore SPAS (Special Purpose Automatic Shotgun) was first revealed in 1979 and, after the inevitable minor modifications, it became widely used as the SPAS Model 12.

One glance at the SPAS shows that it is no ordinary shotgun. The very shape of the weapon looks ferocious, with its black aluminum alloy receiver, slotted alloy guard over most of the chunky barrel, and a large dark-green plastic foregrip. There is also a green plastic pistol grip and an unusual metal folding stock behind, with a special hook device through which the user can lock his arm to enable the gun to be fired single-handedly (although this requires an extremely strong firer). The SPAS 12 uses gas operation and has a piston and cylinder lying alongside, which operate against the bolt in a similar manner to a gas-operated rifle. It fires from a closed bolt, which is pulled back to load a round and cock the hammer using a handle protruding from the ejection port on the right of the receiver. Seven shots are held in the tubular magazine, and just by pulling the trigger once up to four shots can be fired in a second. Using buckshot, this would allow a firer to put 48 heavy 7.62mm pellets into a man-sized target up to 40m (44yd) away – all that firepower in one second! Two manual safeties are fitted: a thumb-operated lever for storage and transit, and a sliding catch just in front of the trigger guard.

More specialised ammunition often does not generate the recoil or gas energy

Franchi SPAS 12

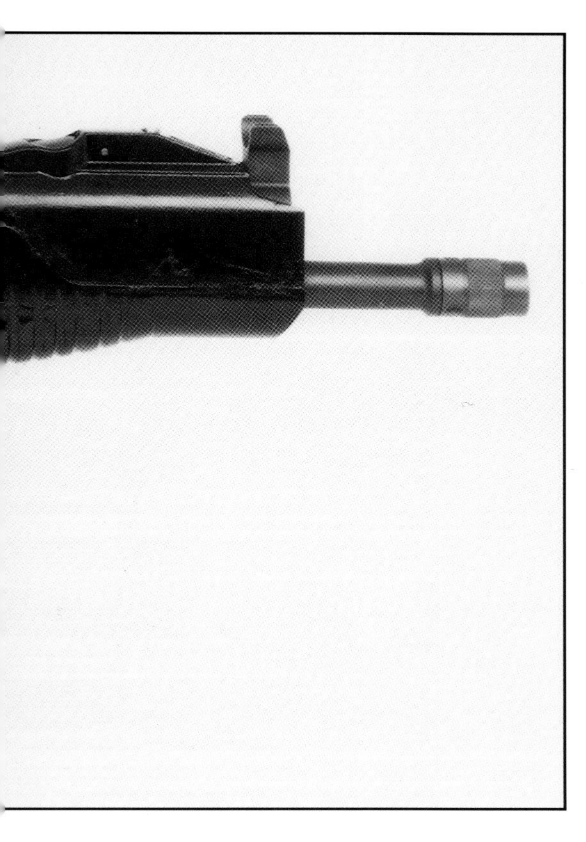

■ LEFT: Franchi's SPAS 15 semi-automatic shotgun. The carrying handle above the receiver protects the cocking handle and can also be used to mount sights.

to cycle a semi-automatic action. The SPAS 12 overcomes this problem by being easily switched to pump-action mode. If a small stud in the fore-end is pressed, it isolates the gas plug and disables the semi-automatic system. The foregrip can then be used to move the bolt just like any other slide-action weapon. Most types of military shotgun ammunition can be fired from the SPAS, including armour-piercing slugs, CS gas, non-lethal pellets and flares. There is an easily attached adaptor which enables high-explosive grenades to be fired, and various muzzle chokes to control the spread of pellets. Powerful, flexible and reliable, the SPAS 12 has found favour with a number of military, police and special forces users, all of whom have procured the SPAS 12 for service around the world. In a reversal of the traditional process, the SPAS has also become popular with sports users.

THE SPAS 15

By the mid-1980s, the United States was looking for some sort of shotgun design to give a close-range, area-fire capability to its conventional and special forces. A number of different design concepts have been tested, but as yet none has been taken up for widespread service. Nevertheless, these extremely tough military requirements have been the spur for designers to create a series of highly effective combat weapons which are seeing military use elsewhere, as well as some more advanced technology demonstrators which have yet to be put in the hands of soldiers.

Franchi responded to the American challenge by redesigning the SPAS 12 to take a detachable box magazine, thereby creating the more advanced Franchi SPAS 15. The lineage is obvious, although the Model 15 resembles an oversized assault rifle rather than a shotgun. The SPAS 15 has a rectangular aluminum receiver topped by a carrying handle/sight unit, which will also take night vision, laser and singlepoint sights. The fore-end retains the large plastic grip, although this time it sits much higher on the barrel, with the gas plug, cylinder and piston above and no tubular magazine below. The unusual stock on the SPAS 12 has been replaced by a more conventional tubular steel folding design. There is also a plastic pistol grip, with the trigger assembly and magazine housing in front.

THE SPAS'S MECHANISM

Ammunition is held in a large, curved box magazine containing up to six cartridges, which clips into a large housing in front of the grip and trigger. The bolt is a typical two-piece item which locks by rotating the front piece against the barrel extension, but its cocking handle is rather awkwardly situated on top of the receiver, beneath the carrying handle. Manual safeties include a thumb-operated lever above the trigger and a button on the front of the grip which must be squeezed before the bolt or trigger can be moved. While the SPAS 15 is

Calibre: 12-gauge
Weight: 4.2kg (9¼lb)
Length: 930mm (36½in) – stock extended; 710mm (28in) – stock folded
Effective range: 40m (44yd)
Rate of fire: single shot
Feed: seven-round tubular magazine
Muzzle velocity: 400mps (1313fps)

Franchi SPAS 15

Calibre: 12-gauge
Weight: 3.9kg (8½lb)
Length: 915mm (36in) – stock extended; 696mm (27½in) – stock folded
Effective range: 50m (55yd)
Rate of fire: single shot
Feed: six-round detachable box
Muzzle velocity: 400mps (1313fps)

meant to be fired as a semi-automatic weapon, it retains the 12's ability to switch to pump-action, although the large box magazine may prove something of a hindrance to smooth operation of the action. The SPAS 15 is able to fire the full range of specialised 12-bore military and police ammunition, and can also make use of a range of muzzle attachments, chokes and other extras.

MORE SEMI-AUTOS

The SPAS 15 has its competitors, notably the Bernadelli B4, another Italian magazine-fed semi-automatic. Much fuss has also been made about the Daewoo Industries USAS-12, a selective-fire shotgun designed in the United States but manufactured in South Korea. In theory, the ability to fire bursts of buckshot ammunition should make this a much-feared weapon, but persistent reports of unreliability indicate that the technology of the full-automatic shotgun still needs to mature (the SAS has reportedly failed the USAS). However, the SPAS and the Bernadelli prove that the semi-automatic weapon is a viable tool for the soldier.

THE FUTURE FOR THE SHOTGUN

The shotgun is undergoing something of a renaissance as a military weapon, with a number of countries looking at advanced designs using new weapons and ammunition technology. The devastating area fire of advanced shotguns would be a useful asset to infantryman engaged in close-range combat, where there is little time for precise aiming and quick-reaction snap shooting is at a premium. Special high-explosive, armour-piercing or even flechette rounds will further increase the destructive potential of the smooth-bore weapon, and much work is being done in this area. At one time the US Army issued a requirement for a new generation close assault weapon system (CAWS) and a number of designs were put forward. Perhaps the most radical was a plastic-bodied, magazine-fed bullpup design with a built-in sight which fired semi-automatic. This was the result of a combination of the design skills of Olin Industries (part of the Winchester Corp) and Heckler & Koch. It makes much use of technology developed from the G11 assault rifle, and is an extremely accurate firearm which transmits very little recoil to the firer. The ammunition is also new: a longer (76mm/3in) brass cartridge in 12-bore holding either eight tungsten alloy pellets (effective up to 150m/165yd) or 20 flechettes (arrows). The CAWS has not been taken up by the US Army, thus unless any government agency expresses firm interest, it is likely to remain an interesting technology demonstrator only.

THE JACKHAMMER

Another pointer to the future can be seen in a bullpup design from the Pancor Corporation, called the Jackhammer. One of the weirdest looking military weapons currently in development, the Jackhammer has a moulded plastic outer casing which completely surrounds the barrel and mechanism, and which also forms the pistol grip and carrying handle. Behind the grip is a large, plastic, revolver-like drum which holds 10 shots of 12-bore ammunition, and behind this is a

■ RIGHT: The Beretta M3P semi-automatic/pump-action shotgun is designed for law enforcement use.

FRANCHI SPAS 15-MIL
F S

WINCHESTER MODEL 12

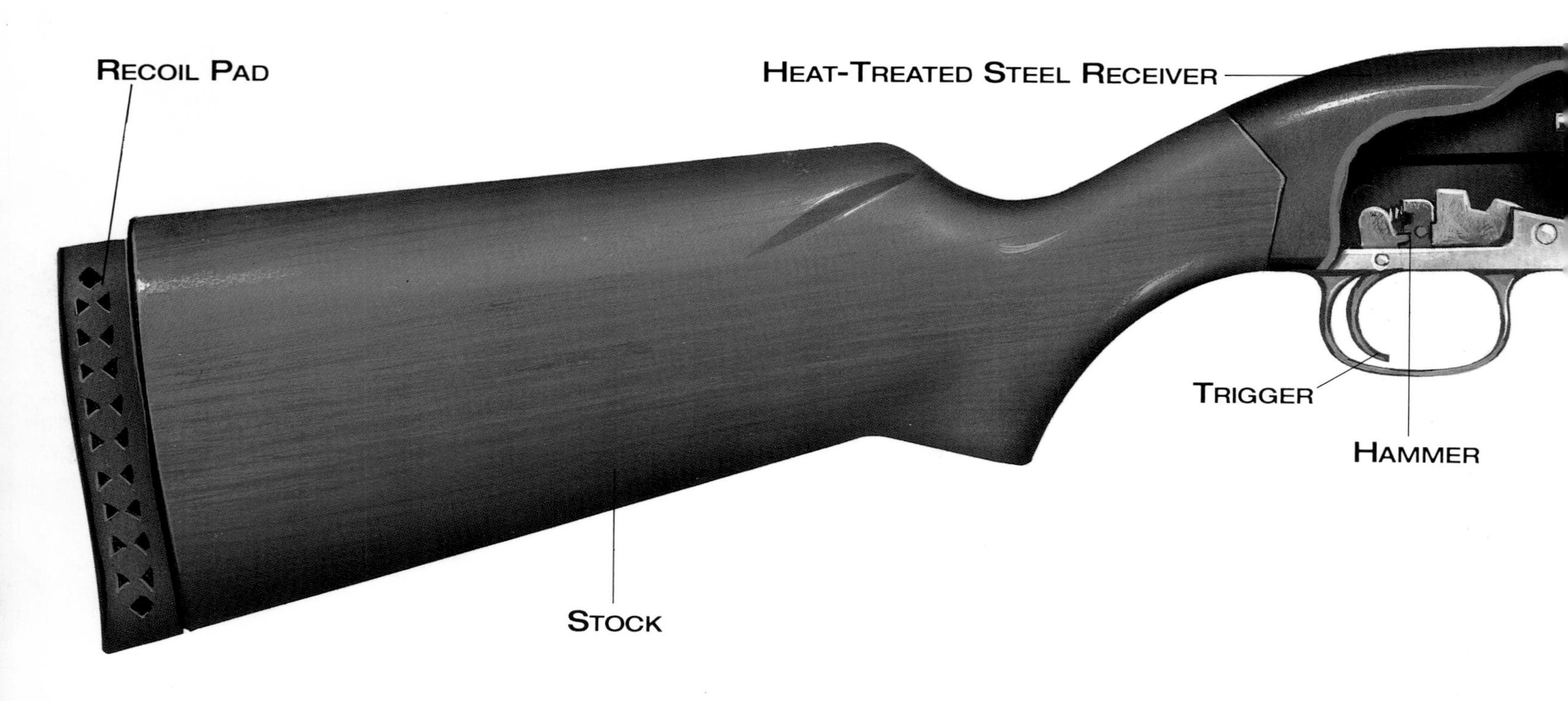

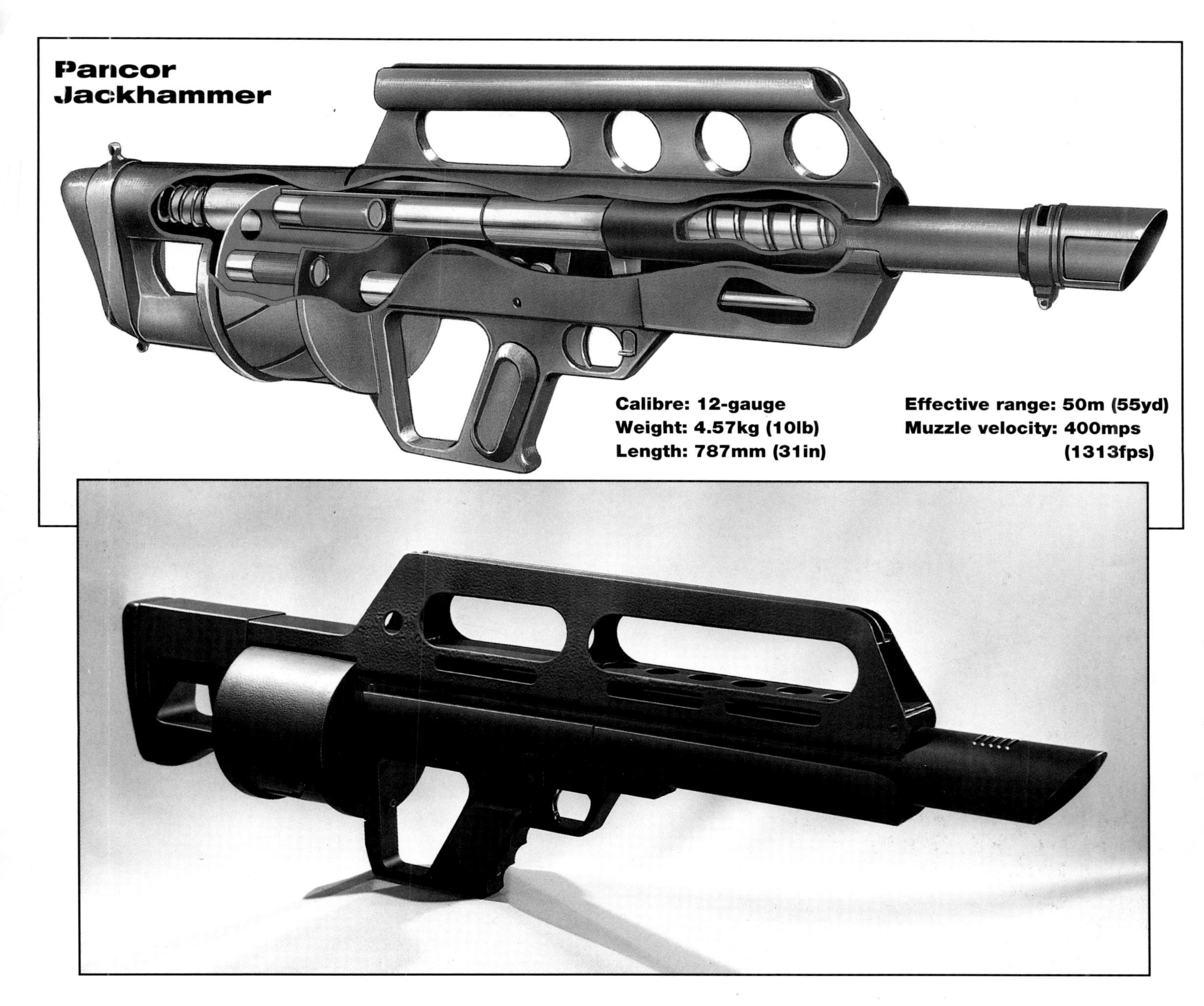

contoured plastic butt. This ammunition drum, or cassette, is supplied pre-loaded with whatever type of ammunition is required, and is simply clipped into the weapon. Once emptied it is easily removed, although the cassette cannot be loaded with single rounds while in the gun, and empty cases are not ejected.

To cock the weapon the firer simply racks the fore-end, although a later version has a lever which cocks or decocks the hammer. The barrel is held against the cassette to give a gas-tight seal, but once the cartridge is fired the gases impinge on a muzzle cap, forcing the barrel to slide forwards and absorbing most of the recoil. This movement releases the cassette, and mechanical energy from the barrel is transferred via an actuating rod to cammed slots on the outside of the cassette, causing it to rotate the next round into position.

Up to four shots a second can be fired, and the whole weapon is a remarkably light, if bulky, source of short-range firepower. An interesting feature is a simple pressure-operated detonator unit which clips onto a fully loaded ammunition cassette. This can then be placed flat on the ground or vertically in an ambush position. Used in such a way, the cassette becomes a makeshift anti-personnel mine or claymore, firing all 12 cartridges in a lethal burst when the pressure plate is moved.

Innovative as they are, it is unlikely that new technology designs such as the Jackhammer will eventually supersede the assault rifle as the standard infantry weapon. For one thing, the problems of bulk and limited ammunition capacity remain to be overcome. To illustrate the magnitude of this, one authority states that 50 rounds of 12-bore shotgun cartridges take up as much carriage space as more than 600 rounds of 9mm Parabellum ammunition. Perhaps, however, the greatest difficulty to be overcome is the limited range of such weapons. Devastating as it is, a 12-bore buckshot cartridge is only really effective up to a range of 40m (44yd), which is inadequate for most military tasks on the battlefield. Improved materials, projectile design and propellants should increase this, but it remains to be seen whether a shotgun will give the required range capability in a package that can be easily handled and transported, and one which is tough enough to withstand being used by the ordinary combat soldier.

■ ABOVE: The radical Pancor Jackhammer, a futuristic-looking automatic, gas-operated 12-gauge shotgun.

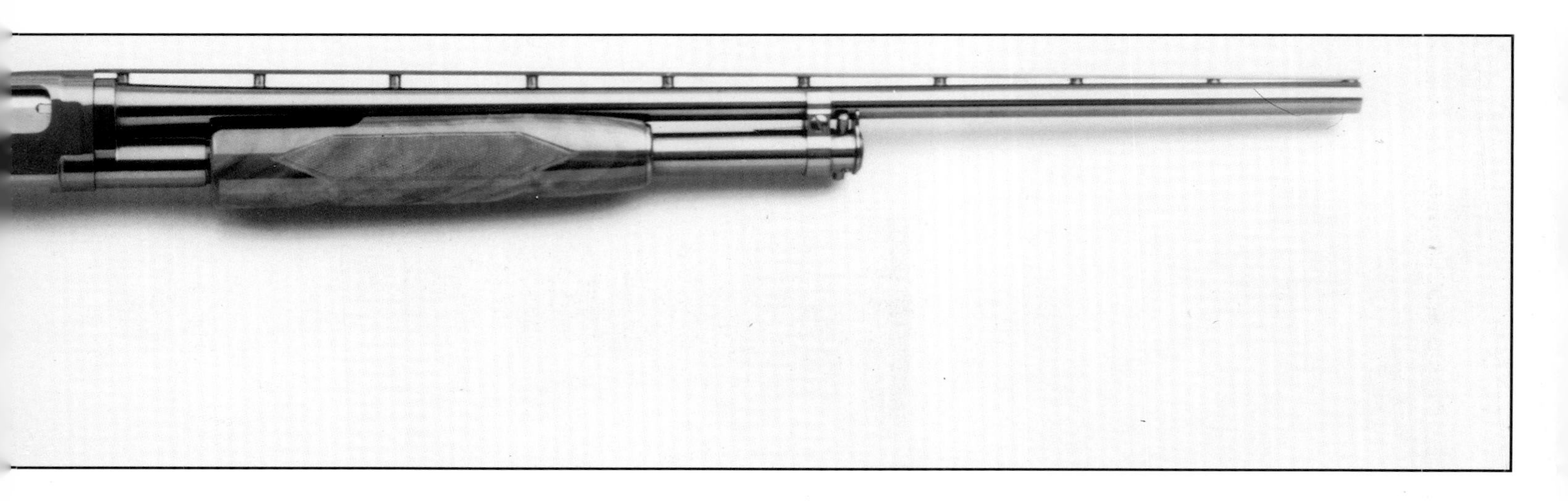

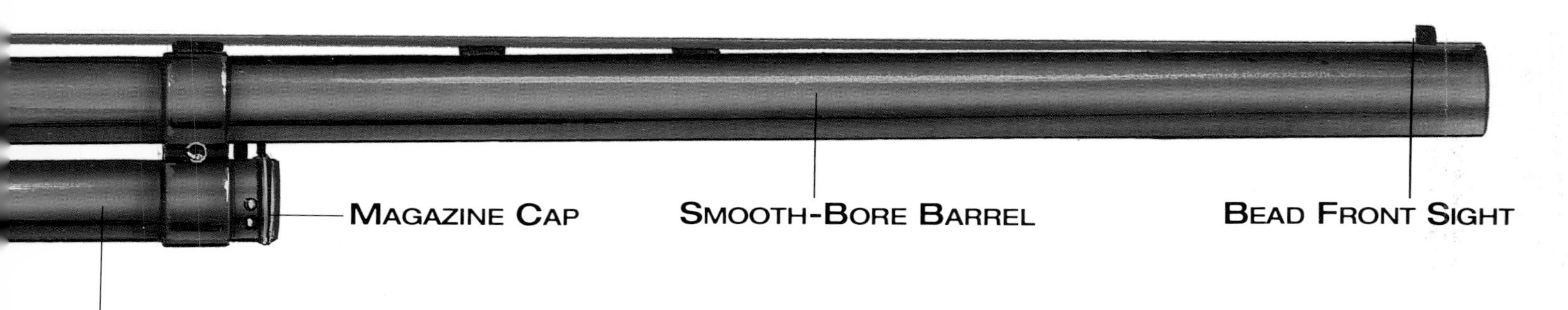

■ **TOP: The Winchester M12 pump-action shotgun. All Winchester shotguns are manufactured to very high standards.**

■ **LEFT: The Winchester Model 1300 pump-action 12-gauge shotgun. The slide action operates a rotating bolt that has four lugs, which gives a very secure breech closure. In addition, unlocking is recoil-assisted, thus resulting in a very fast repeating action.**

Calibre	12-gauge
Weight	3.8kg (8 1/4lb)
Length	1020mm (40in)
Effective range	40m (44yd)
Rate of fire	single shot
Feed	six-round internal magazine
Muzzle velocity	400mps (1313fps)

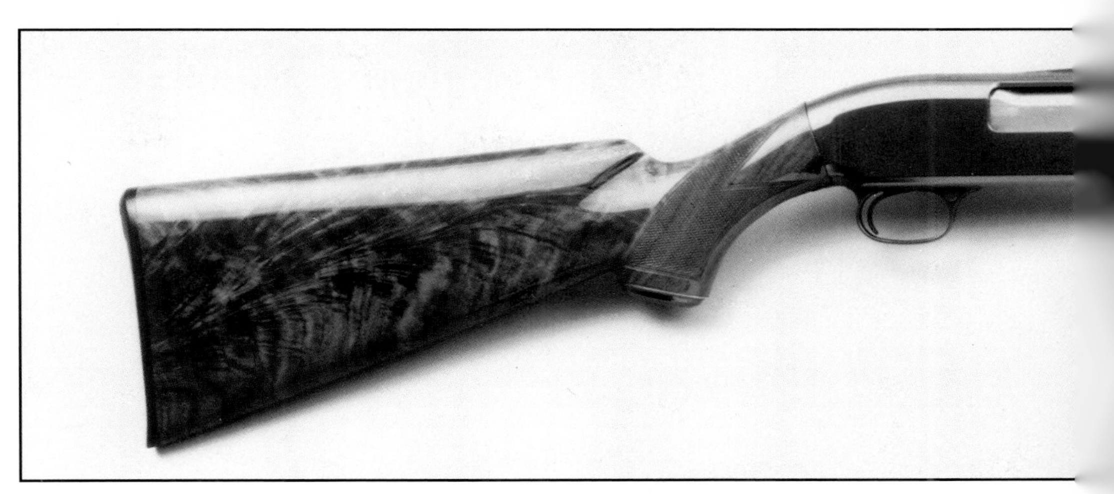

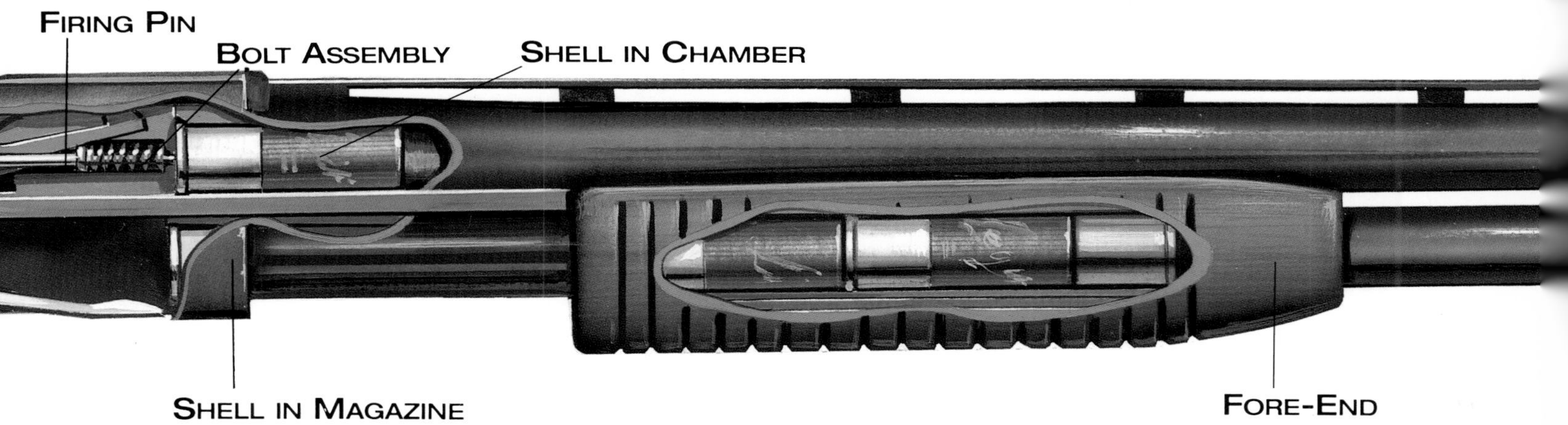

Firing Pin
Bolt Assembly
Shell in Chamber
Shell in Magazine
Fore-End

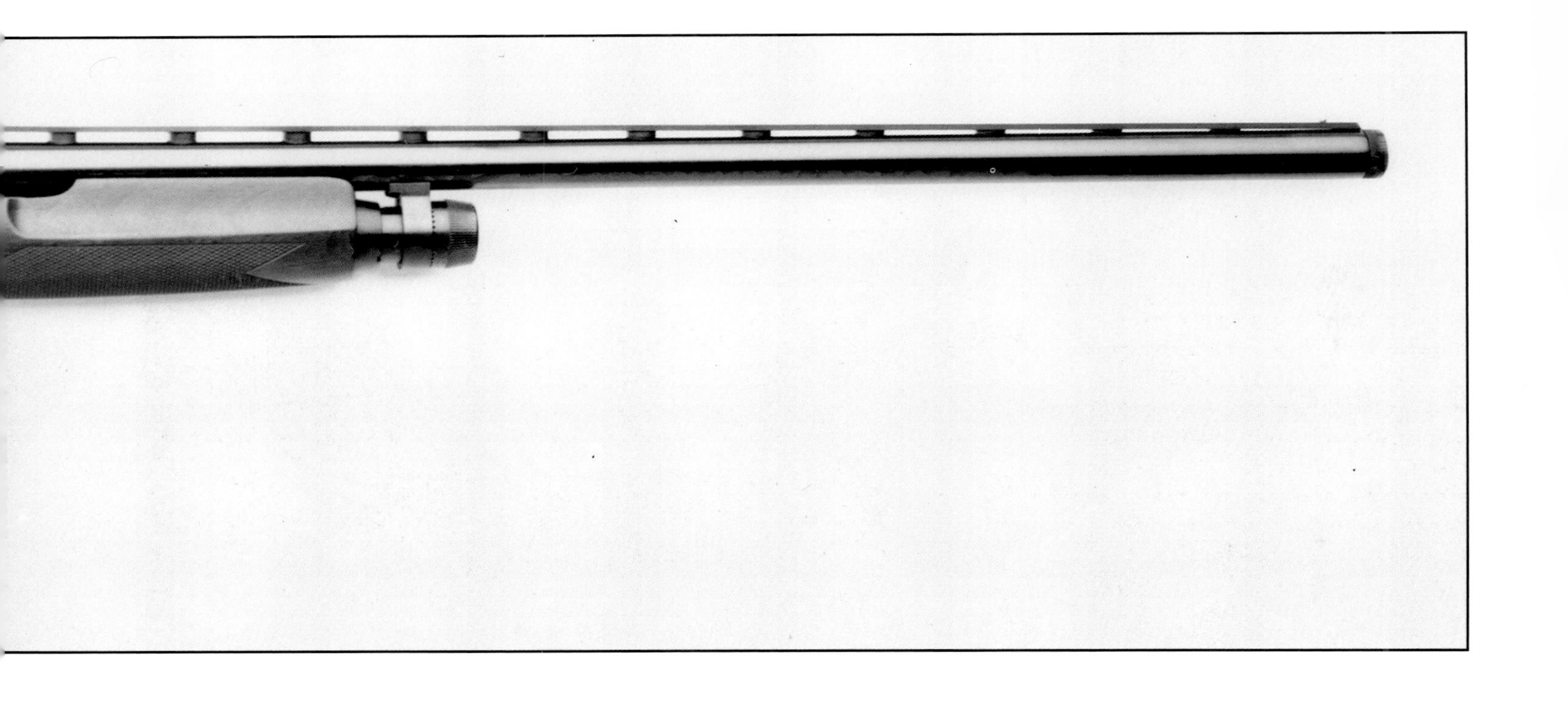

CHAPTER 6
GRENADES AND GRENADE LAUNCHERS

The grenade is one of the oldest explosive weapons on the battlefield, and can trace its lineage back to the days of cast-iron bombs thrown by hand and detonated by a burning fuse. Today's grenades carry out a remarkably wide range of roles, from neutralising enemy defenders in fortifications and trenches, to providing illumination or screening smoke, or to stunning an adversary without causing permanent damage.

TRADITIONAL GRENADES

The most common class of grenade is the hand-thrown, high explosive type, which has a metal casing that generates dozens of fragments when the charge explodes. There is usually some form of fuse which, when set, allows sufficient time for the grenade to be thrown to its target before the explosive is triggered. These devices were used extensively in World Wars I and II by all combatants, especially during infantry assaults in close terrain or during street fighting. The classic wartime grenade, such as the British Mills M36, had a thick, cast-iron casing with the engravings on the outside to give a chunky 'pineapple' effect. The idea was that the grooves would help the casing shatter into the correct size of fragment to maximise the effect on personnel and equipment. The Mills had a screw-in fuse unit which was fitted before combat, and which started the detonation process once a spring-loaded lever was released, ie after the grenade had left the thrower's hand. As a safety precaution the lever was held in place by a split pin, which was removed just before the grenade was thrown.

A problem with grenades of this nature was that the engraving on the outside of the casing actually had little effect on the fragmentation pattern; this turned out to be a few large fragments accompanied by hundreds of extremely tiny 'dust' particles.

LEFT: Heavy metal: the Russian AGS-17 30mm grenade launcher.

The target effects were unpredictable: someone could be standing next to such a grenade and remain untouched, while a heavy chunk of metal could hit another person up to 25m (27yd) away. Research showed that the type of pattern inside the casing had more effect on fragmentation, but to machine grooves on the inside of a grenade is time-consuming and expensive.

The solution chosen by most manufacturers was to include coils of steel wire, notched at short intervals to provide hundreds of fragments of a lethal size that spread in a predictable pattern. This is normally inside a thin metal casing, either with a smooth surface or a pattern (to help the user's grip rather than for fragment distribution). Some designs make use of steel or even tungsten ball bearings, and others have a solid, notched inner casing.

THE M61 GRENADE

A good example of a modern fragmentation device is the US M61, one of the most common hand grenades in service around the world. It weighs about .45kg (1lb) and has a two-piece, thin steel outer casing surrounding a coil of notched steel wire, which in turn surrounds the high-explosive filling. The fuse sits in a thin column running down the centre of the grenade body, with the striker mechanism and safety systems at the top. The striker is operated by a spring-loaded lever, which is held secure by a split pin. As a safety precaution, there is also a small clip which holds the lever in place should the pin be withdrawn accidentally. Normally the clip is removed just before going into action, and the pin taken out just before the grenade is thrown. When the lever is released, the striker slams into a sensitive primer, which detonates and sets off the delay element. The latter forms about half the length of the fuse, and consists of a slow-burning composition which takes between four and five seconds to burn down its length. When this happens the flame reaches a detonating charge, which

L2A2

Weight: 395g (3/4lb)
Height: 84mm (3 1/4in)
Lethal radius: 10m (11yd)

in turn triggers the main filling. As the grenade explodes, hundreds of pre-formed fragments are thrown out in a spherical pattern, and these are guaranteed to cause severe injury or death to any unprotected personnel within a radius of 15m (16yd). There is also have a good chance of causing injuries to others at distances of up to 25m (27yd). The M61 forms the basis of a number of related grenades, including the M26, which is identical apart from the addition of an electrical fuse that detonates on impact, although the grenade retains a pyrotechnic time-delay back-up. The British L2 is basically a copy of the M61, although the British store the grenade and the fuse separately, and only match them up before an operation.

For many years the Soviet equivalent was the longer but lighter RGD5 anti-personnel grenade. Weighing only .31kg (1/2lb), it also has a thin outer casing over a serrated liner, although this time it is made as one piece rather than from coils of wire. A bulky time fuse is fitted which provides a delay of about 3-4 seconds, and the item is an effective fragmentation grenade, with a greater lethal radius than the M61.

A problem with most high-explosive grenades is that the fragmentation pattern extends further than the distance the grenade is normally thrown, which means that the thrower (and his comrades) must be behind cover, or at the very least lying prone, as it bursts. Detonation on hard ground such as tarmac dramatically increases the effective range of the fragments, further causing problems for the thrower. In an effort to get round this, some grenades are designated 'offensive', while others are labelled 'defensive'. An 'offensive' grenade usually has a light plastic casing, no pre-formed fragments,

BELOW: South African troops assault an enemy position during World War II. The soldier on the right is throwing a British M36 pineapple-shaped grenade.

DM 51

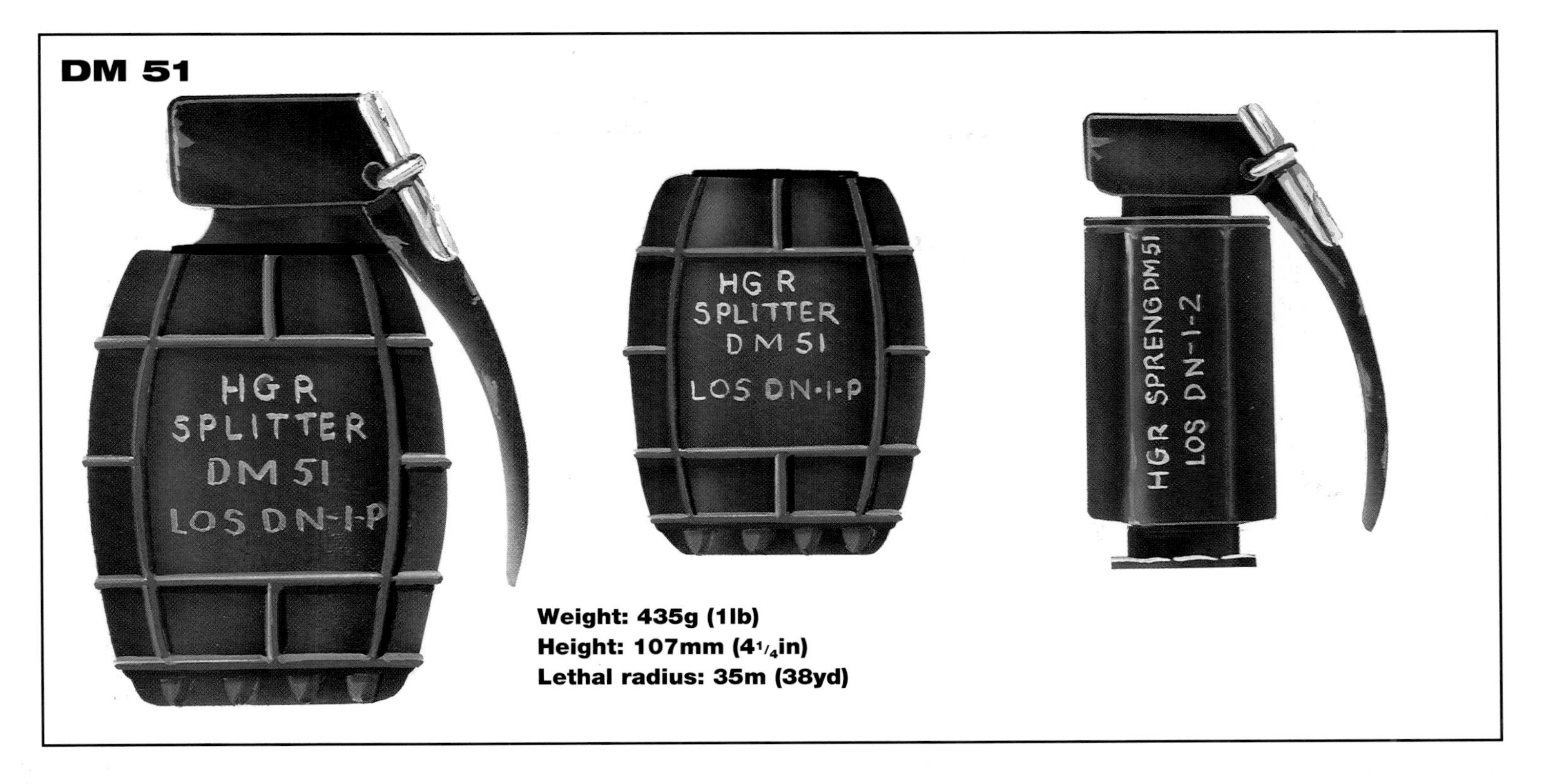

Weight: 435g (1lb)
Height: 107mm (4¼in)
Lethal radius: 35m (38yd)

and a relatively large amount of explosive. This type of grenade relies on the shock effect of the blast and will not cause as much damage in the target area, but it does allow an attacker to follow immediately behind the grenade and reach the enemy positions quickly. A 'defensive' grenade is a traditional fragmentation type, ideal for throwing from behind cover or from a slit trench. Some modern designs such as the German DM51 are dual-purpose, with a non-lethal plastic casing that can be supplemented by the addition of a wrap-around fragmentation outer casing, in this case comprising 3800 steel balls embedded in a plastic sheath.

GRENADES AGAINST TANKS

High-explosive grenades can be used for a variety of tasks, and a number of anti-armour devices have seen service. The most common in use today is probably the RKG3M, an obsolescent Russian design weighing 1.1kg (2½lb) and shaped like a soup can with a metal handle sticking out of one end. When the safety pin is removed and the grenade thrown, a fabric drogue parachute streams out to stabilise the weapon in flight and ensure that the front face impacts on the target. The RKG3M has a shaped warhead, where the front face of the charge has a cone-shaped cutout fixed to a thick copper liner. This cutout focuses the explosive power of the charge into a thin jet that will penetrate up to 165mm (6½in) of steel armour. While the grenade is effective against the top armour of virtually any vehicle, it will take a courageous soldier to get within throwing distance of a main battle tank?

BURNS, BANGS AND SMOKE

Grenades are not just high-explosive or fragmentation weapons, however. They also fulfil many other tasks. Incendiary devices, for example, are useful for clearing enemy trenches and fortifications, or as sabotage and demolition bombs. These tend to be simple steel cans filled with a composition that burns to very high temperatures (around 2500 degrees Centigrade). An example is the United States M14, which weighs .9kg (2lb) and contains a thermite mixture for the destruction of vehicles and equipment.

Smoke is often used to screen the movement of troops and vehicles, and the infantryman has a range of simple hand-thrown grenades which can provide this. The British Army uses the Schermuly Mk 4 smoke grenade, which is a steel can weighing only .65kg (1lb) and filled with a solid pyrotechnic composition. The fuse on the Mk 4 operates like that on any other grenade, giving a few seconds delay before igniting the filling. Once this is burning it gives out a thick grey-white cloud of smoke that obscures any line of sight for over two minutes. Other smoke grenades give off coloured smoke, and are used as signalling devices. If friendly aircraft are attacking enemy positions close to the frontline, troops will usually detonate smoke grenades of a pre-arranged colour just as the aircraft fly in, to help the pilots identify the target area and prevent 'friendly fire' casualties.

One type of screening grenade also has an offensive capability, this being the dreaded white phosphorus (WP) smoke device. This type of grenade has a small bursting charge which throws out fragments of the main filling: a deadly material that burns ferociously on contact with the air and inflicts severe injuries on anyone hit by even a small amount. WP also produces a thick cloud of toxic white smoke that can affect unprotected personnel, causing choking and streaming eyes. Under the terms of the Hague and Geneva Conventions, and in a typical piece of liberal rhetoric, WP is 'a weapon that inflicts unnecessary pain on personnel, so should really only be used to provide signalling or screening smoke'. This ludicrous stricture is cheerfully ignored by most soldiers, who, when under fire, tend to use any weapon they have to hand. WP smoke is extremely hot, so it tends to rise in a pillar rather than roll across the ground, but it can still be a useful screen, as many thermal vision systems find it harder to see through WP than through conventional smoke.

Another type of grenade that was designed specifically for the use of elite forces is the infamous 'flash bang' or stun grenade, first employed when the German GSG 9 hostage-rescue team stormed a Lufthansa airliner held captive in Mogadishu. The concept behind this type

M26

Weight: 454g (1lb)
Height: 99mm (3¾in)
Lethal radius: 15m (16yd)

of weapon is to disorientate and stun any terrorists inside a building or aircraft without harming their hostages. The grenade normally consists of a rubber or plastic body containing a special explosive combination optimised to produce an immense bang and blinding flash. The first models had one charge, but later designs such as the British G60/90 have seven separate charges, each creating peak sounds greater than 160dB. The Haley and Weller E182 is a good example of a modern stun grenade. It uses a patent silent electrical ignition system and contains multiple charges in a rubber casing. If one of these devices is thrown into a room, it will disorientate the occupants for the few seconds necessary for the rescue squad to storm through the doors or windows and shoot any armed terrorists. When the Special Air Service 'Pagoda' troop rescued the hostages being held in the Iranian Embassy in London in May 1980, millions of television viewers heard the thumps and crashes of stun grenades as the troopers stormed the building, to be followed by the crackle of automatic fire.

RIFLE GRENADES

Armies have often looked for ways that allow the infantryman to deliver high-explosive charges farther than he can throw them, and for a while the rifle grenade was popular with many armies. Early versions of these consisted of a cup which could be attached to the muzzle of a rifle and in which a grenade could be placed. The user loaded a special 'blank' propelling cartridge in his rifle, then rested the butt against a secure surface, with the barrel pointing skyward. Pulling the trigger and firing the round would catapult the

■ BELOW: The American M26 hand grenade has a body constructed of two pieces of thin-wall sheet steel. Its fuse is of the impact variety.

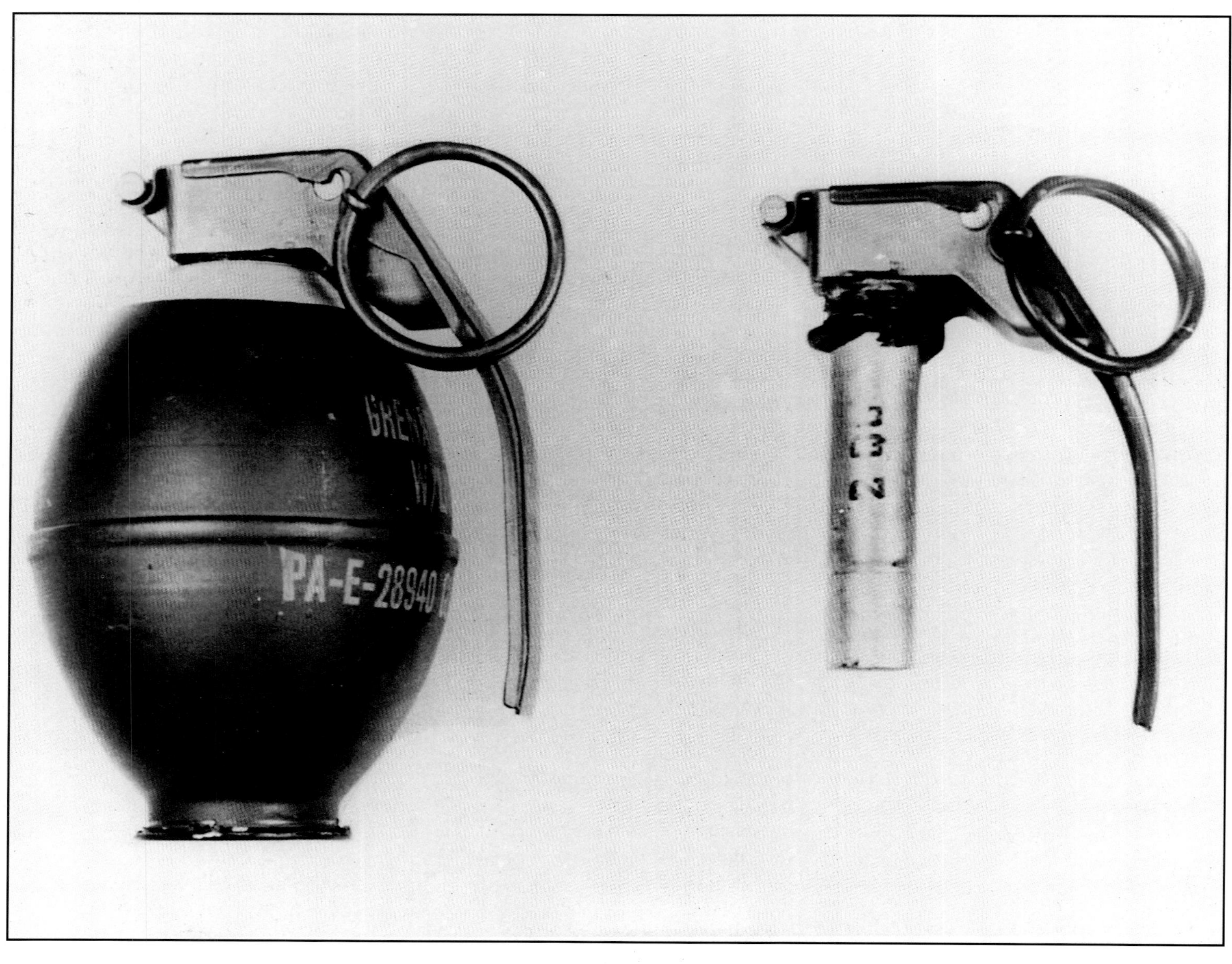

■ **ABOVE: Shown here mounted on a tripod, the AGS-17 grenade launcher can also be fitted to APCs and helicopters.**

grenade into a high-arcing trajectory and give significantly more range than a hand-thrown bomb.

In the 1950s and 1960s, this crude system was largely replaced by specially designed rifle grenades. A grenade of this vintage usually has a long 'stem' which is clipped over the barrel, with the explosive in a streamlined, shaped head at the front. Many can supposedly be fired from the shoulder and come complete with a special flip-up sight attachment. These designs are still less than satisfactory, as the hard-pressed infantryman still needs to load a special propelling cartridge into his rifle, even during the stress and fear of combat. To add to his problems, aiming is difficult, as is accuracy, and the recoil is an immense shoulder-breaking kick. Many armies felt that these disadvantages outweighed any benefits, and no longer use such devices. Some persisted, however, and new technology weapons have made the rifle grenade a much better proposition than before.

The telescopic FN Bullet-Through series consists of some of the most modern rifle grenades available today, and is an example of how technology can be used to ease the difficulties of the ordinary soldier. The base grenade is an anti-personnel fragmentation weapon that comes as a compact package only 189mm (7½in) long and 39mm (1½in) in diameter, and weighs only .32kg (¾lb). The grenade comes complete with a plastic flip-up foresight marker attached to one of the tail fins. To prepare for firing, the rifleman turns his gas plug to the grenade setting, then clips the grenade onto the muzzle of his rifle and unfolds the sight. He then extends the grenade body like a telescope, which now has the explosive part at the front and a long tail holding the stabilising fins. This

OD82

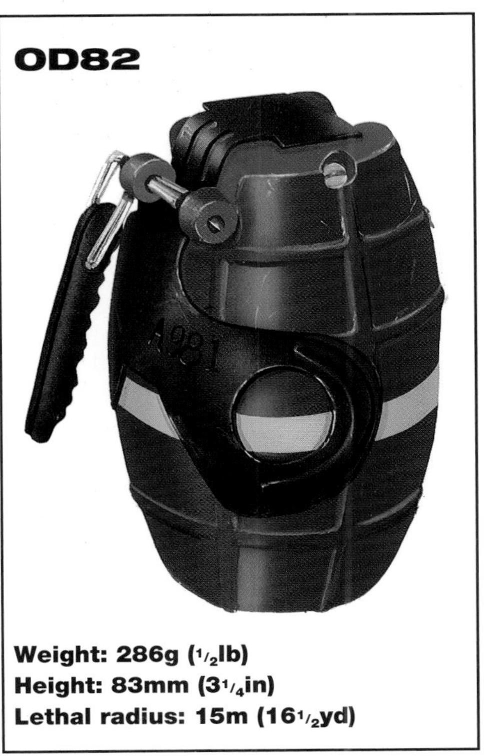

Weight: 286g (½lb)
Height: 83mm (3¼in)
Lethal radius: 15m (16½yd)

N36M

Weight: 224g (1/2lb)
Height: 85mm (3 1/4in)
Lethal radius: 15m (16 1/2yd)

action aligns the fuse firing pin with the detonator and is a safe, positive method of arming the grenade. He estimates the range to his target then aims his rifle using his normal rear sight combined with the grenade's flip-up foresight.

To launch the grenade the rifleman can fire any normal round, including armour-piercing or even tracer. The bullet flies through a central channel in the grenade without any impact, but the gases following behind are trapped and used to propel the whole bomb forward. Recoil forces are well within the limits of controllability and pose no problem to a trained soldier. The grenade now flies to the target, on the way losing the plastic sight and compressing back to its original length. This is the final movement needed to arm the fuse, which, after travelling a fixed safety distance, is set to detonate on impact. The warhead has a lethal radius of about 10m and, fired from a 5.56mm rifle, a maximum range of about 300m (330yd). The complete range of warheads includes an anti-vehicle shaped charge, smoke and a parachute flare. These grenades are easily carried by an infantryman, and are quick and easy to use, even in combat.

Another form of advanced rifle grenade is the 140mm Brunswick RAW (Rifleman's Assault Weapon). A large spherical bomb fits onto a special launching bracket under the muzzle of a conventional M16 rifle. When the launcher is armed, firing a rifle cartridge triggers the RAW firing mechanism, which ignites a tiny rocket propulsion charge in the bomb. The latter flies off, spin-stabilised by the rocket jet, and transfers virtually no recoil force to the firer. The bomb has a large, HE squash-head warhead which will blow a hole in steel-reinforced concrete large enough for a man to crawl through. RAW is also effective against light armour, but its main role is in urban combat, where it can be used to attack enemy fortified positions or to create outflanking or escape routes

■ LEFT: The American Mk 19 grenade launcher, a blowback that can fire high-explosive and anti-armour rounds.

through walls and buildings. The only disadvantage is that each RAW is a relatively large and heavy package, something else for the hard-pressed infantryman to find space for in his equipment.

THE CARTRIDGE GRENADE

When US forces were first engaged in Vietnam, they had a requirement to fire high-explosive grenades over longer ranges than before, but without using the heavy, awkward rifle grenades of the time. The weapon designed to meet this need was the forerunner of a completely new class of grenade launcher, and one which in modified form is still used by many different countries. The M79 entered service in 1961, and is a short, stubby, 40mm calibre weapon that resembles a wide-barrelled shotgun. It weighs 2.95kg (6½lb) and is 737mm (29in) long. The M79 has a rifle-style butt and trigger, and a short, rifled tube for a barrel. It breaks open to allow a grenade to be loaded into the breech.

The projectile is a specially designed high-explosive fragmentation grenade, with its own cartridge case and propellant. The round looks like an extremely large, fat pistol cartridge. The projectile contains a sophisticated mechanical fuse, fragmentation case and explosive filling, and the whole cartridge can be treated just like any other round of ammunition.

THE M79 GRENADE LAUNCHER

An M79 can lob a grenade to around 350m (380yd), although point accuracy is not achievable beyond 150m (165yd). A maximum diameter of 40mm (1½in) is small for a fragmentation weapon, especially as the explosive competes for space with a large fuse, so the destructive power of one of these projectiles is not as great when compared to a hand grenade. Smoke, illumination and signalling rounds have all been developed, and the M79 has proved to be a useful addition to an infantry squad's firepower, and it has seen widespread service with many armies.

A disadvantage with the M79 system is that it requires a dedicated operator, ie one who cannot use a rifle at the same time. By the late 1960s, the AAI corporation had come up with a solution: the M203 launcher. Again a 40mm single-shot device, the M203 is designed to clip underneath the barrel and foregrip of a standard M16 assault rifle. Simple quadrant sights are clipped to the rifle carrying handle, and the addition of the launcher leaves the operation of the rifle unaffected, apart from the problem of aiming with an extra 1.63kg (3½lb) under the muzzle. The M203 fires the same 40mm ammunition as the M79, and allows a squad to put down withering high-explosive suppressive fire while retaining its full rifle capability. A later model, the M203PI (Product Improved), has revised mounting brackets and is capable of being used on the vast majority of 7.62mm and 5.56mm assault rifles. The MP203PI can also be fired dismounted, attached to its own lightweight pistol grip and stock unit.

A number of competitors exist, although virtually all of them use the same 40mm calibre ammunition as the M203. Some manufacturers have attempted to increase the squad's firepower by designing much larger weapons holding multiple grenades in a revolver-type cylinder magazine. The South African Armscor MGL, for example, is an example of this, and has up to six 40mm cartridges in its magazine, bestowing fearsome rapid firepower in a bulky package. This seems to be more useful for firing irritant gas or baton rounds during an internal security operation rather than on the battlefield, as it is a large, awkward weapon demanding a dedicated operator. An American counterpart is the 12-shot MM-1, which is reported to be in service with US Special Forces units.

NR20

Weight: 390g (¾lb)
Height: 104mm (4in)
Lethal radius: 10m (11yd)

Israeli No 5 Smoke Grenade

Weight: 800g (1¾lb)
Height: 150mm (6in)

The Russians have also developed their own rifle-mounted launcher, but it is one that uses a very different type of projectile from any currently used in the West. The BG-15 clips underneath an AK rifle, and looks like a short M203. It was first seen in Afghanistan in 1984, mounted below the barrel of an AK-47 assault rifle. Quadrant sights, marked up to a range of 400m (440yd), sit alongside the launcher, although the BG-15 must be regarded as an inaccurate area-fire weapon at this range. The launcher does not break open; rather, the round is fed in tail first from the muzzle and, instead of having a separate cartridge case, the grenade carries its own propellant behind the explosive section, with 10 tiny gas ports in the tail. When the trigger is pulled, a firing pin drives into a primer cap, which ignites the propellant. Gas is driven through the vent ports and propels the grenade out of the launcher rather like a short, stubby rocket. The projectile has a narrow driving band which engages in the rifling to provide the necessary spin stabilisation.

GRENADE MACHINE GUNS

Perhaps the ultimate in grenade launchers is the tripod-mounted, belt-fed automatic system, first seen in 1967 when the United States deployed the 40mm Mk 19 automatic grenade launcher. Initially

mounted on river patrol boats in Vietnam, this fearsome weapon is now in use with all branches of the US armed forces and also with British special forces. The current model is the Mk 19 Model 3, a large (1024mm/40in long) and heavy (34kg/75lb) monster which looks like a stubby, short-barrelled medium machine gun. Ammunition is fed from the left side of the blocky, rectangular receiver in a 50-round metal disintegrating link belt, although most configurations include a box to hold the belted rounds. The rounds themselves are impressive: 40mm projectiles which achieve a muzzle velocity of over 240mps (787fps) and have an effective range of over 1600m (1750yd). The Mk 19 fires from an open bolt and uses blowback to operate the mechanism, relying on the forward momentum of the bolt to keep the chamber closed until the gas pressure falls. The sights, grips and cocking mechanism are similar to those used on the M2 machine gun. The cyclic rate of fire is over 350 rounds per minute, although practical rates are nearer 60 rounds per minute. Ammunition types include high-explosive, anti-personnel, armour-piercing, smoke and illumination, and the weapon has excellent capabilities against both personnel and vehicles. It can be mounted on a tripod or, more usually, on light vehicles, boats and in remote-controlled turrets on combat helicopters.

■ LEFT: RAW, a weapon specifically designed for fighting in an urban terrain.
■ RIGHT: Russian RGK3 anti-tank hand grenades. When thrown, a small parachute comes out of the handle to stabilise its flight. It also allows it to drop onto the top of an armoured vehicle.
■ BELOW: The Russian RGD5 grenade.

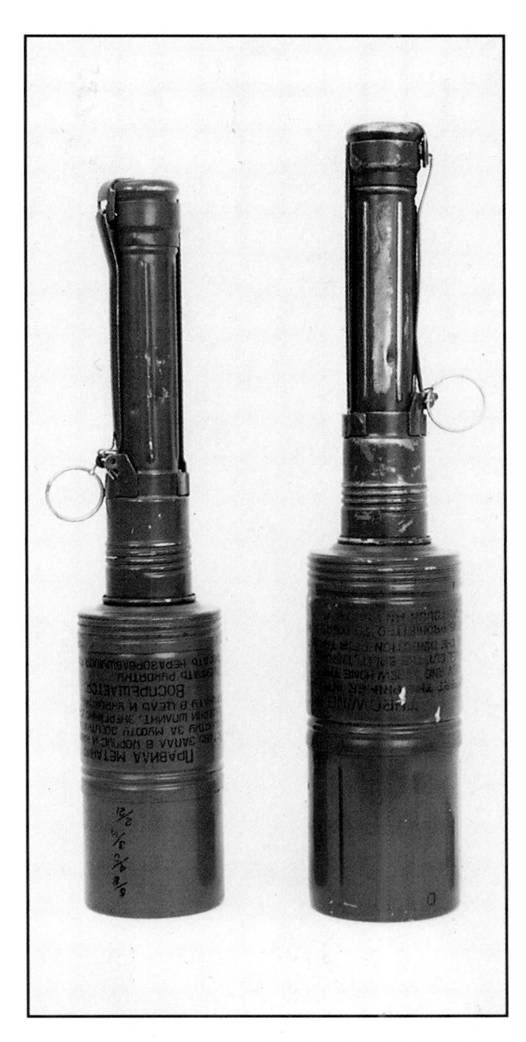

■ ABOVE: The FN Bullet-Through rifle grenade. When the rifle is fired, the bullet passes through the axis of the grenade. However, its propellant gas is retained and utilised in projecting the grenade.
■ LEFT: A close-up of two Bullet-Throughs.

The Russian equivalent of the MK 19 is the AGS-17 *Plamya* (Flame), which is widely issued to CIS infantry companies as a fire support weapon. The AGS-17 is also an open-bolt, blowback design with a hydraulic buffer to absorb some of the recoil. The grenade fired is a long, cylindrical projectile 30mm (1 1/10in) in diameter, with a thin casing surrounding a fragmentation sleeve of steel balls embedded in wax. A short, brass case holds the propellant and provides a gas seal when firing. While a 30mm grenade means less explosive at the target area, it also means a significantly lighter weapon than the Mk 19. In fact, without the tripod the *Plamya* weighs only 18kg (39 1/2lb). The AGS-17 is also some 190mm (7 1/2in) shorter than the American weapon, which makes it a reasonably portable alternative to a medium machine gun. The ammunition is stored in a 29-round metal belt held in a

Stun grenade

Weight: 250g (1/2lb)
Height: 120mm (4 3/4in)

40mm HE Grenade

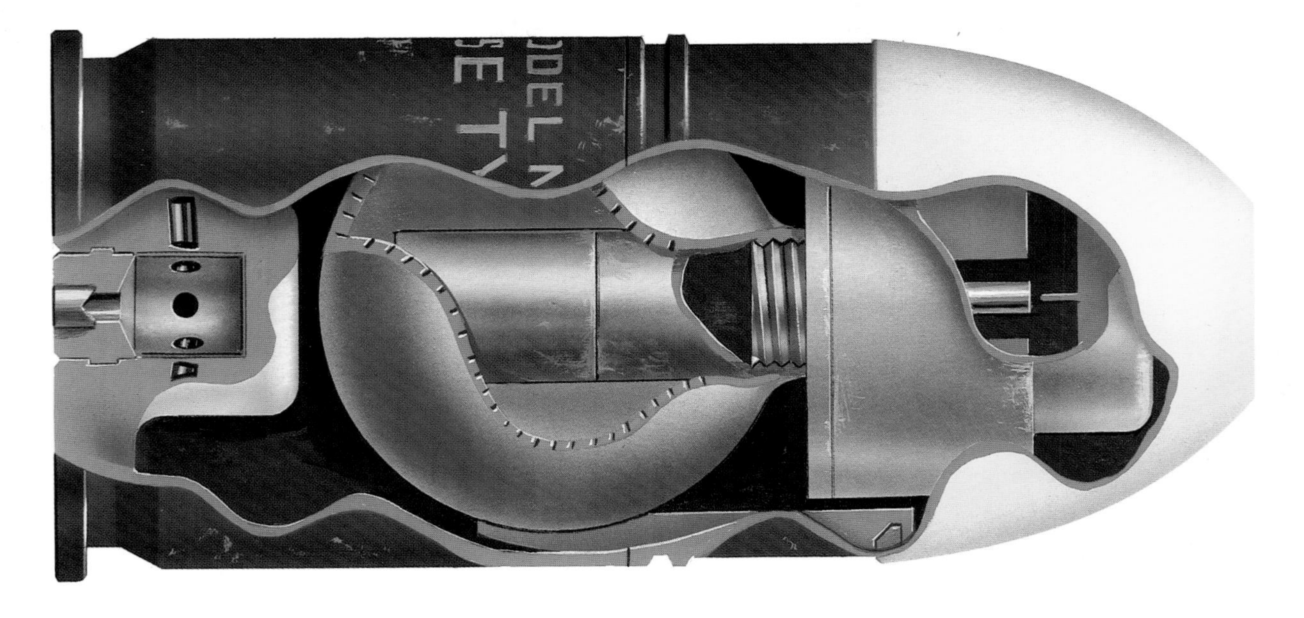

Muzzle velocity: 75mps (246fps) Effective range: 350m (380yd)

round metal drum, which clips onto the left side of the receiver. Types include high-explosive, armour-piercing or incendiary rounds. The effective range of this weapon is slightly less than the Mk 19 – around 1200m (1300yd) – and it has a practical rate of fire of about 45 rounds per minute. The AGS-17, which is normally mounted on a light tripod, can also be mounted on vehicles, either on a pintle mount or in a turret, and there is a heavier version that can be fitted to helicopters.

FUTURE GRENADES

It seems as if the grenade will form part of the soldier's arsenal for the forseeable future, both as a hand-thrown and launcher-projected device. The flexibility of a range of ammunition types bestows increased capabilities on the infantryman, and should ensure continued development of explosive and fragmentation technology. New weapon designs may see the infantry-portable grenade launcher merge with the shotgun to provide an improved area-fire system or even an assault rifle. However, long-range capability and ammunition bulk are always likely to remain a problem. A less radical solution may be to combine the grenade launcher and conventional rifle in an integrated package to give soldiers the ability to provide high-explosive area fire as a secondary role.

Heavy systems such as the Mk 19 or the *Plamya* may also be the forerunners of a new class of grenade machine gun, which would greatly enhance the destructive firepower of company-level fire support groups. Heckler & Koch (H&K) is developing such a new-generation weapon, although ready ammunition supply is still only a single drum holding 15 grenades of 40mm calibre. H&K argues that the improved accuracy of its closed-bolt system reduces ammunition expenditure, but at 20kg (44lb) the prototype is still much heavier and bulkier than a GPMG. In the final analysis, one cannot help but feel that the good old solid lead bullet will be the main battlefield projectile for many years to come, and that the infantry soldier, the little guy, will continue to be a 'rifleman' well into the twenty-first century.

M79

Calibre: 40mm
Weight: 2.95kg (6½lb)
Length: 737mm (29in)
Effective range: 350m (380yd)
Rate of fire: single shot
Muzzle velocity: 76mps (250fps)